Volume II

Quantessence:
how quantum theory works

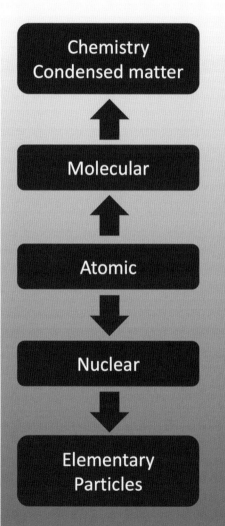

Chemistry
Condensed matter

Molecular

Atomic

Nuclear

Elementary
Particles

Volume III:
Hierarchies:
the emergence of diversity

Quantum Physics

Volume II:
Quantessence:
how quantum
theory works

Volume I:
The journey: from
classical to quantum worlds

Contents

Table of Contents   **v**

     A preface of prefaces   xi

Introduction   **xvii**

     Nature is quantized   xix

     Physics, mathematics and concepts   xxi

I   The journey:

          from classical to quantum worlds

I.1   The gems of classical physics   **5**

Mission almost completed   5

Newtonian mechanics and gravity   7

     Four laws only   7

     Dynamical systems   11

     Conservation laws   12

     Classical mechanics for *aficionados*   16

         ★ The shortest path ★   . . .   18

Maxwell's electromagnetism   19

     The Maxwell equations   21

     Electromagnetic waves   26

     Lorentz invariance: the key to relativity   . .   29

     Gauge invariance: beauty and redundance   33

     Monopoles: Nature's missed opportunity?   37

Statistical Physics: from micro to macro physics   42

     Thermodynamics: the three laws   42

     Understanding entropy.   44

         ★ Two cultures ★   . . .   47

     Statistical mechanics   48

     Statistical thermodynamics.   51

     The ideal gas.   53

I.2   The age of geometry, information and quantum   **57**

     Canaries in a coal mine   57

The physics of space-time   60

     Special relativity   60

     General relativity   62

     Big Bang cosmology   66

     Cosmic inflation   72

         ★ Much ado about nothing ★   .   77

The physics of geometry   78

     Curved spaces (manifolds) and topology   .   80

     The geometry of gauge invariance   96

The physics of information: from bits to qubits   .   103

     Information and entropy   103

     Models of computation   106

     Going quantum   110

Quantum physics: the laws of matter   115

I.3   Universal constants, scales and units   **119**

Is man the measure of all things?   119

     On time   120

     Reinventing the meter   121

         ★ When the saints go marching in.. ★   122

How universal is universal?   125

Theories outside their comfort zone   128

     The virtue of heuristics   128

     Going quantum   133

     Natural units ©1898 Max Planck   138

Black holes   139

     Black hole thermodynamics   141

     Accelerated observers and the Unruh effect   144

     The magic cube   147

I.4   The quest for basic building blocks   **149**

A splendid race to the bottom   149

Fatal attraction: forces yield structure   153

Atomic structure   156

     The Bohr atom: energy quantization   156

The Schrödinger atom: three numbers . . 157
The discovery of spin 161
    ★ Behind the scenes ★   . . 162
Fermions and bosons 163
Atoms: the building blocks of chemistry . . 165
Nuclear structure 166
    Isotopes and nuclear decay modes 167
    Positron-emission tomography (PET) . . . 170
    Transmutation: Fission and fusion 170
        ★ Chysopoeia?★   . . . 172
    ITER: the nuclear fusion reactor 175
Field theory: particle species and forces 176
    The Dirac equation: matter and anti-matter 177
    Quantum Electrodynamics: QED 182
Subnuclear structure 186
    The Standard Model 186
    Flavors, colors and families 186
    The strong interactions 190
    The electro-weak interactions 196
    A brief history of unification. 197
    Supersymmetry 200
Superstrings 205
    Strings: all fields in one? 207
    M-theory, D-branes and dualities 217
    Holography and the AdS/CFT program . . 219
At home in the quantum world 222

Indices   **225**
Subject index Volume I 225
Name index Volume I 230

II   Quantessence:
          how quantum theory works

Contents   5

II.1   The quantum formalism: states   11
Quantum states: vectors in Hilbert space 12
        ★ Reader alert ★   . . . 12
Quantum versus classical 13
        The correspondence principle 14
Classical states: phase space 15
        The mechanics of a bit 16
Quantum states: Hilbert space 19
        States of a quantum bit 20
        The scalar or dot product 22
        A frame or basis 23
        The linear superposition principle 24
            ★ Ultimate simplicity ★   . . 24
        Ultimate simplicity: a single state system? . 24
        Qubit realizations 29
Entanglement 29
        Multi-qubit states 30
        Entangled states 31
        Schrödinger's cat 32
        Entangled vs separable states 34
        From separable to entangled and back . . 36
        Mixed versus pure states 37
        The density operator 39
        Quantum entropy 41
        Entanglement entropy 41
            ★ Botzilla ★   42
        Decoherence 43

II.2   Observables, measurements and uncertainty
                                                          47
Quantum observables are operators 47
        Sample spaces and preferred states 49
            ★Barbies on a globe ★   . . 51
        Spin or qubit Hamiltonians 52
        Frames and observables 53

Unitary transformations   55
Photon gates and wave plates   55
Incompatible observables   56
Projection operators   58
Raising and lowering operators   59
Quantum measurement   61
★ Leaving a trace ★   . . .   63
No cloning!   64
The probabilistic outcome of measurements   65
The projection postulate   66
Quantum grammar: Logic and Syntax   71
★ wavefunction collapse ★   . .   72
The case of a classical particle   74
The case of a quantum particle   74
The case of a quantum bit   77
Certain uncertainties   78
The Heisenberg uncertainty principle   . . .   79
A sound analogy   81
Heisenberg's derivation   82
Qubit uncertainties   83
★ Vacuum energy ★   . . .   84
The breakdown of classical determinism .   84
Why does classical physics exist anyway? .   85

II.3   Interference   89
Classical wave theory and optics   89
Basics of wave theory   89
Reflection, transmission, etc.   92
Beamsplitters and polarization   94
Photon polarization: optical beamsplitters .   96
Spin polarization: the Stern-Gerlach device   97
★ A Barbie's choice ★   . . .   99
Interference: double slit experiments   99
A basic interference experiment   104
A delayed choice experiment   107
The Aharonov-Bohm phase.   109
The Berry phase   113
Spin coupled to an external magnetic field.   115
Probing the geometry of state space   116
The Berry connection.   119

Quantum tunnelling: magic moves   120

II.4   Teleportation and computation   123
Entanglement and teleportation   123
The Einstein–Podolsky–Rosen paradox . .   123
The Bell inequalities   126
Hidden no more   129
A decisive three photon experiment   130
Quantum teleportation   133
★ Superposition ★   . . .   136
Quantum computation   137
Quantum gates and circuits   138
Shor's algorithm   139
Applications and perspectives   142

II.5   Particles, fields and statistics   145
Particle states and wavefunctions   145
Particle-wave duality   146
The space of particle states   148
A particle on a circle   150
Position and momentum operators   152
Energy generates time evolution   154
Wave mechanics: the Schrödinger equation   154
Matrix mechanics: the Heisenberg equation   156
Classical lookalikes   157
The harmonic oscillator   161
Coherent states   163
Fields: particle species   166
★ The other currency ★   . .   169
Particle spin and statistics   171
Indistinguishability   171
Exclusion   172
The topology of particle exchange   173
The spin-statistics connection   177
Statistics: state counting   179
More for less: two-dimensional exotics . .   182

II.6   Symmetries and their breaking   185
Symmetries of what?   186
Symmetries and conserved quantities   187

The full symmetry of the hydrogen atom . . 191
Symmetry algebra and symmetry group 192
Gauge symmetries 195
Non-abelian gauge theories 198
The Yang-Mills equations 201
The symmetry breaking paradigm 204
The Brout–Englert–Higgs (BEH) mechanism 209
Symmetry concepts and terminology . . . 212

Indices   **215**
Subject index Volume II 215
Name index Volume II   220

III   Hierarchies:
the emergence of diversity

Contents   **5**

III.1   The structural hierarchy of matter   **11**
Collective behavior and
the emergence of complexity   11
The ascent of matter 13
Molecular binding 16
The miraculous manifestations of carbon   .   18
Nano physics 21
The molecules of life 23

III.2   The splendid diversity of condensed matter   **31**
Condensed states of matter 31
Order versus disorder 38
Magnetic order 44
The Ising model 45
★ Swing states ★   . . .   50
Crystal lattices 51
Crystalization and symmetry breaking 55
Liquid crystals 58
Quasicrystals 60

III.3   The electron collective   **67**
Bands and gaps 67
Electron states in periodic potentials 67
Semiconductors. 71
Superconductivity 74
The quantum Hall effect 78
Topological order 81

III.4   SCALE   dependence   **87**
Scaling in geometry 89
Self similarity and fractals 89
The disc where Escher and Poincaré met . 91
Scaling in dynamical systems 94
The logistic map 95
Scaling in quantum theory 98

CONTENTS

Quantum mechanics 98
Quantum field theory 101
The Euclidean path integral 104
Scaling and renormalization 106
★ The quantum bank ★ . . 109
Running coupling constants 110
Mechanical analogues 110
Gauge couplings 113
Grand unification: where strong joins weak 115
Phase transitions 116
On the calculation of quantum corrections 117
Perturbation theory 117
Quantum fluctuations in QED 121
A realistic example: Vacuum polarization . 123
The cut-off and the subtraction point 125

III.5 Power of the invisible   **129**
Summary and outlook 130
The *quantessence* in retrospect. 131
Three volumes. 132
Three layers. 133
Common denominators. 136
Scenarios for past and future 139
The double helix of science and technology. 140
Trees of knowledge 141

A   Math Excursions   **151**
♣ On functions, derivatives and integrals 151
♢ On algebras 157
♡ On vectors and matrices 158
♠ On vector calculus 165
♣ On probability and statistics 170
♠ On complex numbers 174
♡ On complex vectors and matrices 176
♢ On symmetry groups 179

B   Chronologies, ideas and people   **187**

Indices   **195**
Subject index Volume III 195
Name index Volume III 199

List of Figures 201
List of Tables 207

Acknowledgements   **209**

About the author   **209**

The other side is usually a dark place?

Not necessarily. I think it has more to do with curiosity. If there is a door and you can open it and enter that other place, you do it. It's just curiosity. What's inside? What's over there? So that's what I do every day. [....,] once I start writing, I go somewhere else. I open the door, enter that place, and see what's happening there. I don't know–or I don't care–if it's a realistic world or an unrealistic one. I go deeper and deeper, as I concentrate on writing, into a kind of underground. While I'm there, I encounter strange things. But while I'm seeing them, to my eyes, they look natural. And if there is a darkness in there, that darkness comes to me, and maybe it has some message, you know? I'm trying to grasp the message. So I look around that world and I describe what I see, and then I come back. Coming back is important. If you cannot come back, it's scary. But I'm a professional, so I can come back.

The Japanese author Haruki Murikama in an interview by Deborah Treisman in The New Yorker (2019)

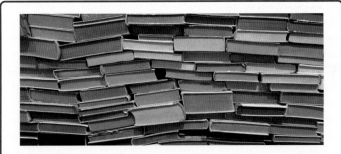

General references on quantum theory for Volume II:

— *Introduction to Quantum Mechanics*
David J. Griffiths
Pearson Education (2018)

— *Quantum Mechanics*
Franz Mandl
Wiley (2013)

— *Quantum Physics for Beginners*
Carl J. Pratt
Independent (2021)

— *The Feynman Lectures on Physics*
R.P. Feynman (Author), R.B. Leighton (Contributor), M. Sands (Contributor)
Pearson P T R; (3 Volume Set) 1st Edition (1970)

— *Quantum Mechanics: The Theoretical Minimum*
Leonard Susskind
Penguin Group (2017)

— *Principles of Quantum Mechanics*
R. Shankar
Springer (reprint of the original 1980 edition) (2013)

— *Foundations of Quantum Mechanics: An Exploration of the Physical Meaning of Quantum Theory*
Travis Norsen
Springer(2017)

Chapter II.1

The quantum formalism: states

There's no sense in being precise when you don't even know what you're talking about.

John von Neumann

Quantum theory has kept the community of physicists under its spell for over a century. It has opened new horizons for understanding a myriad of fundamental phenomena that were observed at ever deeper levels of nature, and it has produced a huge quantity of crucial results for the applied sciences. It has manifested itself in virtually all subfields of physics and from there entered into other adjacent fields like chemistry, engineering, informatics and even biology. And this process is still going on.

In this Volume we focus on the 'quantessential' features of the theory. This means that we will go into more detail with respect to the mathematical formalism underlying the theory. For pedagogical reasons we will apply it only to simple systems, and this may well give the impression that I am using a sledgehammer to crack peanuts.

The basic structure of the theory we are about to explore has far-reaching logical consequences. It will keep us busy in the following chapters on qubits, measurements, interference, entanglement and dynamics. We develop these concepts starting from the perspectives of classical physics, quantum physics and information physics. The starting point is always to define the system by the identification of its 'degrees of freedom' or basic dynamical variables.

These can be 'external', like position, momentum, angular momentum or energy, or 'internal' where one may think of electric charge or something more exotic like intrinsic spin, isospin or color charge.

In Chapter II.1 we focus on the basic notions related to quantum states, such as state vectors, Hilbert space, separable versus entangled states, pure versus mixed states and the concepts of a density matrix and quantum entropy. In Chapter II.2 we discuss the notions of observables as operators, and the probabilistic nature of a quantum measurement. We also introduce the concept of incompatible observables, frames of reference and the Heisenberg uncertainty relations.

Chapter II.3 is about quantum interference in various double slit type of experiments, but also its manifestation in the so-called Berry phase.

In Chapter II.4 we turn to quantum teleportation and quantum computation. Teleportation is the consequence of the quantessential possibility of entangled states, which will be illustrated in a number of famous experiments and paradoxes. The results of recent experiments lead to the inescapable conclusion that quantum theory is correct. This means that theories built on hidden variables and local realism are no longer tenable in view of these experiments. Concerning quantum computation we introduce the notions of quantum gates and circuits, and discuss the factorization algorithm of Shor in some detail.

In Chapter II.5 we turn to the quantum theory of particles, fields and strings and illustrate a number of quantessential properties, such as the quantum statistics of particles and the spin-statistics connection. Volume II closes with Chapter II.6, where we give an overview of the role that symmetry and symmetry breaking play in physics and quantum physics in particular.

Quantum states: vectors in Hilbert space

If we describe a physical system in the classical realm, the relevant variables like position, velocity or momentum and energy are part of the definition of the system. They are observables in that we can measure them, thereby producing dimensionful values as an outcome.

We have mentioned what in quantum physics the states look like: they are vectors in some rather abstract state space called the Hilbert space, and in this section we will show how and to what extent the ordinary physical variables can be retrieved from the state vector.

The crucial fact is that in the quantum formalism observables are not represented by just numbers but are defined as *matrices* or *operators* acting on the state space. That sounds complicated, and yes, it is. It illustrates a remark made by Paul Dirac who stipulated that matters, which at a certain moment may be considered merely as pastimes for mathematicians and logical thinkers, may turn later into tools that are indispensable for understanding nature. And if understanding nature is our goal it may be worthwhile to familiarize ourselves with these mathematical concepts, just like the pioneers of quantum theory had to do a century ago.

In this chapter we point out the quantessential differences between classical and quantum systems for the simplest of all quantum systems, the *quantum spin* or *qubit*. This two-level system plays a fundamental role in many applications of quantum theory, but is also a favorite toy-model.

The ability to control and manipulate arrays of qubits is the holy grail of quantum technology as it entails the production of quantum information processing devices that enable for novel applications, varying from quantum key distribution and teleportation to quantum computation. It is a major challenge to find physical implementations of a basic qubit that can be reliably manipulated and at the same time can be scaled to large arrays.

 Reader alert. Remarkably, in talking about quantum concepts and meaning, formulas are often easier to understand than words. However, if you are not familiar with the notion of operators and matrices, don't despair! The philosophy of the book is not to shy away from them, but to plug and play with them in the simplest imaginable cases to gain familiarity with them. As with driving lessons, you don't have to drive all the way from Spokane to Miami Beach and back to get a proper appreciation for what a highway is. I kindly request that you accept the definitions for what they are, then we will play around a bit so that you will end up throwing matrices around like ordinary numbers.

I will supplement the rather abstract algebraic language of matrices and the like, whenever possible, by more geometric images; for most people imagery provides more insight and is easier to remember. And talking about vectors and matrices, I should like to remind you of the respective *Math Excursions* at the end of Volume III, because those intros will make understanding the forthcoming chapters a lot easier. The use of a symbolic language will at least keep us from slowly getting lost in a dense fog of ever more cryptic quantum terminology and quantum vagueness. Take my word, or rather, my equations for it. □

This challenge is approached from many different angles, like quantum optical systems, superconducting devices, atoms in optical latices, ions in traps, and topologically ordered phases. Progress is rapid which means that quantum devices exploiting the fundamental features of quantum theory may well be with us in a decade or two.

Quantum versus classical

I think it is safe to say that no one understands quantum mechanics. Do not keep saying to yourself if you can possibly avoid it: 'But how can it be like that?' because you will go down the drain 'into a blind alley from which nobody has yet escaped. Nobody knows how it can be like that.'

Richard Feynman

We start by comparing the quantum and classical world generally. The fundamentally different concepts and formulations have profound consequences for the logical and deductive structure of the theories. Where do these worlds meet or separate? Actually, do they?

Classical systems. In classical physics it is usually quite obvious what the system consists of and what the possible states are. If we talk about a *particle* for example we will typically specify the state by assigning it a mass m, a position x, and a velocity v. Given the state at some initial time, Newton will tell us what the state will be at any later time, provided we know the forces that act on the particle along the way. For a *field* like the electromagnetic field we specify the field configuration, by which we mean that we give the electric E and magnetic B fields over all of space. Then the Maxwell equations tell you all about the time development of that initial field configuration, provided we know what the external charges and currents, usually called *sources*, are. The evolution of the gravitational field is described in a similar way by the Einstein

equations. Subsequently we have to combine the frameworks of Newton, Maxwell and Einstein to get the actual time development of the complete classical system of particles with and without charge and gravitational and electromagnetic fields. The structure of the theory is absolutely unambiguous, based on a clear methodology.

Yet, the coupling of the different components of fields and sources makes the system extremely nonlinear and therefore hard to solve explicitly. For example there is the intricate problem of the 'back reaction': the fields will not only change as a consequence of the movement of the charges, but in addition the accelerated charges will radiate. There are certain simple cases that can be dealt with analytically through closed expressions in terms of standard functions, but mostly that is not the case. Whereas we can solve the Newtonian two-body problem analytically, this is not the case for the three-body problem. One has to resort to numerical procedures which can become extremely cumbersome, if one insists on high accuracy, which is the case if one wants to make predictions about the behavior of the system on long time-scales. This point leads us to an additional observation that should be made concerning classical physics.

Nonlinear dynamics and deterministic chaos. We just stated that if we know for example the position and velocity of a particle at a given instant in time, the time evolution is completely fixed by Newton's laws provided we know the forces acting on the particle. This implies that any uncertainty in its evolution is driven by the limited accuracy of the initial conditions. This is not as innocuous as it sounds even if one has a huge zoo of advanced computers at one's disposal. What we have learned in the last half century from studying simple nonlinear systems is that already on a classical level, such systems – *in spite of being completely deterministic* – can exhibit chaotic behavior. In such situations it is not possible to make precise long-term predictions, because small initial uncertainties can be amplified exponentially in time by the chaotic dynamics of the nonlinear system. These systems exhibit an extreme sensitivity on initial conditions often referred to as the *butterfly effect*, meaning that a tiny change in the initial condition may lead to vastly different consequences a relatively short time afterwards. However, what concerns us here is that within classical physics there is no fundamental limit on the accuracy of measurements – by measuring more and more carefully, we can predict the time evolution of a system more and more accurately. The system is fundamentally deterministic. This is no longer true in the quantum world because there we will run into a fundamental limit on the accuracy of the simultaneous measurement of physical observables.

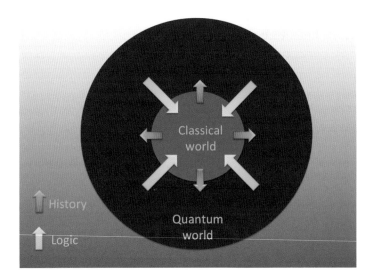

Figure II.1.2: *Classical versus quantum.* We were born in a classical world, but after exploring the nature of things we have discovered the existence of a much larger quantum world. Once these discoveries were made, we understood that the logic should be reversed: it is the classical world that can be logically deduced from the quantum world, and not the other way around.

The correspondence principle

Where classical and quantum meet. At the most basic level there are fundamental differences between the classical and the quantum frameworks. On macroscopic scales, meaning relatively large scales of space, time and energy, where we know classical physics works well, the predictions of classical and quantum theories of course have to agree. This requirement is known as the *correspondence principle*. There is no logical path that brings you from classical physics to quantum physics, but the converse is certainly possible and even mandatory. We should insist on understanding the emergence of all of classical physics from the underlying quantum description. This turns out not to be straightforward at all, but then, nobody promised us it would be. In Figure II.1.2 we have symbolically indicated the classical and quantum worlds. We contrast the direction of the historical process of scientific evolution, moving us out of the classical into the quantum domain, versus the direction of logical deductions and implications which go the opposite way. It warns us that we should not strive for an interpretation or representation of quantum content in classical terms, that would be a terribly misguided effort indeed. So, historically, quan-

tum theory emerged out of the classical theories, but logically it is the other way around, and that is inherent to the way knowledge transcends itself in the process of scientific progress.

Classical phenomena with quantum explanations. As we discussed in the previous Volume, for example in Chapter I.2, the scale of the quantum regime is set by Planck's constant h, or *h-bar* defined as $\hbar \equiv h/2\pi$, which has dimensions of $\mathrm{energy} \times \mathrm{time}$ (or equivalently $\mathrm{momentum} \times \mathrm{length}$). Because of the tiny value of this constant, we expect the quantum properties to become manifest at small time and length scales, and low temperatures. However, collective macroscopic behavior is to a large extent an indirect manifestation of the properties of the basic constituents of the system, and of the interactions between them and the environment. After all, not withstanding the striking similarities between an ant colony and human society, the even more striking differences between them can be largely traced back to the differences between an individual human being and an individual ant. Looking at matter in a similar way, one expects that radically different properties at a microscopic scale (say at the level of atomic and molecular structure) may in turn lead to fundamentally different collective behavior of these basic building blocks and therefore to different emergent properties on a macroscopic scale. So, one certainly should expect quantum manifestations on a macroscopic scale after all. Indeed, most phases of condensed matter realized in nature, such as crystals, ordinary conductors, semiconductors, superconductors or magnetic materials, all involve forms of collective behavior that can only be understood from a quantum perspective. The (meta-)stability and structure of matter is intimately linked to the quantum behavior of its fundamental constituents.

The quantum domain. Returning to the question of states, as we will see in this and the following chapters, the quantum states of bits, particles or fields are very different from their classical precursors and in the beginning it was even far from evident what the space of states would be. However, once we found out, we learned that the structure of the state-space tells us a lot about the generic features of quantum systems and how these may radically differ from their classical analogues. Studying the underlying mathematical structure will enable us to anticipate what we might expect in real physical situations. With some exaggeration one could say that everything that is not forbidden is compulsory, and henceforth will manifest itself somewhere in Nature. Nature *is* quantum.

Many exotic quantum features like particle interference or entanglement derive directly from its underlying structure, but that didn't make it any easier to demonstrate these features through experiment. Many predictions of quantum theory have lingered on the margins, waiting for experimental techniques to develop to the required level of precision. There are quite a few examples where it has taken

more than half a century before predictions could be put to the test. Science requires not only brilliance but also patience. Nowadays, many quantessential phenomena can be beautifully demonstrated by experiments exploiting superconductivity and quantum optics. There is still much more to discover, which is why we want to explore these quantum state spaces and their remarkable properties in this separate second volume. Whereas the present state of modelling real systems in nature within the quantum mechanical framework is described in the Volumes I and III, this volume is dedicated to the 'cosmic code' itself.

Classical states: phase space

The state at some time t *of a classical system is specified by assigning values to a minimal subset of dynamical variables from which all possible other variables can be calculated. We say that the state of the system corresponds to a point in phase space* $\mathcal{F}_{\mathrm{ph}}$. *We are going to discuss the case of a basic particle and work out the discrete 'Newtonian' dynamics of an Ising spin or classical bit as an example.*

Phase space. To specify the state of a simple particle, which may have a mass m and a charge q, we have to give its position $\mathbf{x}$ and its velocity $\mathbf{v}$ or momentum $\mathbf{p} = m\mathbf{v}$. The space of positions is usually called *configuration space* and denoted as $\mathcal{X}$. In three-dimensional space both position and velocity have three components because they are $\mathrm{vectors}$, and thus the *phase space* $\mathcal{F}_{\mathrm{ph}} \simeq \{\mathbf{x}, \mathbf{p}\}$ has six dimensions. From the point of view of particle dynamics, mass and charge are just fixed external parameters. Note that other dynamical variables of a particle, like its energy or angular momentum, can be expressed in terms of velocity and position and therefore can be calculated once the point in phase space is given.

A *property* corresponds to a subspace of the phase space.

A state of the system can be assigned a property, in the sense that one can decide whether a property is true or false by determining whether the point representing the state of the system is lying in or outside that subspace.

The dynamical system will develop in time according to some dynamical equations like Newton's equations of motion, and the point describing the state will move in phase space correspondingly. Furthermore in classical physics it is assumed that the point can in principle be determined to arbitrary precision by a simultaneous measurement of the basic variables thereby fixing the point in phase space. And one also assumes that observations can be made which do not disturb the system, and hence do not affect the trajectory in phase space. These assumptions are an essential Volume of the classical physics paradigm.

The mechanics of a bit

Let us now turn to a system even simpler than a single particle, which I call a *dynamical bit*. We are going to do a bit of bit mechanics. I have chosen this system because it links basic classical mechanics to basic information theory, and defines a simple quantum system as well. As we all know, a bit has two states (positions) labeled $z = 0$ and $z = 1$, so its configuration space consists of two isolated points. Introducing a discrete time step (like the clock in a computer) allows us to define a *discrete dynamics*. We distinguish two possibilities: after the time step the bit changed to the other state or it stayed where it was. This begs for an additional binary state variable which we appropriately call the *bit-momentum* p. So its value labels two distinct states of motion, where $p = 0$ means 'at rest' or $p = 1$ meaning 'on the move.'

Both the classical position and the classical momentum space consist of two points, and therefore both bit-position and bit-momentum are binary variables, which means that

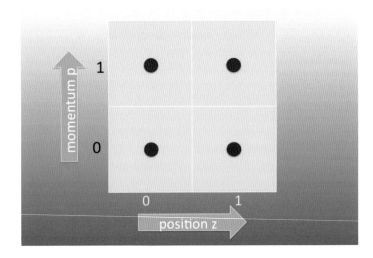

Figure II.1.3: *Phase space.* The phase space of the dynamical bit consists of four points.

all values can be added $\mathrm{mod}\,2$, meaning in particular that $1 + 1 = 0$.

Binary mechanics. The phase space for this dynamical bit corresponds to four points

$$\mathcal{F}_{\mathrm{ph}} \simeq \{p, z\} = \{0, 0; 0, 1; 1, 0; 1, 1\}$$

as indicated in Figure II.1.3. To push the comparison with Newtonian mechanics even further, one could say that the dynamical state in the absence of further interactions would be characterized by the conservation of momentum. Then with $p = 0$ the bit would be 'at rest' indefinitely, in which case the position is conserved as well, but with $p = 1$, the bit stays constantly hopping between the two position states. Depending on the initial condition one finds two fixed points and one two-cycle. The phase space picture of the possible dynamics is given in Figure II.1.4 (top). Maybe you have already noted the amusing possibility of introducing a *bit-force* F, defined *à la* Newton as the change in bit-momentum. Also F takes a binary value; $\mathrm{F} = 0$ leaves the momentum unchanged, while with $\mathrm{F} = 1$ the momentum value changes, which leads to a different dy-

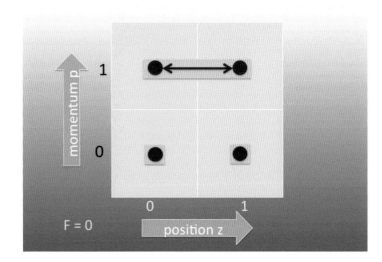

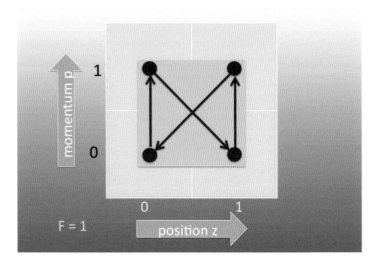

Figure II.1.4: *Bit mechanics*. Phase space picture of 'Newtonian' bit-dynamics with a binary force F being either 0 (top) or 1 (bottom). For F = 0 there are two fixed points and one two-cycle, for F = 1 there is only one four-cycle.

namic consisting of the four-cycle depicted in Figure II.1.4 (bottom). These variables are elements of a *Boolean algebra*, discussed in the *Math excursion* on algebras in Volume III.

Complementary representations. The system is clearly completely deterministic, because given the initial binary z and p values, its future states after an arbitrary number of time steps can be calculated. These discrete dynamics are like a little automaton, an updating procedure for the z-bit that depends on the p-bit. Updating means that the states of the two-bit system change and therefore the dynamics define a logical gate in the sense of digital computation. So we have arrived at four alternative ways to characterize the dynamics of the bit:

(i) as an *updating algorithm* or *iterative map* $|in\rangle \to |out\rangle$,

(ii) as a *diagram* representing the gate,

(iii) as a two-bit to two-bit *input-output table*,

(iv) and as a 4×4 matrix acting on the column vector of two-bit in-states $(p, z) = \{0, 0; 0, 1; 1, 0; 1, 1\}$.

For F = 0 this looks as follows: (i) the algorithm generating the dynamics is just,

$$(p, z) \to (p, (z + p) \bmod 2),$$

which corresponds to the (ii) diagram, (iii) state map, or (iv) the (block-diagonal)matrix as given in Figure II.1.5.

Gates and information dynamics. From the picture we learn that the two-bit dynamic is in fact generated by a two-bit gate which is well known as the *controlled* NOT- or CNOT-gate. The diagram should be read as follows: the horizontal lines correspond to the two incoming (left) and outgoing (right) bits. It is a conditioned gate, which is indicated by the vertical line from the p-bit to the z-bit. The encircled plus symbolizes a NOT-gate acting on the z-bit, but its action is conditioned on the value of the p-bit: it is activated if $p = 1$ and not if $p = 0$. The dot on the p-line indicates that it is the control bit, not changing value by passing the dot. With this interpretation it is straightforward to compute the entries of the input-output table. One puts the input state on the lines at the left and then follows the lines through the diagram to the right performing the instructions one encounters.

This matrix acts like a permutation matrix on the input column vector of two-bit in-states. Indeed, we see that on the

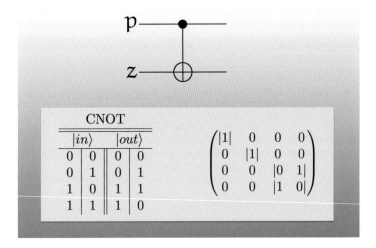

Figure II.1.5: *Three representations*. The $F = 0$ bit dynamics is generated by the CNOT-gate. In the 'block-diagonal' matrix representation on the right, we marked the two fixed points and the two-cycle.

top two entries it acts like a unit matrix, while on the bottom two entries (x) it acts like a NOT-gate.

The NEWTON gate. Imagine that we also include the 'bit-force' we defined as a third force-bit F. Then we obtain an interesting three-bit gate for the complete dynamics of the system. One finds that it can be characterized by the updating algorithm:

$$(F, p, z) \rightarrow (F, (p + F) \bmod 2, (z + p) \bmod 2),$$

which corresponds to the diagram and state map of Figure II.1.6 and the matrix in equation (II.1.1).

On the first four rows it acts like a CNOT, and in the second block it performs some sequence of permutations. In that sense this NEWTON-gate actually computes something on three bits, but from the diagram we see that it is not an irreducible three-bit gate, rather it is composed of two sequentially applied CNOT-gates. It has the following 8×8

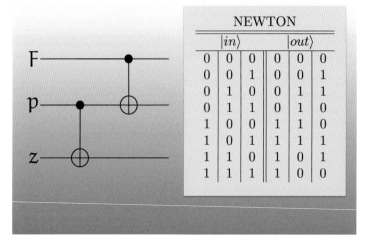

Figure II.1.6: *NEWTON-map*. The three-bit *NEWTON-gate* and the corresponding $|\text{in}\rangle \rightarrow |\text{out}\rangle$ map acting on the column vector of (F, p, z) states.

matrix structure in a basis given by the first three columns of the $|\text{in}\rangle$ states of the table in Figure II.1.4. Note that due to the four bottom entries corresponding to $F = 1$, the fourth power of the NEWTON-gate is equal to the unit matrix. Hence, the dynamics generated has indeed period four, as one would expect if the force is constant. That causes p to hop with period two and z with period four. It is the dynamics of the bottom diagram in Figure II.1.4.

$$\text{NEWTON}: \begin{pmatrix} |1| & 0 & 0 & 0 & 0 & 0 & 0 & 0 \\ 0 & |1| & 0 & 0 & 0 & 0 & 0 & 0 \\ 0 & 0 & |0 & 1| & 0 & 0 & 0 & 0 \\ 0 & 0 & |1 & 0| & 0 & 0 & 0 & 0 \\ 0 & 0 & 0 & 0 & |0 & 0 & 1 & 0| \\ 0 & 0 & 0 & 0 & |0 & 0 & 0 & 1| \\ 0 & 0 & 0 & 0 & |0 & 1 & 0 & 0| \\ 0 & 0 & 0 & 0 & |1 & 0 & 0 & 0| \end{pmatrix} . \quad \text{(II.1.1)}$$

The matrix corresponding to this NEWTON-gate, displayed above, is unitary in the sense that the transpose of the matrix is indeed its inverse. But the matrix is not symmetric, meaning that it is not a time reversal invariant process, because then the matrix would have to be its own inverse. This, however, *is* the case for the CNOT-gate represented by the matrix in Figure II.1.5 .

Conserved energies. In classical Hamiltonian mechanics one may derive the equations of motion, or the time evolution once the energy function is given, as we showed in Chapter I.1 . In the case of discrete dynamics it is less straightforward as we cannot take derivatives in the normal way. Because all variables are binary, small variations are nonexistent! The role of the Hamiltonian is played by the updating algorithm because that generates the time translation of the system. It is that mapping, which by repeated application maps out the time trajectory of the system in phase space. In these discrete cases one may invert the question by asking whether there is a (binary) energy function $E(z, p)$ that is conserved in the time series, i.e. whose value does not change for the subsequent points on a given orbit in phase space.

Let us look at some simple candidates. These can come across as slightly unusual, exactly because the energy is also a binary variable, implying that it can take only two possible values. The good thing about that is that the energy stays always bounded and therefore the system is always well-defined.

Example 1: $E = p$. You would expect the energy of a free particle to be proportional to p^2, and since p is Boolean variable we have that $p^2 = p$. The free particle does not experience any force and so one expects that the Newtonian dynamics rule $(p, z) \to (p, z + p)$ will apply. This is indeed the case where $F = 0$ which we discussed before and p is preserved. It has two fixed points with $E = 0$ and one periodic orbit of length two with $E = 1$:

$$(0, 0) \; ; \; (0, 1) \; \text{and} \; (1, 0) \leftrightarrow (1, 1)$$

Example 2: $E = F = 1$ This is the case of a non-zero constant force conserved under the Newtonian rule $(p, z) \to$

$(p + 1, z + p)$. Its action corresponds to one periodic orbit of length four with energy $E = 1$.

$$(0, 0) \to (1, 0) \to (0, 1) \leftrightarrow (1, 1) \to (0, 0) \to \cdots$$

Example 3: $Q = p + z$. The function Q is a conserved 'charge', or 'constant of the motion' under the clearly not Newtonian rule $(p, z) \to (p + 1, z + 1)$. Again it has two periodic orbits of length two which are now along the diagonals of the phase space, one with $E = 0$ and the other with $E = 1$:

$$(0, 0) \leftrightarrow (1, 1) \; \text{and} \; (1, 0) \leftrightarrow (0, 1)$$

Quantum states: Hilbert space

We discuss the generic setting of a quantum system. For a quantum system we have a set of states denoted $\{|\Psi\rangle\}$, which are vectors that correspond to elements of the so-called Hilbert space $\mathcal{H}$ of the system. The basic quantum setting introduces two novel ingredients, one is the com-plexification, and the other the linear superposition principle of states. These have dramatic consequences.

The Hilbert space of states. To explain the basic ideas of quantum theory, or for that matter of quantum information, we will in this section restrict our attention again mainly to the *qubit*, which can be viewed as the basic building block of quantum information systems. The physical state of a quantum system is described by a wavefunction which can be thought of as a vector in an abstract multidimensional space of states, called the *Hilbert space* denoted by $\mathcal{H}$. For the moment, this is just a finite dimensional vector space where the vectors have complex, rather than real, coefficients, and where the length of a vector is the usual length in such a space, i.e. the square root of the sum of the (absolute) squares of its components along the axes.

Hilbert space replaces the concept of phase space in classical mechanics. Collections of observables, or measurable variables such as spin, charge, position, or momentum, can be used to set up an orthogonal basis for the Hilbert space.

As we will see, a dramatic difference from classical mechanics with tremendous consequences is that many quantum mechanical quantities, such as position and momentum, or spin components along the x-axis and the y-axis, *cannot* be measured simultaneously. Another essential difference from classical physics is that the dimensionality of the state space of the quantum system is huge compared to that of the classical phase space. To illustrate this drastic difference, think of a particle that can move along an infinite line with an arbitrary momentum. From the classical perspective it has a phase space that is two-dimensional and real (a position x and a momentum p), but from the quantum point of view the particle is described by a wavefunction Ψ of one variable (typically the position x or the momentum p). The state is thus determined by specifying a function for all points x. As the state corresponds to a function, the state space must be a 'space of functions.' Formally such a wavefunction corresponds to an element of an infinite-dimensional Hilbert space which is a space of functions that satisfy certain restrictions. So, we go from two real numbers classically to a complex function of one variable in the quantum domain. That is quite a difference indeed! We will address the topic of quantum particles in detail in Chapter II.5.

States of a quantum bit

Now you might have thought that this is not such a big deal, because the classical state corresponds to a point in phase space and that point can be characterized by a vector in phase space. But this is not the way to think about it. We just mentioned the dynamical bit as an example of an almost trivial dynamical system. To this classical system corresponds a quantum system called the quantum bit or *qubit* for short, and the statement is that to every point in the configuration space of the classical bit we associate a basis vector of the Hilbert space. So the bit-position space consists of two points $\{1, 0\}$, and hence the Hilbert space of the qubit is two-dimensional and may be thought of as spanned by two orthogonal unit vectors $\{|1\rangle, |-1\rangle\}$.[1]

A general state of a qubit is described by a wavefunction or *state vector* $|\psi\rangle$, also called a *ket* or *ket vector*, which can be written as

$$|\psi\rangle = \alpha|+1\rangle + \beta|-1\rangle \text{ with } |\alpha|^2 + |\beta|^2 = 1, \quad (\text{II.1.2})$$

where α and β are complex numbers.[2] *Any* linear combination of the two basis states corresponds to an admissible quantum state, as long as it satisfies the *normalization condition*, meaning that the sum of the squares of the components equals one. This means that you can think of $|\psi\rangle$ as a unit vector in the 2-dimensional complex vector space, denoted $\mathbf{C}^2$ spanned by the two basis vectors $|1\rangle$ and $|-1\rangle$.

The geometry of qubit state space. What we have learned so far is that a finite state classical system will lead to a finite-dimensional complex vector space for the corresponding quantum system. Let us describe the geometry of the quantum configuration space of a single qubit in more detail. The constraint $|\alpha|^2 + |\beta|^2 = 1$ says that the state vector has unit length, which defines the complex unit circle in $\mathbb{C}^2$, but if we write the complex numbers in terms of their real and imaginary parts as $\alpha = a_1 + ia_2$ and

---

[1] We switch from a '1, 0' labeling in the classical domain, to a '1, −1' labeling in the quantum domain, these are matters of notation and of mathematical convenience as we will see later.

[2] For a tailor-made introduction to complex numbers and vectors see the *Math excursions* on pages 174 and 176 of Volume III. It is important for complex numbers that basic algebraic operations like addition, subtraction, multiplication and division can be defined. It is almost like in the musical *Annie get your Gun*: 'Everything you can do I can do better.'

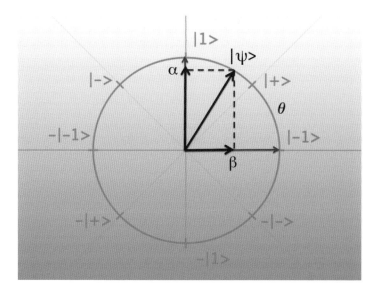

Figure II.1.7: *State decomposition.* Decomposition of a real qubit state vector $|\psi\rangle$, the purple arrow, into its components α and β with respect to the blue basis or frame $\{|+1\rangle, |-1\rangle\}$. The circle represents the subspace of the real states, and in that case we clearly have that $\alpha = \sin\theta$ and $\beta = \cos\theta$. We have marked some of the other real states that we will refer to in the text.

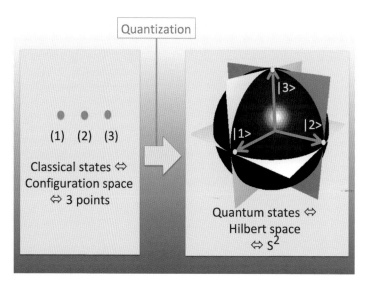

Figure II.1.8: *Configuration versus Hilbert space.* A classical system with a configuration space corresponding to a set of three points. The quantum Hilbert space for this system would correspond to the unit-sphere in the complex three-dimensional space $\mathbb{C}^3$. In the figure we show the restriction of that space to real states forming a two-sphere. Classical and quantum spaces are structurally very different. There is a 'world' in between which is described by the formalism we are about to explore.

$\beta = b_1 + ib_2$, then we obtain $|a_1 + ia_2|^2 + |b_1 + ib_2|^2 = a_1^2 + a_2^2 + b_1^2 + b_2^2 = 1$. The geometry of the space described by the latter equation is just the three-dimensional unit sphere S^3 embedded in a four-dimensional Euclidean space, $\mathbb{R}^4$ with coordinates a_1, a_2, b_1, and b_2. This three-dimensional sphere is in physics referred to as the *Bloch sphere*.

Complex rotations. At this point it is appropriate to make a side comment. As the state of a qubit is a normalized two-dimensional complex vector, the state space of a qubit corresponds to a complex circle, which in turn equals S^3. All states on the complex unit circle can be obtained by acting with all complex rotations on a given qubit state in $\mathbb{C}^2$. This is by definition the group $SU(2)$ and having argued that these vectors can be transformed into each other by the elements $U \in SU(2)$, we can also conclude that the

space of all $SU(2)$ transformations is in one-to-one correspondence with the points on the three-sphere S^3. We will use these geometric representations of state spaces and transformation groups later on, because they are easier to understand than just formulas.

Real states. For pedagogical reasons it is advantageous to limit ourselves for the moment to the subspace corresponding to $\texttt{real}$ states. This means that one only considers states for which α and β are real and the condition $\alpha^2 + \beta^2 = 1$ imposes that the states lie on an ordinary circle in $\mathbb{R}^2$. The real states are depicted in Figure II.1.7, where we have also marked some special states. Many of the formal quantum properties can be explained within this real subspace.

Alternative notations. We may represent the state by the column vector of its components:

$$|\psi\rangle \Leftrightarrow \begin{pmatrix} \alpha \\ \beta \end{pmatrix}.$$

If you like you can also map the states of the classical configuration space in the quantum picture, then the classical bit would only have the two states $|\pm 1\rangle$, corresponding to the basis vectors

$$|\pm 1\rangle \Leftrightarrow \begin{pmatrix} 1 \\ 0 \end{pmatrix}, \begin{pmatrix} 0 \\ 1 \end{pmatrix},$$

while the qubit can be any normalized linear combination of these two basis states. This makes the dramatic difference between the classical and quantum setting quite visible indeed. Each point in the configuration space $\mathcal{Z}$ of the classical system corresponds to an orthogonal basis vector of the Hilbert space, and consequently adding a point to the configuration space $\mathcal{Z}$ adds a dimension to $\mathcal{H}$. So in this picture the classical states correspond to the corners of a unit hypercube in that higher dimensional space, while the quantum states lie on the unit-hypersphere embedded in that space. This is illustrated in Figure II.1.8 for a three-state system.

The scalar or dot product

Ordinary, say 'high school' vectors are called *real* vectors. You may remember how the length $|a|$ of a vector $\mathbf{a}$ was defined as the square root of the sum of the squares of its components $|a| = \sqrt{a_1^2 + a_2^2 + \dots}$. And the dot or inner product of two vectors $\mathbf{a}$ and $\mathbf{b}$, wassimilarly as $\mathbf{a} \cdot \mathbf{b} = \sum a_1 b_1 + a_2 b_2 + \dots = |a||b|\cos\theta$, with θ the angle between them.

Conjugate states. For the state or ket vectors $|\psi\rangle$, we basically want to do the same thing, but because the vectors are complex, it is slightly more complicated. However,

once you understand the definition, a notation introduced by Dirac will make it like 'real' vectors. We first define the *dual* of the vector space in $\mathbf{C}^2$ with dual or conjugate vectors, called *bra vectors*, that can either be represented as row vectors with complex conjugated elements, where $\alpha^* \equiv a_1 - ia_2$ etc. Following the notation introduced by Dirac we write this like,

$$\langle\psi| = \langle 1|\alpha^* + \langle -1|\beta^*. \tag{II.1.3}$$

This somewhat strange nomenclature of *bra* and *ket* vectors makes more sense once you realize that they allow you to make a *bracket*, and this bracket is nothing but a scalar product of two vectors.

The inner product The *scalar (or inner, or dot) product* maps a bra-and-ket-pair into a complex number (the scalar). So if we have two state vectors $|\psi\rangle$ and $|\phi\rangle = \gamma|1\rangle + \delta|-1\rangle$ then their bracket is defined as

$$\langle\phi|\psi\rangle = \langle\psi|\phi\rangle^* = \gamma^*\alpha + \delta^*\beta. \tag{II.1.4}$$

As the components of the state vectors are complex, the dot product of two vectors is also, and it is thus no longer true that it equals the product of the lengths of the vectors and the cosine of the angle between them. But, just like in the real case, we call two vectors whose dot product vanishes *orthogonal* or *perpendicular*. Similarly, the inner product of a vector with itself, which is always a real number, is defined as the length squared of that vector.

Probability amplitudes. It turns out that the dot product of state vectors has an important physical interpretation as a *probability amplitude*, and it plays a fundamental role if we are going to talk about quantum measurements. We will discuss this extensively later in this chapter, but it is useful to preview here already the basic idea. Let us look at Figure II.1.7, where we have a state $|\psi\rangle$, and if we want the outcome with respect to the blue $\{|1\rangle, |-1\rangle\}$ frame, then the probability to find the outcome $+1$ would be the probability amplitude squared:

$$p_{+1} = |\langle 1|\psi\rangle|^2 = \langle\psi|1\rangle\langle 1|\psi\rangle = \alpha^* \alpha = |\alpha|^2 . \qquad (\text{II}.1.5)$$

This assignment of a probability to the inner product of two state vectors is called the *Born rule*, after Max Born, the quantum pioneer who proposed the probability interpretation of quantum mechanics. It is also referred to as the *Kopenhagener Deutung*, or *Copenhagen interpretation*. Clearly a similar calculation for the -1 outcome would give the probability $p_{-1} = |\beta|^2$. The normalization of the state vector is just the statement that the total probability for finding one of the two possible outcomes is one: $p_{+1} + p_{-1} = 1$. Making a measurement means that we get new information on the state and that affects the probabilities for the measurements after that. This means that the state vector has to change, because it has to reflect the probabilities of measurement outcomes at any instant. In this simple example the following happens, if we obtain $+1$ the state will change to the plus one state: $|\psi\rangle \rightarrow |1\rangle$. So the state gets 'projected' on the state, which gives that measurement outcome with unit probability. This you can interpret as saying that if you measure a quantum system and find a certain outcome, then if you repeat the measurement immediately afterwards you will find the same outcome.

Projectors. There is an alternative way to read equation (II.1.5). One needs to first look at the object,

$$P_1 = |1\rangle\langle 1|; \qquad (\text{II}.1.6)$$

this is not an inner product, but rather a *projector* on the state $|1\rangle$. If this operator acts on an arbitrary state $|\psi\rangle$, it produces the projection equal to $\langle 1|\psi\rangle$, along the $|1\rangle$ basis vector:

$$P_1 |\psi\rangle \rightarrow |1\rangle\langle 1|\psi\rangle .$$

So the probability to find an outcome $+1$ is also obtained by 'sandwiching' the projector P_1 in the state $|\psi\rangle$:

$$p_{+1} = \langle\psi| P_1 |\psi\rangle .$$

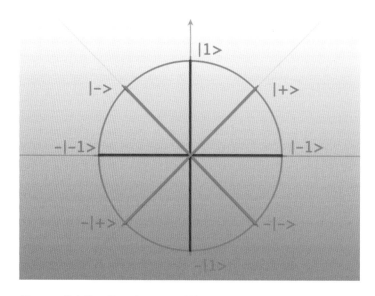

Figure II.1.9: *Two frames.* We have depicted two different frames for the two-dimensional qubit Hilbert space. The blue basis consists of the states $\{|\pm 1\rangle\}$, whereas the green basis consists of the states $\{|\pm\rangle\}$.

These probability and measurement definitions will be used extensively in the next chapter.

A frame or basis

It is convenient to choose an *orthonormal frame* consisting of unit length, mutually orthogonal basis vectors that 'span' the vector space. This amounts to choosing a set of basis vectors $|i\rangle$ with $i = -1, 1$, which have the property that:

$$\langle i|j\rangle = \delta_{ij} , \qquad (\text{II}.1.7)$$

with the Kronecker 'delta' symbol defined as follows: δ_{ij} equals one if $i = j$, and equals zero otherwise.

Note that if you think of the qubit as a spin, then the states with spin up or down point in parallel but 'opposite' directions in real space but they are represented by two *orthogonal* vectors in the state space of the quantum spin. The state space picture therefore looks similar to that of the two polarizations of a photon, which are also in real space orthogonal. Yet there remains an essential difference, the qubit is what we call a spinor while the photon is a real vector. Note also that there are many choices of frame possible, for example the states $|+\rangle$ and $|-\rangle$ also form an orthonormal frame, as is depicted as the 'green frame' in Figure II.1.9.

The linear superposition principle

The expression (II.1.2) is an expansion of the state vector $|\Psi\rangle$ in an orthonormal basis $\{|i\rangle\}$. This a general rule: for any state vector in any $D-$dimensional Hilbert-space and any choice of basis one may write:

$$|\Psi\rangle = \Sigma_i^D \, \alpha_i \, |i\rangle \, , \qquad (\text{II}.1.8)$$

where once more the α_i are the components of the state vector in that particular basis. This *linear superposition principle* is a general property and is a consequence of the fact that the Hilbert space of quantum states is a vector space. Any linear combination of state vectors is (after normalization) again a possible quantum state. It follows from there also that any state can be expanded in a complete set of basis vectors, a property we have used above.

We can now show what it means to say that a state vector $|\Psi\rangle$ has unit length by writing:

$$\langle\Psi|\Psi\rangle = \Sigma_{i,j}\alpha_j^*\alpha_i\langle j|i\rangle = \Sigma_i|\alpha_i|^2 = 1 \, . \qquad (\text{II}.1.9)$$

With what I just said, you may get worried about the Hilbert space for a real particle, because already in one dimension the configuration space is a line, corresponding to a continuum of classically allowed positions. But how then can you ever build a vector space of that continuous collection of points? That space has to be *infinite*-dimensional for a start.

Yes indeed, but in fact this can be done in a rigorous way! Our mathematical friends have shown that the space of functions on configuration space of the system is exactly the infinite-dimensional (!) Hilbert space of the type one needs to describe a particle with. The particle states correspond to functions on the classical configuration space, and as you may have guessed these are the famous wavefunctions quantum people always talk about, the functions we introduced in Chapter I.4. The functions have to satisfy the additional condition that their squares are normalizable, so that they can be interpreted as probability densities. We will explore quantum states for particles and fields in more detail in Chapter II.5.

Ultimate simplicity: a single state system?

 Let us make a small detour and imagine for a moment that you were to ask the silly question about what the quantum theory would look like for a system that has only a single state. A particle that only can be in one point. Should we waste our time with such a thing, which seems worse than thinking about how many angels can dance on the point of a needle, as the great theologian Thomas Aquinas appears to have worried about in the 13th century.

The quantum formalism would then say that this pin-point particle has a one-dimensional Hilbert space, so there is only one complex state vector that has to be normalized to one. It would look like:

$$|\psi\rangle = \alpha|0\rangle \text{ with } |\alpha|^2 = 1 \Rightarrow \alpha = e^{i\theta} \, .$$

There is only one phase and that phase is an overall phase which is not observable, as it drops out of the only possible probability amplitude $\langle 0|0\rangle = 1$, and so that finishes off the subject.

Except if we allow ourselves a minute amount of

freedom, maybe then....

So, let us imagine that this single state system represents the ground state of some real physical medium, and furthermore that possible other states in that medium have much higher energy, unreachable for the system all by itself, after all where would the energy come from? And if it were to jump up spontaneously by some quantum magic, it would plunge down instantly anyway. So we have a one-state Hilbert space for this system that corresponds to its ground state.

Now the critical readers are supposed to scratch their head and ask whether it is permitted to have two chunks of that material, both in that same ground state, but of course each with its own 'unobservable' phase. And they ask me: Sir, are two unobservable phases not a bit too much of obscurity? After all, what does *overall phase* mean in this context? Aha! Your point is well-taken. Two chunks making one system have one overall phase, but that leaves us with exactly one *relative phase*. But what is that good for, I may ask you in return. The puzzling point is indeed that we have two exactly identical pieces of exactly the same material, and we know all there is to know about them. There is nothing we can learn about them by making more measurements.

Well, let us sit back for a moment, and try to imagine some classical situations that are vaguely similar. I have two big chunks of material and I only talk about one variable, say temperature. There happen to be no thermal fluctuations because the material has infinite thermal conductivity! What you suggest is that we put one chunk in the freezer, and the other we keep exactly at room temperature. Each chunk in its own habitat is boring and stupid and nothing happens. But imagine we bring them out in thermally isolated boxes and put them on the table, and

then take away the isolation at two facing sides and move them quite close. Sure enough the temperature difference will have an effect and heat will start flowing from the hot chunk to the cold chunk. In spite of the gap in between, there will be a thermal flow which is caused by the temperature difference. After this poor classical analogue (poor, because the temperature (difference) is of course a directly measurable observable for the individual subsystems), we rush back to our quantum chunks each with their own quantum vacuum phase angle. What we did pick up is the idea that we should bring them close together and see what happens.

The Josephson junction

Often things don't have to be complicated to be interesting. What I am telling you is basically the story of the Josephson junction, referring to an effect that explains that having two slabs of superconducting material in the same superconducting ground state, but with different phase angle, one can indeed obtain a 'tunneling current' from one piece to the other! This is a truly remarkable physical effect, entirely due to the phase difference of two one-dimensional Hilbert spaces describing the same ground state. In spite of the fact that the slabs are not touching, they may quantum interact if you bring them close. And that quantum interaction turns the phase-difference into an observable.

So, how can we understand this more precisely using the Schrödinger equations for this system? We have two parts to the system with wavefunctions $|\psi_i\rangle$ $(i = A, B)$.

$$|\psi_i\rangle = e^{i\theta_i}|0\rangle.$$

The state is just the lowest state and is constant over the sample, and taking the inner product gives the Cooper pair density, the normalization is therefore that $\langle\psi_i|\psi_i\rangle = \langle 0|0\rangle = n$, because the phases cancel. This state itself is a rather non-trivial affair but that doesn't concern us here. We just have a well-defined single state. If there is no coupling between the two pieces of super-conducting material, then this is the end of the story. The situation is completely static. We find ourselves talking chunks of superconducting material, in which nothing happens as long as you stay below the energy needed to break up a Cooper-pair.

so once they are very close they can interact quantum mechanically, but not classically, the insulating material in between acts like a high potential barrier. Yet, the two pieces interact, which means that there is some weak coupling w. This situation is depicted in figure (b) and the interaction leads to

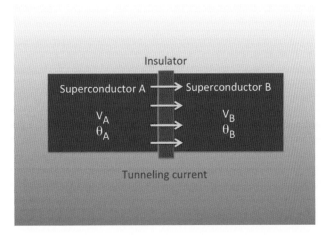

(a): *Josephson junction.* Two 'identical' slabs of superconductor with an insulating layer in between. The ground states have few parameters, a homogeneous charge density $ne \simeq |\psi|^2$, a Potential V, and a phase angle θ.

Then life gets simple again, effectively it only has an angle which is hidden and does not really count as a degree of freedom. Trivial! So that's why we discuss it here as a case of ultimate simplicity, it really is less than a single particle, less even than a qubit!

But, imagine we bring the two pieces very close, then the wavefunction will decay exponentially outside the the space in between the two pieces,

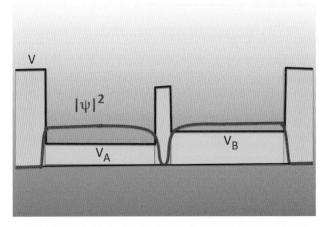

(b): *Charge density.* Potential landscape (purple curve) and charge density (red curve). The potential is minimal in the slabs, so the charges (Cooper pairs) are well confined. But at the boundaries of the slabs the wavefunction will decay exponentially, also on the insulator side, so if the insulator gap is narrow enough the wavefunctions of slab A and B will overlap and represent an interaction.

cross terms in the equations as follows:

$$i\hbar \frac{d|\psi_A\rangle}{dt} = eV_A|\psi_A\rangle + w|\psi_B\rangle, \qquad \text{(II.1.10)}$$

and a corresponding equation for $|\psi_B\rangle$ with the same V_B and a term $-w|\psi_A\rangle$.

A DC current. We start by considering the case with $V_A = V_B$. Now we don't have to solve the problem in all detail as we mainly want to know what the effect of the interaction on the charge densities is. We know that the electric current(density) J is defined as the time derivative of the charge (density), where the charge density is just $\rho = e\langle\psi_A|\psi_A\rangle$, with $-2e$ the charge of a Cooper-pair,

$$J = \frac{d\rho}{dt} = e\,\frac{d\langle\psi_A|\psi_A\rangle}{dt}\,. \qquad (II.1.11)$$

The right-hand side of this equation can be directly calculated from,

$$\frac{d\langle\psi_A|\psi_A\rangle}{dt} = \frac{d\langle\psi_A|}{dt}|\psi_A\rangle + \langle\psi_A|(\frac{d|\psi_A\rangle}{dt})\,.$$

After substituting the right-hand side of the equation (II.1.10) and its mirror we arrive at the following expression for the current:

$$J = \frac{-iew}{\hbar}(\langle\psi_A|\psi_B\rangle - \langle\psi_B|\psi_A\rangle) = \frac{2ewn}{\hbar}\,\sin(\theta_B - \theta_A)\,.$$

Defining the phase difference $\theta = \theta_B - \theta_A$, we obtain that

$$J = J_0 \sin\theta \quad \text{with} \quad J_0 = 2ewn/\hbar\,.$$

This is a stunning result! Apparently there is a DC current flowing through the junction without any potential difference, the current is basically driven by the phase difference between the two superconducting slabs!

An AC current. There is another important equation, which follows if we now in addition apply a voltage across the barrier. Then $V_A \neq V_B$, we can just solve for the phase difference θ to obtain

$$\frac{d\theta}{dt} \simeq \frac{2e}{\hbar}V\,, \qquad (II.1.12)$$

where V equals the potential difference $V \equiv V_B - V_A$. So we see that if we apply a voltage over the junction, the current becomes an AC current. This Josephson junction is a quantum device that has the remarkable feature that the frequency of the current measures the voltage!

The power delivered to the junction. Now the amount of energy is the power delivered to the junction over time, where the power is equal to the product of the current and the applied voltage $J\,V$. We can write this in terms of our fundamental angular variable:

$$U(\theta) = \int_0^t J\,V\,dt = \frac{J_0\hbar}{2e}\int_0^{\theta(t)} \sin\theta\,d\theta\,,$$

$$\rightarrow U(\theta) = \frac{J_0\hbar}{2e}(1 - \cos\theta)\,. \qquad (II.1.13)$$

We find that this energy is periodic in the phase difference, which is not so surprising if you realize that the whole setup is periodic from the start. Yet, to get to a more complete understanding we should take another contribution to the energy into account.

The charging energy. You can think of this junction as a (super) capacitor, with two (super-)conducting plates and an insulator in between. We have an AC current $J(t)$ going through, so that a charge $Q(t)$ and a related voltage $V(t)$ will build up on the capacitor. The defining relation for the *capacity* C of the capacitor is $Q = CV$, and C is a property of the junction which does not depend on time.

There is a charging energy U_Q that builds up in the capacitor, which is given by the time integral,

$$U_Q = \int_0^{Q(t)} V\,dQ = \frac{1}{2C}Q^2\,. \qquad (II.1.14)$$

A mechanical analogue. Think of the total energy function as a Hamiltonian

$$H(Q, \theta) = \frac{1}{2C}Q^2 + \frac{J_0\hbar}{2e}[\cos\theta - 1].$$

with of course also the relation,

$$Q = CV = \frac{\hbar C}{2e}\frac{d\theta}{dt}.$$

This reminds us of a simple particle Hamiltonian where the first term is the like the kinetic energy proportional to the momentum squared (the velocity being $d\theta/dt$), and the second like a potential energy. It describes a particle running around on the unit circle with an (angular) momentum Q proportional with the angular velocity $d\theta/dt$ in a nice periodic potential $U(\theta)$. This particle has a mass proportional to C and the strength of the potential is proportional to J_0. One can now check with the material we discussed in Chapter I.1, with $p = -Q$ and $q = \theta 2e/\hbar$, that (i) the dynamical equations correspond with the equations we derived for J and V, and (ii) that the total energy is indeed conserved for this mechanical system.
So this, in essence, basic quantum system, could in the end be mapped to a familiar classical system, where one can effectively apply one's good old Newtonian mechanics skills and intuitions.

This closes our Josephson-junction detour. Now you can appreciate the remarks we made in Chapter I.2 on units, equation (II.1.12) displays a direct relation between a frequency and the ratio of two universal constants which is by the way the fundamental unit of magnetic flux, $\Phi_0 = h/2e$. You can use this relation to measure that ratio, but also the other way around, knowing that ratio you can measure voltages extremely accurately. Indeed, this Josephson junction has many generalizations

called Josephson's effects with ample applications.

This answers the so-called 'silly' question we started off with. The answer is that by introducing the interaction between two 'trivial' systems they become one, and there is only one unobservable phase left, while the other, relative, phase becomes a dynamical variable and acquires physical meaning of the utmost importance.

This intermezzo illustrates in my opinion something interesting about doing physics: it is not always a matter of taking as much as possible into account, but rather, it is rather that after stripping the problem back to its minimal form that essential insights are obtained. In other words, my advice to the alert reader would be: keep pestering your teachers with silly questions, because as you see, they may not be so silly after all and may lead to stunning answers!

By the way, it was the the Welshman Brian Josephson, who won the physics Nobel prize in 1973 at 33 years of age for the discovery of what is now called the *Josephson junction*, which is in essence the system we just described. He did the work in Cambridge as a student at the age of 22. In other words, we are never too old to learn and never too young to make a difference! We will come back into more detail to these matters in Chapter III.3 on condensed matter physics in Volume III of the book.■ □

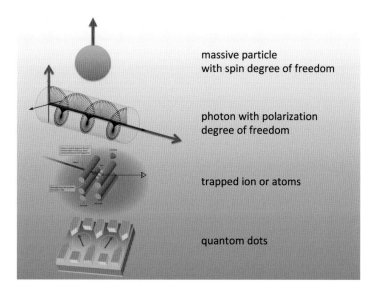

massive particle
with spin degree of freedom

photon with polarization
degree of freedom

trapped ion or atoms

quantum dots

Figure II.1.10: *Qubit realizations.* Four possible qubit realizations: (i) an atom or particle that carries spin one-half like the electron, (ii) the photon, (iii) particles trapped in optical lattices having two well-separated levels, and (iv) spins in quantum dots.

Qubit realizations

Any well-defined two level quantum system can be thought of as representing a qubit. This could also mean we restrict ourselves to a subset of two specific states of a more elaborate quantum system. Examples of two state quantum systems are:

(i) *a particle that carries half a unit of spin* like the electron, the proton or neutron. These possess two basic spin states. If we measure its spin along any direction, we always find either spin 'up' or 'down'. This spin-$1/2$ property basically has no classical analog; we have introduced its discovery and its meaning on page 161 of Volume I.

(ii) *a photon* with a fixed frequency, which possesses two basic polarization states. The photon can oscillate in any direction perpendicular to its direction of motion, and as the photon necessarily moves with the velocity of light and just cannot be put to rest, this frame is always well defined. The polarization state can always be decomposed

into two perpendicular basis states, say 'horizontal' and 'vertical'. We can arbitrarily designate one quantum state as 'spin up', represented by the symbol $|+1\rangle$, and the other 'spin down', represented by the symbol $|-1\rangle$. We illustrated some typical polarization states of a photon in Figure II.1.11. If both components are in phase with each other, we say that the photon is linearly polarized. If they are out of phase we speak of circular or elliptically polarized light, where we distinguish 'left-handed' or 'right-handed' polarization.

A photon is a qubit that necessarily travels with the speed of light. If we generate an electromagnetic wave, what we really do is making a beam of photons, and depending on the type of source, this beam maybe polarized or unpolarized. But if we make an ultra-short light pulse, it is possible to only produce a single photon.

(iii) *A particle (say atom or molecule) in one of two lowest energy states* which are well separated from the rest of the spectrum of states. A well-known example is the trapping of ions in an optical lattice.

(iv) In *quantum dots* it is possible to individually manipulate spin carrying degrees of freedom such as polarized electrons, and therefore these can in principle be assembled into quantum information processing devices.

Entanglement

It is in multi-particle and multi-qubit states that some of the most counter-intuitive and powerful aspects of quantum theory surface: in particular the notion of entanglement. In Figure II.1.12 we give a 'state of the union', a schematic overview of the multi-qubit type of states and how they are related. This schematic summarizes the content of this section.

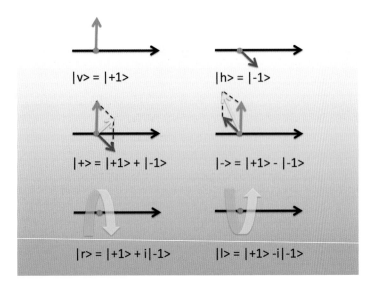

Figure II.1.11: *Photon polarizations.* Polarization states of the photon decomposed into the standard basis vectors $|+1>$ and $|-1>$. The top four are linearly polarized states, while the bottom two are circularly polarized. The polarizations in the three lines correspond to the eigenstates of the basic qubit observables, Z, X, and Y which will be defined after equation (II.2.2).

Multi-qubit states

A quantum computer needs systems of multiple qubits, called *quantum registers*. You may think of an array or network of n particles, each with its own spin. (As stated before, the formalism does not depend on the precise implementation, and it is possible to have examples in which the individual qubits correspond to degrees of freedom other than spin). The quantessence doesn't talk about how the qubits are realized, but about their underlying structural properties. The mathematical space in which the n qubits live is the *tensor product* of the individual qubit spaces, which we write as $\mathbf{C}^2 \otimes \mathbf{C}^2 \otimes ... \otimes \mathbf{C}^2 = \mathbf{C}^{2^n}$. For example, the Hilbert space for two qubits is $\mathbf{C}^2 \otimes \mathbf{C}^2$. This is a four-dimensional complex vector space spanned by the vectors $|1\rangle \otimes |1\rangle$, $|-1\rangle \otimes |1\rangle$, $|1\rangle \otimes |-1\rangle$, and $|-1\rangle \otimes |-1\rangle$. So tensor products are not about multiplying numbers or functions, but about multiplying spaces, where the product

refers to the dimensions: the product of an m-dimensional and a n-dimensional space gives an $(m \times n)$-dimensional space. So multi-qubit states live in an exponentially larger state space ($d = 2^n$). For convenience we will often abbreviate the tensor product by omitting the tensor product symbols, or by simply listing the spins. For example

$$|1\rangle \otimes |-1\rangle \equiv |1\rangle|-1\rangle \equiv |1,-1\rangle .$$

The tensor product of two qubit states with state vectors $|\psi\rangle = \alpha|1\rangle + \beta|-1\rangle$ and $|\phi\rangle = \gamma|1\rangle + \delta|-1\rangle$ is the state

$$|\psi\rangle \otimes |\phi\rangle \equiv |\psi\rangle|\phi\rangle =$$
$$= \alpha\gamma|1,1\rangle + \alpha\delta|1,-1\rangle + \beta\gamma|-1,1\rangle + \beta\delta|-1,-1\rangle .$$

An basic feature of the tensor product is that it is distributive, i.e. $(\gamma|1\rangle+\delta|-1\rangle)\otimes|\psi\rangle = \gamma|1\rangle\otimes|\psi\rangle+\delta|-1\rangle\otimes|\psi\rangle$. We emphasize once more that whereas the classical $n-$bit system has 2^n states, the $n-$qubit system corresponds to a vector of unit length in a 2^n-dimensional complex space. It is a continuous space in fact a complex hypersphere. For example a three-qubit can be expanded as:

$$\begin{aligned} |\psi\rangle \ = \ & \alpha_1|1,1,1\rangle + \alpha_2|1,1,-1\rangle + \alpha_3|1,-1,1\rangle \\ + \ & \alpha_4|-1,1,1\rangle + \alpha_5|1,-1,-1\rangle + \alpha_6|-1,1,-1\rangle \\ + \ & \alpha_7|-1,-1,1\rangle\alpha_8|-1,-1,-1\rangle . \end{aligned}$$

As before it is convenient to denote the state vector by the column vector of its complex components $\alpha_1, \alpha_2, ..., \alpha_{2^n}$.

When dealing with multi-qubit states, we have to make clear distinctions between various types of states. These are important in discussions to come later, yet I want to present them here all at once, without elaborating too much on their specific roles yet. It is nice to compare them and contrast them with each other. First of all there are the so-called *pure states* and those are the states we have been talking about so far. The pure multi-qubit or multi-particle states break up into two types, the *separable* and the *entangled* states. The notion of entanglement and its dramatic physical implications are the subject of Chapter II.4,

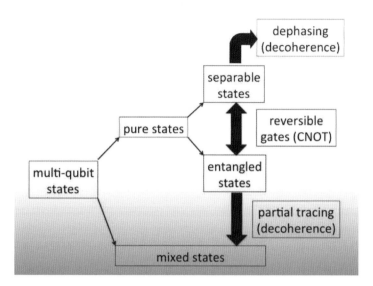

Figure II.1.12: *Multi-qubit states.* An overview of the types of multi-qubit states and the relations between them.

fluence the systems separate again, they can no longer be described in the same way as before, viz. by endowing each of them with a representative of its own.

I would not call that *one* but rather *the* characteristic trait of quantum mechanics, the one that enforces its entire departure from classical lines of thought. By the interaction the two representatives [the quantum states] have become *entangled.*

E. Schrödinger, 1935

Entanglement is a direct consequence of the linear superposition principle applied to multi-qubit or multi-particle states. If qubits are entangled this means that successive measurement outcomes on the two qubits will be highly correlated, implying that quantum theory is fundamentally non-local.

about the Einstein–Podolski–Rosen paradox and quantum teleportation.

If we talk about realistic quantum systems that couple to some environment or 'classical' measurement device, we often have to deal with states that are not pure but *mixed* states. To deal with both pure and mixed states it is convenient to introduce the *density operator*, which provides a unified framework for all types of states. This concept was introduced by Von Neumann in the early days of quantum theory as an alternative to the wavefunction or state vector approach. These are the topics that I will focus on in the remainder of this section.

The quantum states of systems consisting of spatially separated components (e.g. two particles) can be *entangled*, which implies that they can no longer be treated independently and therefore measurements made on one can have instantly consequences for the other! This is indeed a quantessential feature of reality that dramatically departs from the classical description of such a system. It is this 'entanglement' property that lies at the root of a zoo of so-called quantum paradoxes, such as Schrödinger's cat and the EPR paradox and more generally the quantum measurement problem. But it is also essential for understanding the Bell inequalities which pose a rigorous quantitative bound on classically allowed correlations; bounds that have been observed to be violated in quantum systems. Entanglement furthermore plays an essential role in fashionable and promising subjects like quantum teleportation. We return to these topics in Chapter II.4. In this section we will merely touch on some of these aspects.

Entangled states

When two systems, of which we know the states by their respective representatives, enter into temporary physical interaction due to known forces between them, and when after a time of mutual in-

Figure II.1.13: *Bohr and Einstein in one of their debates.* (Source: (Photo made in 1930 by Paul Ehrenfest, courtesy AIP Emilio Segrè Visual Archives)

Schrödinger's cat

When we have more than one qubit an important practical question is when and how measurements of a given qubit depend on measurements of other qubits. Because of the deep properties of quantum mechanics, qubits can be coupled in subtle ways that produce consequences for measurement that crucially differ from classical bits. Understanding this has proved to be important for questions relating to quantum computation and information transmission. To explain this we need to introduce the opposing concepts of separability and entanglement, which describe whether measurements on different qubits are statistically independent or statistically dependent.

This notion of entanglement as a necessary consequence of the quantum postulates led to the infamous problem of

Schrödinger's cat. This problem was well described by Schrödinger himself:[3]

> '[...]Man kann auch ganz burleske Fälle konstruieren. Eine Katze wird in eine Stahlkammer gesperrt, zusammen mit folgender Höllenmaschine (die man gegen den direkten Zugriff der Katze sichern muss): in einem Geigerschen Zählrohr befindet sich eine winzige Menge radioaktiver Substanz, so wenig, dass im Laufe einer Stunde vielleicht eines von den Atomen zerfällt, ebenso wahrscheinlich aber auch keines; geschieht es, so spricht das Zählrohr an und betätigt über ein Relais ein Hämmerchen, dass ein Kölbchen mit Blausäure zertrümmert. [...]'

and[4]

> [...] Hat man dieses ganze System eine Stunde lang sich selbst überlassen, so wird man sich sagen, dass die Katze noch lebt, wenn inzwischen kein Atom zerfallen ist. Der erste Atomzerfall würde sie vergiftet haben. Die Psi-Funktion des ganzen Systems würde dass so zum Ausdruck bringen, dass in ihr die lebende und die tote Katze

---

[3]It is also possible to construct very burlesque fables. A cat is locked into a steel chamber, together with a poisoning contraption consisting of a hammer and a flask (which must be secured against direct access by the cat): and a Geiger counting tube containing a minute amount of radioactive substance, so little that in the course of an hour perhaps one of the atoms breaks up, but equally probably none; if it happens, then the counting tube responds and, via a relay, releases the hammer that crushes a little flask with blue-acid.

[4][...] After one has left this whole system for an hour, one will say that the cat is still alive if no atom has decayed, as the first atomic decomposition would have poisoned it. The wavefunction of the whole system would thus express the fact that in it the living and the dead cat are mixed or smeared in equal parts. That an indeterminacy confined to the atomic realm translates into indiscernible indeterminacy, which can then be removed by direct observation. This prevents us, in such a naive way, from considering such a 'washed out model' as an image of reality ...

Figure II.1.14: *Schrödinger's cat state.* Artist impression of a quantum cat in the state: $|\psi_{cat}\rangle = |alive\rangle + |dead\rangle$. (Source: JSTOR Daily.)

(s. v. v.) zu gleichen Teilen gemischt oder verschmiert sind. Das Typische an solchen Fällen ist, dass eine ursprünglich auf den Atombereich beschränkte Unbestimmtheit sich in grobsinnliche Unbestimmtheit umsetzt, die sich dann durch direkte Beobachtung entscheiden lässt. Das hindert uns, in so naiver Weise ein "verwaschenes Modell" als Abbild der Wirklichkeit gelten zu lassen...'

A cat in our classical world can either be dead or alive, and taking this quantum assumption to its logical extreme, this cat could in principle be in a state that it is a linear superposition of 'alive' and 'dead'. This property of quantum mechanics is simple to spell out but is radically different from the way we talk about physical states in classical physics. This difference derives directly from the quantessential principle that allows us to consider linear superpositions of states, which therefore seems problematic from the start.

The cat sits in a closed box with some food but also with

a lethal contraption consisting of a small quantity of a radioactive substance, or a single metastable atom for that matter. If that atom decays, it emits a photon that hits a detector which subsequently triggers a device which breaks a little capsule filled with a poisonous gas that in turn will kill the cat. This unfortunate scenario suggests that in this situation the states of the atom labeled $|decayed\rangle$ or $|not\ decayed\rangle$ are entangled with the states $|alive\rangle$ or $|dead\rangle$ and we write:

$$|\psi_{cat}\rangle = |not\ decayed\rangle \otimes |alive\rangle + |decayed\rangle \otimes |dead\rangle ,$$

because the other states in the $atom \otimes cat$ state space have zero coefficient, and we have assumed that both terms are equally probable. What the formula above expresses is that the undetermined state of the atom is entangled with the states of the cat.

It seems a far-out proposal of a fundamental theory of nature to take such states seriously. At the heart of this problem lies the following question: if quantum mechanics is the underlying reality of everyday life described by the laws of classical physics, then it should be possible to understand these classical laws from the quantum laws. There may be no logic that leads you from classical to quantum theory but there should be a derivation of the laws of classical physics starting from the quantum laws, because classical physics is just an approximation of quantum physics, and such approximations should be well understood. We should compare this to how classical Newtonian mechanics can be obtained as the limit of relativity where we send the speed of light c to infinity. The analogy suggests that in quantum theory we just have to send Planck's constant $\hbar$ to zero, and yes, in many cases this is what we have to do, but such direct approaches do not resolve issues like Schrödinger's cat. The question has lead to numerous deep philosophical arguments among physicists and philosophers right from the inception of quantum mechanics in the beginning of the twentieth century, and we will return to 'Schrödinger's cat' in later chapters. For the moment we just want to give a more accurate definition of the different types of states for simpler systems.

Entangled vs separable states

Let us now turn to precise definitions of multi-qubit states. The n-qubit state is called *separable* if it can be written as a single product of n single-qubit states[5], i.e. if it can be written as $n - 1$ tensor products of sums of qubits, with each factor depending only on a single qubit. An example of a separable two-qubit state is

$$|\psi\rangle = \frac{1}{2}(|1, 1\rangle + |1, -1\rangle + |-1, 1\rangle + |-1, -1\rangle),$$

because it can be written like

$$|\psi\rangle = \frac{1}{2}(|1\rangle + |-1\rangle) \otimes (|1\rangle + |-1\rangle) = |+\rangle |+\rangle.$$

If an n-qubit state is separable, then measurements of individual qubits are statistically independent, i.e. the probability of outcomes of a series of measurements of different qubits can be written as a product of probabilities of the measurements for each qubit. These outcomes are uncorrelated and the overall outcome is therefore independent of the order in which these measurements are performed.

If an n-qubit state is not separable, then it is per definition *entangled*. An example of an entangled two-qubit state is,

$$|\psi\rangle = \frac{1}{\sqrt{2}}(|1, 1\rangle + |-1, -1\rangle), \qquad (\text{II.1.15})$$

which indeed is a linear superposition which cannot be factored into a single product. If we have a pair of qubits in an entangled state, subsequent measurements of the individual qubits do depend on each other. If you first make a measurement on the first bit, then that measurement will *instantaneously* affect the two-bit state and possibly the

---

[5]Strictly speaking this is only true for pure states, which we define in the next section.

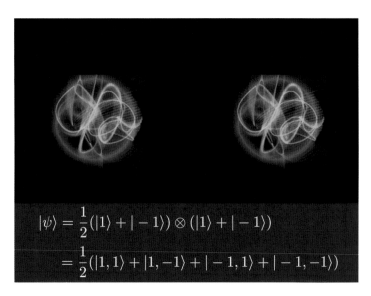

Figure II.1.15: *Separated pair.* The state vector for the pair is a product of the individual state vectors.

state of the other bit, even if that is spatially arbitrarily far away. The measurement thereby influences a later measurement outcome of the second bit. Now the use of that word 'instantaneous' should make you feel uneasy in view of the theory of relativity, and correctly so. Some great physicists – like Einstein to mention one – felt the same way and preceded you. This thought-provoking question unleashed a deep, but also longwinded debate about the foundations of quantum theory, already among its founders.

Let me illustrate this point for the examples we gave above. Suppose we do an experiment in which we measure the spin of the first qubit and subsequently measure the spin of the second qubit. For both the separable and entangled examples, there is a 50% chance of observing either spin up or spin down on the first measurement. Suppose it gives spin up. For the separable state this transforms the

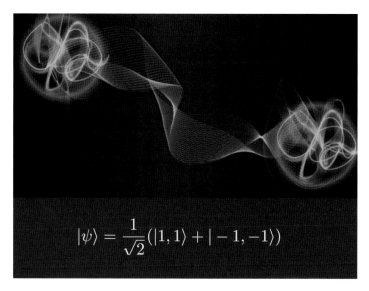

$$|\psi\rangle = \frac{1}{\sqrt{2}}(|1,1\rangle + |-1,-1\rangle)$$

Figure II.1.16: *Entangled pair.* Artist impression of what an entangled state of a pair would look like. It gives at least a feeling for it, maybe more so than the formula below telling you exactly what it is.

state vector as follows:

$$\frac{1}{2}(|1\rangle + |-1\rangle) \otimes (|1\rangle + |-1\rangle)$$
$$\rightarrow \frac{1}{\sqrt{2}}|1\rangle \otimes (|1\rangle + |-1\rangle) = \frac{1}{\sqrt{2}}(|1,1\rangle + |1,-1\rangle),$$

it means that the measurement projects the initial qubit state $|\psi\rangle$ on the first line onto the state $|\psi'\rangle$ in the second line. One may verify that the probability amplitude in analogy with equation (II.1.5) equals $|\langle\psi'|\psi\rangle|^2 = 1/2$ as it should. The same probability would have resulted for the spin down measurement.[6]

So only the $|1\rangle$ component of the first qubit survives after the measurement. If we now measure the spin of the second qubit in the state $|\psi'\rangle$, the probability of measuring spin up or spin down is still 50%. And as mentioned before, the previous measurement on the first qubit has no

[6]We will deal with the observables and measurements more extensively in the next chapter.

effect on the second measurement. As we have already noted, it is a generic property of separable states that subsequent measurement outcomes on individual spin states are independent, and the outcomes do not depend on the order in which we perform the measurements.

Let us now consider a similar experiment on the entangled state of equation (II.1.15) and observe spin up in the first measurement. This changes the state-vector to

$$|\psi\rangle = \frac{1}{\sqrt{2}}(|1,1\rangle + |-1,-1\rangle) \rightarrow |\psi'\rangle = |1,1\rangle. \quad \text{(II.1.16)}$$

(Note the 'disappearance' of the factor $1/\sqrt{2}$ due to the necessity that the projected state vector remains normalized). If we now measure the spin of the second qubit, we are certain to observe spin up! Similarly, if we observe spin down in the first measurement, we will also see that in the second qubit with 100% certainty. For this entangled example the measurement outcomes are completely correlated – the outcome of the first completely determines the second, and the state is therefore called maximally entangled. As this also holds for entangled qubits which are light years apart, this instantaneous effect on the state implies a puzzling if not bizarre form of non-locality in the quantum world that at first sight appears to violate causality.

Bertlmann's socks. There has been a debate among physicists like John Bell and others about what it is that sets quantum entanglement really apart. The conundrum goes by the name *Bertlmann's socks.* Mr Bertlmann, a real-life early collaborator of Bell at CERN, happens to always wear socks of a different color. So, Mr Bertlmann, whose socks have risen to eternal fame, constitutes a system which has the unusual property that if you get to see one of his socks to be 'red' for example, then instantaneously you are able to conclude that the other sock has the property 'not red'. So here is a form of non-locality. You measure one sock and are hundred percent sure about a property of the other sock which is elsewhere. So, the conditional probability given sock #1 is red, for sock #2 to be 'not red', is one. Is that not a classical version of quantum entanglement? It looks like it, the states of the socks are highly correlated indeed, and knowing the state of the first affects the probability distribution for the other. It doesn't change the socks or their color: it just affects the probability of measurement outcomes. And there is nothing unusual, absurd or stunning about that. It is very much true that the state of the socks is not affected. There is no signal exchanged between the socks, since they are in a definite state which is there to stay.

The quantessence of entanglement. The quantum catch is that there is one additional feature in the quantum framework that has no classical analogue and which sets the EPR paradox apart. In the qubit experiment there is an additional freedom for making the measurements, one is free to choose the frame or polarization of a measurement. In the example of the entangled state given in (II.1.16), we could have chosen the measurement for the first qubit not in the $(|1\rangle, |-1\rangle)$ frame, but for example of in the $(|+\rangle, |-\rangle)$ frame. Then, given the outcome of that measurement for example to be plus one, we know that the second qubit has to be in the $|+\rangle$ state. Keeping the measurement for the second qubit as before in the $(|1\rangle, |-1\rangle)$ frame, the probability to find the outcome to be plus or minus one is 50% for each. This dependence of the probability of the second outcome on the choice one makes for the first measurement is what makes the situation non-local, because now, dependent on the frame choice and the outcome plus one for the first measurement, the second qubit flips instantaneously to the $|1\rangle$ or $|+\rangle$ state. And this looks very much like an instantaneous action at a distance, the state of the second *is* affected, and therefore causality should be violated. Is it?

The answer is: no! As we have already, and will explore more extensively in the following chapters, the quantum state is like a probability amplitude, which encodes a probability distribution for measurement outcomes. Multi-qubit states, separable or entangled, encode all possible corre-

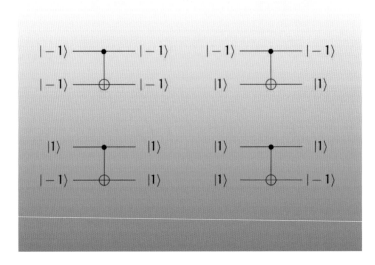

Figure II.1.17: *CNOT gate.* The circuit diagram is basically a two-qubit interaction diagram, representing the action of the CNOT gate on the four possible two-qubit basis states. As pointed out in Figure II.1.5, the dot on the upper qubit denotes the control and the cross is the symbol for the conditional one-qubit NOT gate.

lations that may or may not exist between sequences of measurement outcomes. And a closer look at the examples given above does precisely that, they show how unconditional probabilities, turn into conditional probabilities which are different indeed. And since in the quantum world there are basically only probabilities, the measurements of entangled states are easier to grasp if you think of 'states' as encoding probability distributions. We return to these questions in the section on the Einstein–Podolsky–Rosen paradox in chapter II.4.

From separable to entangled and back

For two qubits in a separable state to get entangled they need to interact somehow. In quantum information language that would mean that they have to be acted upon by some two-qubit gate. Let us take our favorite CNOT-

gate of Figure II.1.5, it acts on the state $|A\rangle \otimes |B\rangle$ as follows:

$$\text{CNOT} : |A\rangle \otimes |B\rangle \Rightarrow |A\rangle \otimes |[-AB]\rangle .$$

In other words, the CNOT gate flips the state of B if $A = 1$, and does nothing if $A = -1$.

For convenience we give the explicit action on the basis states in Figure II.1.17, which allows you to verify that if we let the CNOT gate act on the separable state $|+\rangle \otimes |-1\rangle$ it indeed generates a maximally entangled state (II.1.15):

$$\text{CNOT} : |+\rangle \otimes |-1\rangle \Rightarrow \frac{1}{\sqrt{2}}(|1,1\rangle + |-1,-1\rangle) . \quad \text{(II.1.17)}$$

Note that this gate is reversible, as one can immediately see from the figure, $\text{CNOT}^2 = 1$.

In fact, from an intuitive point of view the ability to generate substantial speed-ups using a quantum computer vs. a classical computer is related to the ability to operate on the high dimensional state space including the entangled states. To describe a separable n-qubit state with k bits of accuracy we only need to describe each of the individual qubits separately, which only requires of the order of nk bits. In contrast, to describe an n-qubit entangled state we need of the order of k bits for each dimension in the Hilbert space, implying that we need of the order of $2^n k$ bits. If we were to simulate the evolution of an entangled state on a classical computer we would have to process all these bits of information and the computation would be extremely slow. Quantum computation, in contrast, acts on all this information at once – a quantum computation acting on an entangled state is just as fast as one acting on a separable state. This is exactly the type of parallelism at the intermediate stages of computing that we referred to before. Thus, if we can find situations where the evolution of an entangled state can be mapped into a hard mathematical problem, we can achieve spectacular speed-ups.

Mixed versus pure states

The states we have been dealing with so far were statistically pure, or more simply, *pure states*. In spite of the quantessential uncertainties in such states, the state vector is the most complete knowledge about a quantum state that is available. In real life however it may prove very difficult to prepare a system in a pure state. After all, quantum phenomena are not that easy to detect, which means that pure states apparently are not so common. Somehow a lot of the quantum stuff gets washed away in ordinary life, quantum does not hit the eye, so to speak. The reason is that quantum systems are permanently interacting with their environment, and it is only in situations where we take exceptional care to protect our quantum system from those influences, that we can observe pure quantum behavior. This is not easy; it certainly is not the case in most situations which arise naturally, and that is precisely why we perceive the world around us as completely classical. Turning this reasoning around you may ask that given the underlying world is entirely quantum, why there is such a thing as the classical world, and how it comes about. How can we understand the laundering of all that quantum exotica? This is the basic question one has to face in a detailed treatment of quantum measurement, which has to account for how we can start up with a quantum process and end up reading dials and counting macroscopic signals like clicks, or pulses and what not. It is here that we have to introduce the concept of a *mixed state*, and contrast it with a pure state whether entangled or not. And indeed it is often through the interaction with the environment that states get 'mixed up', just like humans do. We have to deal with mixed up people all the time, and we learned to deal with that! Let us be pedantic and illustrate the distinction between between a pure and a proper mixed state with the experimental setup depicted in Figure II.1.18. An incoming beam is polarized and each of the particles is in the pure state $|+\rangle$ i.e. with $X \sim +1$. Now we send them through a Z polarizer in (b). What we find

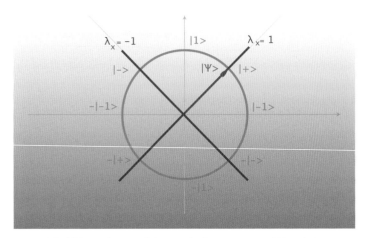

(a) All incoming particles are in the pure state $|\psi\rangle = |+\rangle$.

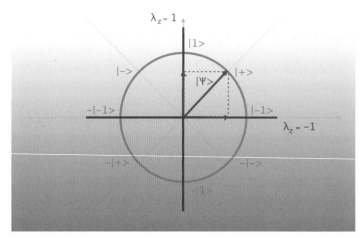

(b) The incoming beam goes through a Z polarizer

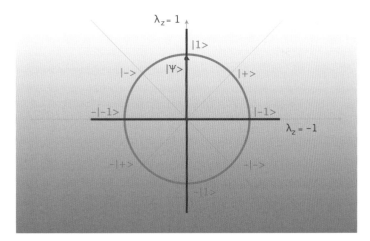

(c) Half of the particles in the outgoing beam are in the pure state $|\psi\rangle = |1\rangle$.

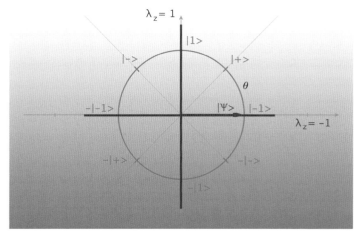

(d) The other half of the particles in the outgoing beam are in the pure state $|\psi\rangle = |-1\rangle$.

Figure II.1.18: *Mixed state.* Graphical representation of how to prepare a beam of particles in a proper mixture and corresponding mixed state. For the incoming particles in figure (a) the density matrix is given by equation (II.1.23), in the outgoing beam (c)+(d) the particles have the density matrix of equation (II.1.24)

behind the polarizer is a beam of particles, but now 50% of the particles is in a pure state $|1\rangle$ (c) and the other 50% is in a pure state $|-1\rangle$ (d). Now we could combine the particles in single beam (without letting them interfere), then each of the particles is still in a pure state, but the beam is now a statistical mixture of particles in $|\pm 1\rangle$ states. The beam represents a classical ensemble of particles that is in a *mixed state*. This is called a *proper mixture* to be distinguished from the improper mixture to be discussed shortly. In the present situation there is a non-zero probability for the particle to be in any one of two pure states. So picking out one particle there is a 50% chance it is in a pure up-state and a 50% chance it is in the down-state, but – and this is crucial – it is not a state corresponding to a linear superposition of the up and down-state, that would just be the 'plus' state, $|+\rangle$!

This mixed state is a classical statistical mixture and not a quantum superposition. What makes this setting a bit confusing is that we now have two types of probability to keep track of, the quantum probabilities we have been talking about so far and in addition the probability distribution of the classical ensemble.

To further clarify this notion, let me point out that a naive but *wrong* way is to write for the state of the particle something like $|\psi_{mix}\rangle = \sum_i p_i |\psi_i >$. This looks dangerously close to the usual expansion of a pure state into a certain basis $|\psi\rangle = \sum_k \alpha_k |\psi_k >$. But there the coefficients are probability amplitudes α_k leading to probabilities $p_k \simeq |\alpha_k|^2$. To put it differently, with the troublesome trial notation I just proposed we would get that the expectation or average value[7] of an observable A in a mixed state $|\psi_{mix}\rangle$ would become $\langle\psi_{mix}| A |\psi_{mix}\rangle \sim \sum p_i p_j \ldots$, an expression that is proportional to probabilities squared, which makes no sense.

---

[7] I apologize for getting ahead of myself, as observables and their expectation values are to be discussed in detail in the next chapter on page 51.

What we want is a weighted average over ordinary pure state expectation values:

$$\langle A\rangle = \sum_a p_a \langle\psi_a|A|\psi_a\rangle . \qquad (II.1.18)$$

In this expansion the states $|\psi_a\rangle$ are some set of pure states. These don't have to be orthogonal, so it could be that $|\psi_1\rangle = |1\rangle$ and $|\psi_2\rangle = |+\rangle$ for example. It is for this reason that once we admit both mixed states and pure states it is almost imperative to use the density matrix formalism because it treats both type of states on an equal footing.

The density operator

The famous mathematical physicist John von Neumann developed an alternative formalism for quantum mechanics in terms of what is called a *density operator*, which basically replaces the wavefunction, or state vector, right from the start.

The density operator formulation, as we will see shortly, leads in a natural way to the definition of what is called the *Von Neuman entropy* for a quantum system.

Proper mixtures. Consider as we just did, a mixed state in which there is a probability p_a for the system to have wavefunction ψ_a and an observable A with an expectation value (II.1.18). The density operator defined for a pure state is just the projection operator we introduced in (II.1.6) for that state:

$$\rho = P_i = |\psi_i\rangle\langle\psi_i| ,$$

and the density operator for a properly mixed state is quite naturally defined as:

$$\rho = \sum_i p_a |\psi_a\rangle\langle\psi_a| , \qquad (II.1.19)$$

which reduces naturally to the pure state case above if $p_a = p_i = 1$ for a single value of i. To obtain the *density matrix*, we have to expand this operator in an orthonormal basis. We start with

$$\rho = \sum_{ajk} p_a \alpha_j^{(i)} \alpha_k^{*(i)} |\chi_j\rangle\langle\chi_k|,$$

where the $\alpha_j^{(i)}$ are the expansion coefficients of the pure state $|\psi_a\rangle$ in the $\{|\chi_j\rangle\}$ basis. The density matrix is defined by the matrix elements of the density operator:

$$\rho_{mn} = \langle\chi_m|\rho|\chi_n\rangle = \sum_i p_i \alpha_m^{(i)} \alpha_n^{*(i)} \qquad \text{(II.1.20)}$$

With density matrices the notion of a trace is convenient. Recall that the trace of a matrix is the sum of the diagonal elements, so we have for example that,

$$\mathrm{tr}\,\rho = \sum_i p_i (\sum_m \alpha_m^{(i)} \alpha_m^{*(i)}) = \sum_i p_i = 1,$$

because the sums over m equal one for each value of i. The expectation value (II.1.18) is compactly expressed as:

$$\langle A\rangle = \mathrm{tr}\,(A\rho), \qquad \text{(II.1.21)}$$

and because the trace $\mathrm{tr}(A\rho)$ is independent of the chosen basis this expression can be evaluated in any convenient basis, and so provides an easy way to compute expectation values in any state. Note that for a pure state $p_a = 1$ for one particular value of $a = i^*$, and $p_a = 0$ for $a \neq i^*$. In this case the density matrix has rank one. This becomes clear if we write the matrix ρ in a basis in which it is diagonal, because then there will only be one non-zero element. When there is more than a single non-zero value of p_a it is a mixed state and the rank is larger than one.

Finally note that if we chose the unit matrix as the trivial observable we get the trace of ρ itself, which equals one by definition. This property will be used if we consider partial traces, which refer to the density matrix of subsystems, later on. The best way to think about the density matrix of a proper mixture is as a classical distribution over pure quantum states. It is an essential concept if we want to

understand and describe quantum measurements in more detail. In particular if we are to include the measurement apparatus in the analysis, and want to understand how we get from quantum to classical physics: from a pure quantum state to a macroscopic pointer on a dial.

To get a better feeling for how a density matrix works, consider a few simple examples of single qubit states. First look at a spin in a pure state with $|\psi\rangle = |1\rangle$. The density operator corresponds to the corresponding projection operator.

$$\rho = |1\rangle\langle 1| \Leftrightarrow \rho_{mn} = \begin{pmatrix} 1 & 0 \\ 0 & 0 \end{pmatrix}. \qquad \text{(II.1.22)}$$

The expectation of the spin polarization operator along the z-axis becomes

$$\mathrm{tr}(Z\rho) = \mathrm{tr}\left(\begin{pmatrix} 1 & 0 \\ 0 & -1 \end{pmatrix}\begin{pmatrix} 1 & 0 \\ 0 & 0 \end{pmatrix}\right) = \mathrm{tr}\begin{pmatrix} 1 & 0 \\ 0 & 0 \end{pmatrix} = 1,$$

as expected. Likewise we could construct the *density matrix* corresponding to another pure state $|+\rangle$ as

$$\rho = |+\rangle\langle +| = \frac{1}{2}(|1\rangle + |-1\rangle)(\langle 1| + \langle -1|) \Leftrightarrow \frac{1}{2}\begin{pmatrix} 1 & 1 \\ 1 & 1 \end{pmatrix}.$$
$$\text{(II.1.23)}$$

Now the expectation value of Z is

$$\mathrm{tr}(Z\rho) = \frac{1}{2}\mathrm{tr}\left(\begin{pmatrix} 1 & 0 \\ 0 & -1 \end{pmatrix}\begin{pmatrix} 1 & 1 \\ 1 & 1 \end{pmatrix}\right) = \frac{1}{2}\mathrm{tr}\begin{pmatrix} 1 & 1 \\ -1 & -1 \end{pmatrix} = 0,$$

as it should. If, however, the system is in a mixed state with 50% of the population spin up and 50% spin down the density matrix becomes

$$\rho = \frac{1}{2}(|1\rangle\langle 1| + |-1\rangle\langle -1|) \Leftrightarrow \frac{1}{2}\begin{pmatrix} 1 & 0 \\ 0 & 1 \end{pmatrix}. \qquad \text{(II.1.24)}$$

In this case the expectation of the spin along the z-axis, which is $\mathrm{tr}(Z\rho)$, is zero again as it should be, because the probability for a particle in the mixed state to contribute $+1$ is equal to the probability to contribute -1 to the expectation value. The particle represents a classical statistical ensemble of particles that are either in a definite quantum 'up' or a definite quantum 'down' state.

Quantum entropy

The introduction of the density matrix allowed Von Neumann to extend the fundamental concept of entropy to the quantum domain. He defined the entropy of a quantum state in analogy with the Gibbs entropy for a classical ensemble as

$$S(\rho) = -\mathrm{tr}\,\rho \log \rho = -\sum_i p_i \log p_i. \qquad \text{(II.1.25)}$$

Where the right-hand side directly follows from the definition (II.1.19). *The entropy of a quantum state provides a quantitative measure of 'how mixed' a system is because the entropy of a pure state is equal to zero, whereas the entropy of a mixed state is always greater than zero.* Let us check this with the examples of the previous subsection. In the cases with pure states we have first considered (II.1.22) where $p(+1) = 1$ and $p(-1) = 0$ which for the quantum entropy yields $S_{\mathrm{pure}} = -1 \log 1 - 0 \log 0 = -1 \cdot 0 = 0$. This reflects that if you know the pure state a system is in, you know everything there is to know about it, and therefore there is no hidden information and the entropy should be zero and happily that is true. For the properly mixed case of (II.1.24) we found $p(+1) = p(-1) = 1/2$, and we obtain that $S_{\mathrm{mixed}} = -2 \cdot \frac{1}{2} \log \frac{1}{2} = \log 2$, which corresponds to the information of one bit. And it is here that we make contact with the definition by Shannon of information being proportional to the entropy as defined by Boltzmann and Gibbs. We see quite generally that a mixed state corresponding to an equal probability distribution over the pure states one has $\rho = \frac{1}{N} \sum |i\rangle\langle i|$, which will have the maximal entropy $S = \log N$ corresponding to the good old Boltzmann formula. All this underscores the remark that a (properly) mixed state is just a classical distribution over quantum states.

Entanglement entropy

We just saw how the Von Neuman entropy yields a quantitative measure of 'how mixed' a quantum state is. The entropy of a pure state (that may be entangled or not) is always equal to zero, whereas the entropy of a mixed state is always greater than zero. So, why inventing the term *entanglement entropy* if the entropy of an entangled state is always zero? The logic is somewhat oblique in that the term in fact refers to the entropy of a mixed state which is obtained after one traces out 'part' of the density matrix of an entangled state. For this reason such states are referred to as *improper mixtures*, in contrast to the *proper mixtures* which refer to the cases we discussed before where the state is a statistical mixture of pure states.

Partial traces and improper mixtures. In certain situations there is indeed a close relationship between entangled and mixed states, and that is what I would like to explain next. It entails a mechanism that plays a vital role in explaining the all-important fact that the world we perceive is classical rather than quantum, and this explanation involves the phenomena of *decoherence* that we'll get into shortly. The crucial observation is that an entangled but pure state in some higher-dimensional multi-qubit space can appear to be a mixed state when looked at from the point of view of a lower-dimensional subspace. Such mixed states that may appear when restricting the density matrix to a subspace by (partially) tracing out the other part are referred to as *improper mixtures*, and these are clearly essentially quantum because they derive directly from a pure (though entangled) state of the system.

Take a situation where we only koot at part of the system. It might be that we can only measure certain qubits and not others and without being aware of it. This is frequently the case because systems interact continuously with their environment. Studying the quantum behavior of a system, requires extraordinary precautions to make sure

A qubit named Botzilla. Once upon a time there were two qubits who had nothing to do with each other and therefore the two were in a separable state, say $|+\rangle_B \otimes |1\rangle_A$. We have a two-qubit system where qubit Botzilla is our object of study, while qubit Abigail is the girl out there who wants to get entangled (a form of quantum common-law marriage, so to speak) with our beloved Botzilla. Abigail, having studied equation (II.1.17), decided to bring in her charming friend CNOT to make it happen. If you lead us through the Gate, eternal gratitude will be yours! And this is what happened. Both of them, not so young, not-lovers really, went through the Gate anyway, and came out entangled indeed. As you may have anticipated, they did not live a long and happy life ever after. Abigail turned out to be a Botwoman and managed to one day disappear from the air, leaving Botzilla behind in a severely mixed-up state (basically making him the classical example of a quantum divorcee).

To understand the deplorable state Botzilla finds himself in, we have to perform what is called a *partial trace* in the quantum jargon. The point is that he can make only observations which concern himself, though, whether he wants or not, he is still entangled with Botwoman Abigail. This means that he only has a small subset of observables to his disposal of the type $\mathcal{B} \otimes \mathbf{1} \in \mathcal{O}$. So calculating the expectation value of such an observable involves tracing over the Abigail qubit. This amounts to just establishing the fact that Abigail is still there' with unit probability, yet because the state is entangled, the effect of her 'being somewhere' is non-trivial. it leads to a result which can be described by saying that Botzilla is calculating the expectation value of

just the operator $\mathcal{B}$ in his own system, but in a particular mixed state. So, he may ignore Abigail, but then has to pay the price of being in a mixed state. Let us now 'trace out' Abigail and see what trace she left on Botzilla's state. This is achieved by summing over all the states associated with the subspaces we want to ignore, or better, about which we know nothing in particular. This means that we have to add up the diagonal entries with Abigail indices. We know already that Botzilla and Abigail ended up in the entangled state of equation (II.1.15), which we have to trace with respect to the second (Abigail) qubit. This we do by making use of the fact that $\mathrm{tr}(\mathbf{1}\,|\psi\rangle\langle\phi|) = \langle\psi|\phi\rangle$. Using labels A and B to keep the qubits apart, and remembering that because we are using orthogonal basis states the calculation can be written like,

$$\rho_B = \mathrm{tr}_A\left(|\psi_{BA}\rangle\langle\psi_{BA}|\right)$$
$$= \frac{1}{2}\mathrm{tr}_A\left[\left(|1\rangle_B|1\rangle_A + |-1\rangle_B|-1\rangle_A\right)\right.$$
$$\left.\left(\langle-1|_A\langle-1|_B + \langle1|_A\langle1|_B\right)\right]$$
$$= \frac{1}{2}\left(|1\rangle_B\langle1|_B\langle1|1\rangle_A + |-1\rangle_B\langle-1|_B\langle-1|-1\rangle_A\right)$$
$$= \frac{1}{2}\left(|1\rangle_B\langle1|_B + |-1\rangle_B\langle-1|_B\right). \qquad \text{(II.1.26)}$$

This is the density matrix for Botzilla in a mixed state with probability $1/2$ to either be spinning up or spinning down. The corresponding entropy is also higher: In base-two $S = -\log(1/2) = 1$ bit, while for the original pure state $S = \log 1 = 0$. The whole operation of tracing out Abigail is non-unitary and irreversible, as we moved from two qubits to one. Indeed, exactly one bit of information got lost to the environment (it was taken along by Abigail). In fact we could of course also calculate the entropy for the state Abigail finds herself in, then we have to trace over Botzilla's states. The situation is entirely symmetric, and her entropy will also be 1 bit. So there is some justice after all! This is what happens, the system Botzilla + Abigail is in a pure state all along and the total entropy remains zero therefore, but looking at subsystems this is no longer true. What remains true is that if we divide the system up into two complementary parts, the entropy in each of them increases equally.

Generally it is the case that if we begin with a statistically pure separable state and perform a partial trace we will still have a pure state, but if we begin with an entangled state, and we perform a partial trace, we will get a mixed state as we just saw. In the former case the entropy remains zero, and in the latter case it increases. It is precisely in this sense that the Von Neumann entropy yields a useful measure of entanglement.

This observation is relevant for the understanding of real quantum systems, because most realistic quantum systems are strongly entangled with their environment. We don't know exactly how and with what, but it means that we tacitly trace out all kinds of things we are not aware of. What we know is that these systems behave quite classically in the end, and that in fact we should not be too surprised about that because they are in a strongly mixed state. □

that it does not engage in interactions that we have no control over. Such 'unknown knowns' might well wash away the quantum effects we were looking for. Quantum effects depend on the subtle phase relations that make quantum states in fact highly coherent. What to do if part of our system is out of sight? It boils down to a quantum, yet touching variant of the Romeo and Juliet story called 'A qubit named Botzilla.'

Event horizons revisited. The Botzilla tale we have just worked through may have reminded you of the black hole information paradox, which we addressed in the section on black holes in Chapter I.3 on page 139. We know that the Hawking-Bekenstein analysis leads to a macroscopic black hole entropy and temperature of the horizon. And we discussed that this is a property that can be assigned in a frame of reference where an event horizon is perceived. Our discussion of quantum entropy clearly allows for a microscopic mechanism, generating the entropy. We imagine the creation of a particle-antiparticle pair in a pure maximally entangled state, where one of the two particles falls through the horizon. This means that the Hilbert space factor corresponding to the lost particle gets traced out, which in turn tells us that the left-over particle finds itself in a mixed (maximal) entropy state. Very much like the Botzilla story. The entropy is the quantum entropy that arises because we are forced to take a partial trace. I have to admit that whether and how this perspective would fit into the 'quantum gravity' scenarios is still under serious debate.

Decoherence

Decoherence is the effect that a quantum system in a pure state loses its quantum coherence due to interaction with a complicated environment. It is one of the reasons why the world around us obeys the laws of classical physics.

Of course a quantum system may be in a pure state but if we do not take care it may quickly, through random interactions with the environment, end up in a mixed state. It is basically in a classical state where there are no quantum interference effects left and probabilities add, not quantum amplitudes. The quantum state 'decoheres'.

If we talk about qubit systems, then a way to think of these interactions is of course to think of gates that effect the state and thereby cause decoherence. For example we may have a qubit in the $|+\rangle$ state, and have it interact with some phase gates, like a photon going through a random sequence of phase plates. The action of the phase-gate $P_z(\theta)$ corresponds to the unitary operator:

$$\begin{pmatrix} \alpha \\ \beta \end{pmatrix} \rightarrow \begin{pmatrix} 1 & 0 \\ 0 & e^{i\theta} \end{pmatrix} \begin{pmatrix} \alpha \\ \beta \end{pmatrix} = \begin{pmatrix} \alpha \\ e^{i\theta}\beta \end{pmatrix}.$$

Let us see what happens to the corresponding density matrix:

$$\rho_0 = \frac{1}{2}\begin{pmatrix} 1 & 1 \\ 1 & 1 \end{pmatrix} \rightarrow \rho(\theta) = P_z\,\rho_0\,P_z^* = \frac{1}{2}\begin{pmatrix} 1 & e^{-i\theta} \\ e^{i\theta} & 1 \end{pmatrix}.$$

Next we randomize the phases with some normal distribution as to represent 'the environment'. This means that we choose the density of dephasing agents to be Gaussian

$$f(\theta) \simeq e^{-\theta^2/\lambda}, \tag{II.1.27}$$

and then the effect of the random sequence of gates is obtained by averaging the above expression:

$$\sqrt{\frac{2i}{\lambda\pi}} \int f(\theta)\rho(\theta)\,d\theta = \frac{1}{2}\begin{pmatrix} 1 & e^{-\lambda/4} \\ e^{-\lambda/4} & 1 \end{pmatrix} \Rightarrow \frac{1}{2}\begin{pmatrix} 1 & 0 \\ 0 & 1 \end{pmatrix}.$$

What this calculation shows is that only the classical probabilities on the diagonal are left and the off-diagonal phase coherence of the quantum state ρ_0 has disappeared. By choosing λ large enough we wash out all quantum correlations and end up with a classical distribution over up and down states. This calculation merely illustrates a mechanism that leads to decoherence. Clearly, one would like to actually compute also the time-scales over which this decoherence takes place, this depends of course on the details of the environment or measurement apparatus.

Let us close this section by another toy model of decoherence. We start with a separable two-qubit state which we entangle using the CNOT gate as we did in (II.1.17). Then we use the $\mathrm{Botzilla} - -\mathrm{Abigail}$ mechanism by taking

the partial trace with respect to Abigail as in (II.1.26) ending up with the mixed state for Botzilla. This basically turns the story into a decoherence phenomenon.

In other words, we imagine an interaction of a qubit B in a state $|\psi_B\rangle$ with the environment (a qubit A in some state $|\psi_A\rangle$) to generate an entangled two-qubit state $|\psi\rangle = |\psi_{BA}\rangle$ from a separable two-qubit state $|\psi\rangle = |\psi_B\rangle \otimes |\psi_A\rangle$. When viewed from the perspective of a single qubit, the resulting state after tracing out the A qubit, becomes incoherent. That is, suppose we look at (II.1.17) in the density matrix representation. Looking at the first qubit only, the state vector of the separable state is $|\psi_B\rangle = |+\rangle$,, a pure state in the density matrix representation given by equation (II.1.23),

$$|\psi_B\rangle\langle\psi_B| = |+\rangle\langle+| \Leftrightarrow \frac{1}{2}\begin{pmatrix} 1 & 1 \\ 1 & 1 \end{pmatrix}.$$

Under the action of CNOT this becomes the maximally entangled state on the right-hand side of equation (II.1.17). After partially tracing the density matrix as in (II.1.26) we end up with the B qubit in a mixed state given by (II.1.24),

$$\rho = \frac{1}{2}\begin{pmatrix} 1 & 0 \\ 0 & 1 \end{pmatrix}.$$

Only the 'classical' probabilities on the diagonal are left and the off-diagonal phase coherence of the quantum state has disappeared due to entangling a degree of freedom in the environment.

Table II.1.1: **Key quantum principles concerning the Hilbert space of quantum states introduced in Chapter II.1.**

	Keyword	Description
(i)	**Hilbert space**	The complex vector space denoted by $\mathcal{H}$ of states of a quantum states. In this chapter we restrict ourselves to the finite dimensional case. We refer to the *Math Excursion* on complex vectors and matrices on page 176 of Volume III
(ii)	**State vector**	A *pure* quantum state is denoted by $|\psi\rangle$ corresponding to a *ket* or column vector in $\mathcal{H}$.
(iii)	**Expansion of state in a basis**	Any state $|\psi\rangle$ has a linear expansion in the basis $\{|i\rangle\}$ given by $|\psi\rangle = \sum_i \alpha_i |i\rangle$, with normalization condition $\sum_i |\alpha_i|^2 = 1$.
(iv)	**Probabilistic interpretation**	A measurement on the above state $|\Psi\rangle$ of the 'property' related to a basis $\{|i\rangle\}$ gives outcome i with probability $|\alpha_i|^2$.
(v)	**Qubit state**	A qubit state is a two-dimensional complex vector: $|\Psi\rangle = \alpha|1\rangle + \beta|-1\rangle$ with normalization $|\alpha|^2 + |\beta|^2 = 1$. A realization is a spin 1/2 degree of freedom where the vector is called a spinor.
(vi)	**Conjugate states**	The complex conjugate or dual state of $|\psi\rangle$ is defined by the *bra* or row vector $\langle\psi| = \sum_i \alpha_i^* \langle i|$.
(vii)	**Bracket or inner product**	For two states $|\Psi\rangle$ and $|\Phi\rangle$ with coefficients α_i and β_i respectively, we define the inner product as the bracket $\langle\Phi|\Psi\rangle = \sum_i \beta_i^* \alpha_i$. The orthonormal frame satisfies $\langle i|j\rangle = \delta_{ij}$. $\langle\Phi|\Psi\rangle$ is a complex number that satisfies $\langle\Phi|\Psi\rangle = \langle\Psi|\Phi\rangle^*$.
(viii)	**Multi-particle or qubit states**	If particle one has a state that is m-dimensional and that particle two is n-dimensional, than the two-particle system has a $(m \times n)$-dimensional state vector, which can be expanded as $|\Psi^{(1,2)}\rangle = \sum_{i,j}^{M,N} \gamma_{ij}|i^{(1)}\rangle \otimes |j^{(2)}\rangle$. A two-qubit state vector is $2^2 = 4$-dimensional, written as: $|\Psi\rangle = \alpha_1|1,1\rangle + \alpha_2|1,-1\rangle + \alpha_3|-1,1\rangle + \alpha_4|-1,-1\rangle$, with $|i,j\rangle = |i\rangle \otimes |j\rangle = |i\rangle|j\rangle$.
(ix)	**Entangled and separable states**	A n-particle state is *separable* if it the state can be factorized in an n-fold product: $\Psi^{(1,2,...,n)}\rangle = |\psi^{(1)}\rangle|\psi^{(2)}\rangle \cdots |\psi^{(n)}\rangle$. A state is *entangled* if it is not separable.
(x)	**Mixed states**	A mixed state is a properly normalized (statistical) mixture of some set $\{|\psi_a\rangle\}$ pure states: $|\Psi\rangle = \sum_a p_a|\psi_a\rangle$, with probability p_a that the system is in the pure state $|\psi_a\rangle$.
(xi)	**Density matrix/operator**	The density operator for a mixed state $|\Psi\rangle$ is defined as $\rho = \sum_i p_a |\psi_a\rangle\langle\psi_a|$ For a pure state there is only one term $p = 1$.
(xi)	**Quantum entropy**	The quantum entropy of a mixed state is given by: $S(\rho) = -\text{tr}\,\rho\log\rho = -\sum_a p_a \log p_a$. For a pure state the entropy is zero.

Chapter II.2

Observables, measurements and uncertainty

It is wrong to think of that past [ascribed to a quantum phenomenon] as 'already existing' in all detail. The past is theory. The past has no existence except as it is recorded in the present. By deciding what questions our quantum registering equipment shall put in the present we have an undeniable choice in what we have the right to say about the past.

John Archibald Wheeler,
Some Strangeness in Proportion (1980)

In the previous chapter we focussed exclusively on states, in particular the space of pure quantum states, the Hilbert space $\mathcal{H}$. In this chapter we consider the physical variables or quantum observables. These are represented by linear operators or matrices which act on the Hilbert space. The fact that physical variables are no longer represented by ordinary numbers or functions like in classical physics, but by matrices or differential operators makes quantum theory fundamentally different. It leads to deep reflections on the logical structure of the theory, on the nature of measurements, and on the fundamental aspects of uncertainty so concisely expressed by the Heisenberg uncertainty relations. And that is what this chapter is about. It should make you feel at home in Hilbert space.
We have summarized and specified the basic ingredients of the mathematical framework and the jargon that comes along with the notion of observables, which forms the sub-ject of this chapter, in the table at the end of the chapter on page 87.

Quantum observables are operators

Physical variables or observables in quantum theory are represented by hermitian operators. In this section we explore what this means in general and work out most of the details for the case of qubits. Operators have a spectrum of eigenvalues that correspond to possible measurement outcomes. To these eigenvalues correspond orthogonal eigenstates (or subspaces), which can be used to define a suitable frame for the Hilbert space. The aim of this section is to exhibit the algebraic structure of the theory, with the observables, projection operators and raising and lowering operators which play essential roles in describing the generic properties of quantum systems.

The algebra of observables. For a quantum system we have a set of dynamical variables called *observables*, $\mathcal{O} = \{A, B, \ldots\}$. In most cases corresponding to the classical variables, but there may be additional variables such as the aforementioned spin, which have no classical analogue. Whereas in classical physics the language of states and dynamical variables is smoothly connected, basically because the states are labelled by the (real) values of the dynamical values. This however is no longer true in the quantum world. In quantum theory we make a clear distinction between the Hilbert space $\mathcal{H}$ of states and the set of observables $\mathcal{O}$. Let us start with some general properties and definitions.

1. *Operators on Hilbert space.* The quantum observables are represented by linear *operators*, that act on Hilbert space.[1] In other words we have that $\mathcal{O} : \mathcal{H} \to \mathcal{H}$, and we write:

$$|\psi'\rangle = A |\psi\rangle ,$$

with $|\psi'\rangle, |\psi\rangle \in \mathcal{H}$ and $A \in \mathcal{O}$.

You should typically think of *matrices* in case the Hilbert space is finite dimensional.[2] In the infinite-dimensional case, we should think of continuous systems like a particle, where the states are described by wavefunctions $\psi(x, t)$, and the operators are typically represented by a differential operator, like the momentum and energy operators:

$$P = -i\hbar \frac{d}{dx} \quad \text{and} \quad H = i\hbar \frac{d}{dt} ,$$

as we mentioned in the previous chapter.

The fact that observables are operators that 'act on states' implies that they may well change the physical state, and strongly suggests the possibility that the act of measurement of such an observable will affect the state of the system.

2. *Linearity.* Linearity implies that for any two states and any observable A we have that,

$$A (|\psi_1\rangle + |\psi_2\rangle) = A |\psi_1\rangle + A |\psi_2\rangle .$$

3. *Hermitian adjoint.* On the algebra $\mathcal{O}$ we can define

---

[1] In this book we adopt the convention to represent quantum observables with uppercase letters while for their values we use lowercase. The set $\{a\}$ of allowed values is called the *sample space* of the observable A.

[2] We refer to the *Math Excursion* on page 158 of Volume III for an introduction to real matrices and vectors, which was extended to the complex case in the *Math Excursion* on page 176.

a hermitian adjoint, or 'dagger' operation, denoted as $\dagger$, where $A \to A^\dagger$. The definition is as follows

$$\langle \phi | A^\dagger | \psi \rangle = \langle \phi | A | \psi \rangle^* \quad \text{for all} \quad |\phi\rangle, |\psi\rangle \in \mathcal{H} . \quad \text{(II.2.1)}$$

Sandwiching the adjoint operator $A^\dagger$ between any pair of states yields a number, which is the complex conjugate of the number resulting from sandwiching A. From the definition it follows that (i) the adjoint of a product satisfies $(AB)^\dagger = B^\dagger A^\dagger$, and (ii) the dagger squares to unity: $(A^\dagger)^\dagger = A$, and is therefore referred to as an *involutive automorphism* of the algebra of observables. For matrices this implies that the hermitian adjoint of A is defined as $A^\dagger = (A^{tr})^*$, or in words: it is the complex conjugate of the transpose of A.

4. *Hermitian or self-adjoint operators.* We require that the eigenvalues of an observable are real numbers, as they correspond to possible outcomes of measurements, and that translates into conditions on the particular type of matrices that can represent physical observables. As a matter of fact the reality condition on the eigenvalues of operators requires that the quantum observables have to correspond to *hermitian* also known as *self-adjoint* operators or matrices. This means that observables satisfy the condition $A = A^\dagger$. A general hermitian matrix is a matrix M with complex entries that can be written as $M = S + iA$, where S is real and symmetric, and A is real and antisymmetric. For the case of a two-dimensional Hilbert space, like in the case of a single qubit or a basic quantum spin, all observables can be expressed as a linear combination of the unit matrix and the three Pauli or spin matrices of equation (II.2.2).

5. *Norm and boundedness.* We like to talk about bounded operators A, meaning that if they work on vectors in Hilbert space they do decent things. So what sets the norm $\|A\|$ for an operator? Here is a reasonable way to do this: (i) you let A work on all states in $\mathcal{H}$, (ii) calculate the norms of all the resulting vectors, and (iii) look at the 'largest value' or 'infimum' that occurs, which is denoted

by $\inf$. So, the definition of the norm of the operator A is then:

$$\|A\|^2 = \inf\{ \langle \psi | A^\dagger A | \psi \rangle : \forall | \psi \rangle \in \mathcal{H} \}.$$

A *bounded operator* has by definition a finite norm: $\|A\| < \infty$. If you think of A as a matrix, this statement boils down to saying that the eigenvalues of the matrix should be finite.

6. Algebraic structure. The observables form an algebra (we want to add and multiply observables). This is easy to understand for matrices as we will show in the *Math Excursions* just mentioned. The restrictions (of boundedness and self-adjointness) are much harder to implement if one passes to the infinite-dimensional cases corresponding to physical systems like particles and fields which have continuous variables. To properly address these problems one needs some quite sophisticated mathematics involving concepts like *Banach spaces* and C^* *('C-star') algebras*. This allows for a mathematically rigorous and consistent formulation of quantum theory. Such axiomatic approaches, however, are far beyond the scope of this book, though one may of course argue that they are quantessential because they address foundational questions. We will follow an operational, less rigorous approach, and comfortingly, it turns out that the typical notation we have introduced doesn't change much after going rigorous. We will treat the expressions using simple rules, glossing over the fact that we manipulate symbols which deep down may refer to rather sophisticated notions.

The qubit observables. The Hilbert space for a qubit is two-dimensional, and therefore the observables can be represented by 2×2 hermitian matrices. A typical set of observables would be the set of so-called Pauli matrices $\{X, Y, Z\}$ with:

$$X = \begin{pmatrix} 0 & 1 \\ 1 & 0 \end{pmatrix}, \ Y = \begin{pmatrix} 0 & -i \\ i & 0 \end{pmatrix}, \ Z = \begin{pmatrix} 1 & 0 \\ 0 & -1 \end{pmatrix}. \quad \text{(II.2.2)}$$

Any one qubit observable can be expressed as a linear combination of the three Pauli matrices and the unit matrix.[3]

In our discussion of classical bit mechanics we already argued that the X matrix, as operator or gate, acts like a momentum or displacement operator on the z-space of the bit, because it acts like the NOT-gate interchanging the two bit states $|1\rangle \leftrightarrow |-1\rangle$. It shows nicely how classical physics (discrete mechanics), and now quantum theory meet in this picture, with a correspondence between dynamical maps, logical (digital) gates, and quantum observables: they are all operators acting on a state.

q-gates. Clearly the three Pauli spin matrices above are one-qubit gates. In classical computation the X-gate corresponds to the NOT-gate, and is the only acceptable one-bit gate. The others are not, because the Z-gate introduces a relative minus sign (which is a phase), and the Y-gate introduces complex components, which are both not admissible for classical bits. This is a first hint that quantum bits offer far more possibilities, so let us get back to the qubit observables.

Sample spaces and preferred states

To each observable A corresponds a set $\mathcal{S}_a = \{a_i\}$ of values it can take. In other words, it is the set of possible outcomes of a measurement of the observable A, which is also called the *spectrum* or *sample space* of A. If we apply the observable A to a state $|\psi\rangle$ and we get a number a_i multiplying that same state, we say that the system is in a state where A takes the value a_i. A state with this property is denoted as $|\psi\rangle = |a_i\rangle$, and is called a *preferred* or *eigenstate* (or eigenvector) of A with *eigen-*

---

[3] The real spin polarization operator has units and equals $S_z \equiv \frac{1}{2}\hbar Z$, involving an essential factor one half. Throughout the book we discuss spin one-half directly in terms of the Pauli matrices $\{X, Y, Z\}$, which in most textbooks are denoted as $(\sigma_x, \sigma_y, \sigma_z)$.

value a_i. These statements are summarized by the following equation,

$$A|a_i\rangle = a_i|a_i\rangle. \tag{II.2.3}$$

Is the eigenvector defined this way unique? No, it is not, we can multiply by any overall constant and it is still an eigenvector. We take care of that by choosing the eigenvector to have unit length, but then there is still an overall phase factor $(e^{i\phi})$ possible. This factor doesn't have any observable consequences.

Qubit eigenstates. Recall that for the classical dynamical bit we introduced a position $z = \pm 1$ and a momentum $p = \pm 1$. In the quantum realm these observables should somehow correspond to certain operators. Let us thereto consider the 2×2 matrices Z and X (related to p) which can act on the states in $\mathcal{H}$.

The basis vectors corresponding to the classical states are indeed eigenvectors of the position operator Z:

$$Z\begin{pmatrix} 1 \\ 0 \end{pmatrix} = \begin{pmatrix} 1 & 0 \\ 0 & -1 \end{pmatrix}\begin{pmatrix} 1 \\ 0 \end{pmatrix} = 1\begin{pmatrix} 1 \\ 0 \end{pmatrix},$$

$$Z\begin{pmatrix} 0 \\ 1 \end{pmatrix} = \begin{pmatrix} 1 & 0 \\ 0 & -1 \end{pmatrix}\begin{pmatrix} 0 \\ 1 \end{pmatrix} = -1\begin{pmatrix} 0 \\ 1 \end{pmatrix},$$

and the eigenvalues $z_\pm = \pm 1$ are the corresponding z values. We conclude that the sample space or spectrum of the observable Z is $\mathcal{S}_z = \{\pm 1\}$.

The operator X does also exactly what you would expect of the 'momentum' operator; it implements the $p = 1$ transition $|\pm 1\rangle \Leftrightarrow |\mp 1 >$ as one may verify explicitly:

$$X\begin{pmatrix} 1 \\ 0 \end{pmatrix} = \begin{pmatrix} 0 & 1 \\ 1 & 0 \end{pmatrix}\begin{pmatrix} 1 \\ 0 \end{pmatrix} = \begin{pmatrix} 0 \\ 1 \end{pmatrix}, \text{ etc.}$$

We also learn that the operator X^2 equals the unit matrix. In fact we have that $X^2 = Y^2 = Z^2 = \mathbf{1}$, which by definition leaves all states invariant and it therefore implements the trivial $p = 0$ transition. This is as far as the 'relation'

between classical and quantum formalism can be traced.

The quantum formalism allows for more because we have the *linear superposition principle* as well as the *complexification* of the state vectors. We have seen that the states $|\pm 1\rangle$ correspond to the eigenvectors of the 'position' operator Z, but in the quantum formalism we can also ask for the eigenvectors of other observables, for example X. One easily verifies that these correspond to the state vectors $|\pm\rangle = (|+1\rangle \pm |-1\rangle)/\sqrt{2}$, with again eigenvalues $x_\pm = \pm 1$ as follows:

$$X\begin{pmatrix} 1 \\ \pm 1 \end{pmatrix} = \begin{pmatrix} 0 & 1 \\ 1 & 0 \end{pmatrix}\begin{pmatrix} 1 \\ \pm 1 \end{pmatrix} = \pm 1\begin{pmatrix} 1 \\ \pm 1 \end{pmatrix}. \tag{II.2.4}$$

The eigenvectors $|\pm\rangle$ are real linear superpositions of the basis states $|\pm 1\rangle$, and we have marked them on the circle of real states in Figure II.1.7.

Is this all? Are we done? The answer is, no! We have indeed identified the eigenstates of momentum, which actually do not have a classical equivalent. This shows the quantessential possibility that the linear superposition principle introduces. However, we have so far only explored real states and real matrices, and it is here that the quantum formalism summons us to proceed. There are other independent choices: the one conventionally chosen is the (complex) matrix Y:

$$Y = \begin{pmatrix} 0 & -i \\ i & 0 \end{pmatrix}.$$

One may verify that $Y = Y^\dagger$, and we see that acting on the basis states it indeed introduces complex coefficients as

$$Y|\pm 1\rangle = \pm i|\mp 1\rangle.$$

So loosely speaking we could say that Y introduces a complex part to the standard classical momentum variable $P \simeq$

X. We should expect its eigenstates to be complex as well:

$$Y\begin{pmatrix} 1 \\ \pm i \end{pmatrix} = \begin{pmatrix} 0 & -i \\ i & 0 \end{pmatrix}\begin{pmatrix} 1 \\ \pm i \end{pmatrix} = \pm 1\begin{pmatrix} 1 \\ \pm i \end{pmatrix},$$

and the eigenvalues are again $y_\pm = \pm 1$.

The fact that all eigenvalues square to one is not surprising if one realizes that the matrices themselves square to the unit matrix: $Z^2 = P^2 = Y^2 = \mathbf{1}$. All quantum observables in this problem can be written as linear combinations of the independent hermitian matrices X, Y, Z and the unit matrix $\mathbf{1}$. These basic observables have identical sample spaces $\mathcal{S}_x = \mathcal{S}_y = \mathcal{S}_z = \{+1, -1\}$. Furthermore, as we just showed, they have no eigenvectors in common. It signals the important fact that these three observables are incompatible with each other, a notion we will return to later on. It raises the question of what that means in terms of measuring these observables in such a non eigenstate.

Expectation values. We may now also define the notion of the expectation value of an observable A in a quantum state $|\psi\rangle$ as:

$$a = <A> \equiv \langle\psi|A|\psi\rangle, \qquad (\text{II}.2.5)$$

which is just a number indeed. The expectation value a is therefore a weighted average of the eigenvalues of A, which depends on which state $|\psi\rangle$ one chooses. This is consistent with the remark we made earlier that the square of the coefficients are probabilities. It means that we 'sandwich' the operator between a row and column vector, for example:

$$\langle +1| Z |+1\rangle = (1\,0)\begin{pmatrix} 1 & 0 \\ 0 & -1 \end{pmatrix}\begin{pmatrix} 1 \\ 0 \end{pmatrix} = (1\,0)\begin{pmatrix} 1 \\ 0 \end{pmatrix} = 1,$$

and similarly:

$$\langle +1| X |+1\rangle = \langle +1| -1\rangle = 0.$$

An expectation value can be calculated for any observable in any state and corresponds to some average of measurement outcomes.

A Qubit is like a Barbie on a globe

 We return to the qubit state space and point out an alternative way to parametrize qubit space by directly relating it to the eigenstates of an operator/observable. This amounts to yet another geometrical representation of the state space of a qubit or quantum spin, and that will be useful in a variety of contexts. We start by choosing a point on the unit two-sphere in X, Y, Z space, as depicted in the figure (a). The point represents a unit vector $\hat{n}$, but we want to use it to label a qubit state, which as we saw is a point on a unit three-sphere so we have to do a little more. First we construct a unit sigma matrix $\hat{n} \cdot \vec{\sigma}$, with $\sigma = \{X, Y, Z\}$, which to each point on the sphere associates a particular hermitian (2×2) matrix or observable. This observable is proportional to the spin operator along that axis. The qubit state that we link to the point is the eigenvector $|\chi_1\rangle$ of that observable with the highest eigenvalue ($\lambda_1 = 1$). However the eigenvector is not unique: it is multiplied by a phase factor with some angle ϕ between zero and 2π, so to completely fix the state we have to specify the pair $\{\hat{n}, \phi\}$.

The mathematically alert reader may have experienced a feeling of déjà vu since I am basically repeating the story I told in Chapter I.1 about the Hopf or monopole bundle, where the three-sphere was interpreted as a phase or circle bundle over the two-sphere. So the three-sphere is a physically relevant object, we have seen it appear as the bundle associated with the fundamental Dirac monopole in Chapter I.1, as the manifold of the group $SU(2)$ in the *Math Excursion* in Volume III on Groups, and here as the state space of a qubit.

The natural way to represent also the angle ϕ

in the picture is to draw the tangent plane to the sphere at the point chosen, and define ϕ as the polar angle in that tangent plane as we did in the *Math Excursion* on Complex numbers on page 151 of Volume III.

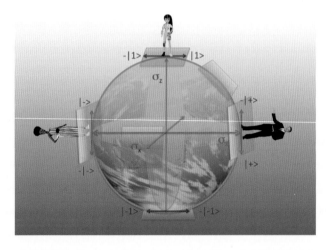

(a): *Choosing a state of a qubit is like setting a Barbie on a globe.*. Choosing a different frame is like choosing the North and South Poles along a different axis.

In the figure we have depicted some of the states we discussed before, on the z-axis we have two points with the operators $\pm Z$ with eigenvectors $|\pm 1\rangle$. So the states are now represented as unit vectors in the tangent plane at the point $\hat{n}$ with phase angle ϕ. So in the plane at the North Pole we find the states $\pm|1\rangle$ at angles $\phi = 0, \pi$.

What we have learned is that we can represent a point on the three-sphere by choosing a point on the two-sphere and an additional phase in that point. This way of choosing coordinates on the three-sphere is indeed completely equivalent to fixing a Barbie on the earth surface by saying *where* (s)he stands, *and* in *what direction* (s)he is looking. In a more sophisticated wording one says one picks a point on the sphere and a frame

in the tangent plane to the sphere at that point as is illustrated in the figure. So now you don't any longer have to say that you cannot imagine how to choose a point on a three-sphere, even a kid can do it! Buy him a Barbie of some sort and a globe and ask him to stick the Barbie on the Globe.

Note that the present picture (a) is essentially different from Figure II.2.2 in that corresponding states are located in different places. For example the North Pole represents the states $\alpha\,|1\rangle = \exp(i\phi)|1\rangle$, where ϕ is the angle of the arrow in the tangent plane.

This set contains in particular the real states $|1\rangle$ for $\phi = 0$ and $-|1\rangle$ for $\phi = \pi$, whereas the states $\pm|-1\rangle$ are located on the South Pole. In Figure II.2.2 the states $|\pm 1\rangle$ are perpendicular, in Figure II.2(a) they are antipodal. Changing the qubit state corresponds to moving around on the three-sphere and that is nothing but walking over the globe and looking in various directions. What is all this good for? This alternative view of the space of states of a qubit or quantum spin has yielded some interesting physical insights to be addressed in Chapter II.3 about probing the state space and measuring the Berry phase, which is exactly like having the Barbie in the figure walking around on the globe. $\square$

Spin or qubit Hamiltonians

A crucial observable in physics is the energy or the Hamiltonian operator denoted by H. The eigenvalues E_n of the Hamiltonian correspond to the allowed energy levels of the system. The possible energy eigenstates $|\psi_n\rangle$ are called *stationary states*, because they have a trivial time dependence that resides in the overall phase factor. Linear combinations of different energy eigenstates would therefore have a non-trivial time dependence. Of particular interest is the lowest energy state or ground state of the system. We consider two examples for the Hamiltonian of a spin or qubit and show their properties. Our first choice corresponds to putting the spin in a magnetic field in the z-direction, the Hamiltonian would be proportional to Z:

$$H_1 = bZ,$$

and its eigenstates are $|\pm 1\rangle$ and have eigenvalues $\lambda_\pm = \pm b$. Another sensible choice for the Hamiltonian would be what is called the total spin operator which is quadratic in the spins:

$$H_2 = b(X^2 + Y^2 + Z^2) = b(\mathbf{1} + \mathbf{1} + \mathbf{1}) = 3b\mathbf{1},$$

Indeed a bit trivial perhaps, because it is just 3 times the unit matrix. Of course, if we act with this Hamiltonian on *any* state, it will return that state with eigenvalue $3b$, i.e. $H_2|\psi\rangle = 3b|\psi\rangle$. In this case you could say that the Hamiltonian is trivial, because all states have the same eigenvalue, they are what we call *degenerate*. Degeneracies are a common feature and usually imply that there is some (hidden) symmetry in the system one considers.

Frames and observables

The *eigenstates* $|a_k\rangle$ of a linear operator A are defined by the equation $A|a_k\rangle = a_k|a_k\rangle$. If A is a $N \times N$ hermitian (matrix) operator, there are N independent (N-dimensional) eigenvectors and the *eigenvalues* a_k are real and generically different. As we will see these eigenvalues are the possible outcomes of a measurement of that observable. Generally the eigenstates can be chosen orthonormal, so that

$$\langle a_j | a_k \rangle = \delta_{jk} \text{ where } \delta_{ij} = 1 \text{ if } i = j, \text{ and } \delta_{ij} = 0 \text{ if } i \neq j.$$
$$(\text{II.2.6})$$

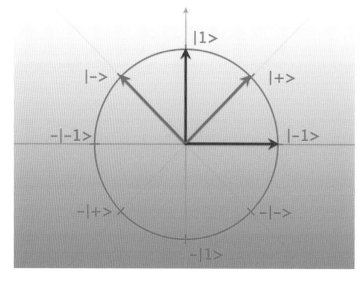

Figure II.2.1: *Two frames.* Two different frames spanning the same two-dimensional space of real qubit states. The blue one is the Z frame $\{|-1\rangle, |1\rangle\}$ and the green one is the X frame $\{|+\rangle, |-\rangle\}$. The frames are related by a rotation over an angle $\theta = 45°$.

This means that the set $\{|a_i\rangle\}$ forms an *orthonormal basis* or *orthonormal frame* for the state space – the Hilbert space – of the system.

Qubit frames. Let us briefly illustrate this: the eigenstates for $A = Z$ are the column vectors

$$|1\rangle \Leftrightarrow \begin{pmatrix} 1 \\ 0 \end{pmatrix}, \qquad |-1\rangle \Leftrightarrow \begin{pmatrix} 0 \\ 1 \end{pmatrix},$$

which have eigenvalues plus and minus one respectively. The eigenstates $|\pm 1\rangle$ of Z form an orthonormal basis for the space of qubit states.

If we choose instead $A = X$, then the normalized eigenstates correspond to

$$|\pm\rangle \equiv \frac{1}{\sqrt{2}}(|1\rangle \pm |-1\rangle) \Leftrightarrow \frac{1}{\sqrt{2}}\begin{pmatrix} 1 \\ \pm 1 \end{pmatrix}$$

and these have eigenvalues ± 1 also. Clearly, the states $|\pm\rangle$ form an alternative basis for the qubit states. In Fig-

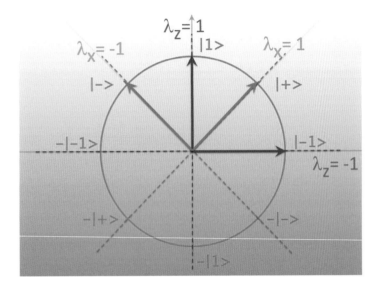

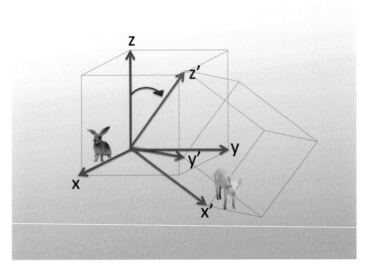

Figure II.2.2: *Frames and eigenvalues.* The frames corresponding to eigenstates of Z (blue) and X (green) respectively. The axes are labeled by the corresponding eigenvalues. The circle represents the normalized qubit states with real α and β .

Figure II.2.3: *Frame rotations.* Two frames spanning the space $\mathbb{R}^3$. The 'rabbit' and the 'pig' frames can be rotated into each other. For example first rotate the z'-axis to the z-axis, then the $x-, x'-, y-$ and y'-axes all lie in the $x - y$ plane. So there they can then be rotated into each other by a rotation around the z-axis. This also holds for frames in higher dimensions because rotations preserve the origin, the length of vectors and also the angles between them. This in fact defines what a rotation is.

ure II.2.2 we have depicted the two frames where the unit circle describes all the states with real coefficients α and β . This picture will return in many guises when we discuss measurements in quantum mechanics. A priori there is no preference for any particular basis, the best choice depends on the questions you want to answer. Clearly if we are going to measure some physical quantity, the eigenstates of the corresponding operator will play an important role.

What the examples just given also show is that the Z and X operators have no eigenvectors in common. That is necessarily the case because the operators do not commute, and they are called *incompatible observables*. We return to this notion in a forthcoming section.

Frame choices. When writing down an explicit expression for a qubit, or in fact for any quantum system, we first have to choose a *basis* $\{|i\rangle\}$ in which the state can be expanded. This basis is a matter of choice. In Figure II.2.1

we have for example depicted the standard blue frame, but also a different green frame consisting of the states $|+\rangle$ and $|-\rangle$. In Figure II.2.3 we have depicted two frames for a three-dimensional vector space. What is quite evident from the figures is that different frames can be transformed into each other by a simple rotation. That is so because rotations by definition not only keep the length of vectors but also the angles between them the same.[4]

---

[4]A rotation in fact preserves the *orientation* of a frame. If we interchange the x- and y-axes in Figure II.2.3, then we also have an orthonormal frame, but it cannot be obtained by rotating the old frame, exactly because its orientation is opposite. The frames in the figure are *right-handed* meaning to say if rotate from x to y the right-handed rotation by the 'like'-rule would point in the positive z-direction.

Unitary transformations

A rotation of a vector or a frame is an operation or a transformation on such a vector or frame. You may in this respect think of a frame as a solid cube, under rotations its shape is conserved, it stays congruent. In a N—dimensional space such rotations can be represented by a $N \times N$ matrix that act on a vector.

An important property of rotations is that they satisfy the *group* property, namely that the result of two successive rotations is again a rotation. This is obvious in the two-dimensional case because you just add the angles. In three dimensions a simple way to see it is to look at the 'rabbit' unit vector in the z—direction in Figure II.2.3. If we would trace out the arrow head under all possible rotations, we should get the unit sphere. Any rotation of a vector around an *orthogonal* axis would move the arrowhead along a *big* circle over the sphere, big because it is a circle of maximal size on a given sphere. It is also true that the shortest distance between two points on the sphere is exactly the unique segment of the unique big circle on which both points lie. So, if we make first a rotation of the vector around some axis $\hat{n}_1$, the vector moves from the first point A over a segment of some big circle to a second point B. Next we move the resulting vector over a given angle around a second axis $\hat{n}_2$, then the vector ends up at a third point C on the sphere. The combined rotation is then just the rotation that moves the vector from A directly to C over the big circle connecting them.

This is all simple to imagine, and therefore let us now translate these simple geometric intuitions into a symbolic language. We start with rotating ket vectors with rotation matrices U_i:

$$|\psi_2\rangle = U_1|\psi_1\rangle$$
$$|\psi_3\rangle = U_2|\psi_2\rangle = U_2 U_1|\psi_1\rangle = U_3|\psi_1\rangle$$
$$\Rightarrow U_3 = U_2 U_1. \tag{II.2.7}$$

This is true for arbitrary vectors and also for arbitrary rotations. Under a frame rotation U, the conjugate bra vector will rotate like:

$$\langle\psi_2| = \langle\psi_1|\, U_1^\dagger,$$

with the conjugated rotation matrix $U^\dagger$, that can be obtained from U by interchanging rows and columns (which is called taking its *transpose* U^{tr}) and also taking its complex conjugate (meaning conjugating all its matrix elements i.e. its entries, so, $U^\dagger = (U^{tr})^*$. We require the length and inner product of vectors to be preserved under rotations, so if we simultaneously rotate arbitrary vectors $|\psi\rangle$ and $|\phi\rangle$ by U, then we have to impose:

$$\langle\phi_2|\psi_2\rangle = \langle\phi_1|U^\dagger\, U|\psi_1\rangle = \langle\phi_1|\psi_1\rangle.$$

From the last equality we conclude that rotations apparently correspond to a *unitary transformation*, satisfying the unitarity condition:[5]

$$U^\dagger U = \mathbf{1}.$$

The rotations in N complex dimensions form a mathematical structure called a *group*, basically because they satisfy the group property, equation (II.2.7). This group is called the *unitary group* denoted by $U(N)$. More precisely it is the *special unitary group* $SU(N)$ because the rotations preserve the *orientation* of the frame (this is the cyclic order X, Y, Z, where by definition $\hat{x} \times \hat{y} = \hat{z}$). We refer to the *Math Excursion* A for further details.

Photon gates and wave plates

One can think of these unitary operations as a transformation on the qubit state vector. And changing the state

---

[5]Note that if we rotate in real space the matrices become real and there is no complex conjugation, therefore real rotations are orthogonal matrices O satisfying the condition that $O^{tr}O = \mathbf{1}$ these matrices also form a closed group under multiplication, denoted as the orthogonal group $O(N)$. Indeed where quantum physicists are married to unitary groups, classical physicists are with the orthogonal ones. It is the difference between being complex and being real.

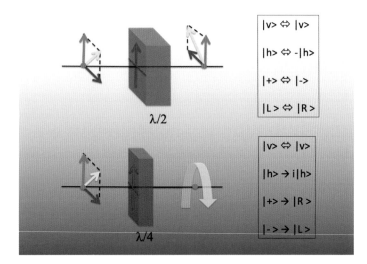

$$|v> \Leftrightarrow |v>$$
$$|h> \Leftrightarrow -|h>$$
$$|+> \Leftrightarrow |->$$
$$|L> \Leftrightarrow |R>$$

$\lambda/2$

$$|v> \Leftrightarrow |v>$$
$$|h> \rightarrow i|h>$$
$$|+> \rightarrow |R>$$
$$|-> \rightarrow |L>$$

$\lambda/4$

Figure II.2.4: *Wave plates*. The wave plates with optical thickness of $\lambda/2$ and $\lambda/4$ can be used to change the polarization state of a photon. They are unitary one-qubit phase gates, and are the physical realizations of the transformations U described in the text, on the states defined in Figure II.1.11. The transformations can be inverted meaning that we reverse the direction in the picture, so, if going to the right corresponds to some U, then going to the left corresponds to $U^\dagger$.

vector really amounts to processing quantum information as the *in-state* gets transformed into some *out-state*. Such manipulations can be performed on real photons relatively simply by what are called *wave plates*. These have two parameters: a principal axis and a given optical thickness as is depicted in Figure II.2.4. We have shown the effect on the polarization state of a photon when it passes through a phase plate with its principal axis along the z-axis in the figure. The plate acts like what is called a *phase-gate* $P(\theta)$; it leaves the polarization along the principal axis unchanged, and rotates the orthogonal component by a phase corresponding with the optical thickness of the plate. So in the case at hand the action is given by,

$$\begin{pmatrix} \alpha \\ \beta \end{pmatrix} \rightarrow \begin{pmatrix} 1 & 0 \\ 0 & e^{i\theta} \end{pmatrix} \begin{pmatrix} \alpha \\ \beta \end{pmatrix} = \begin{pmatrix} \alpha \\ e^{i\theta}\beta \end{pmatrix}.$$

Indeed the $\lambda/2$ plate rotates the lower component over an angle $\theta = \pi$ in the complex plane leading to the phase -1,

while the $\lambda/4$ plate rotates by an angle $\theta = \pi/2$ giving an imaginary factor i.

Incompatible observables

The fact that observables are represented by operators reflects the quantessential property that measurements may alter the state, and therefore that the outcomes of different measurements may depend on the order in which the measurements are performed. This latter property expresses the fact that the operators that represent observables in quantum mechanics do not necessarily *commute*, by which we mean that for the product of two observables A and B one may have that $AB \neq BA$ and we say that such observables are *incompatible*. It is pretty weird to be told that $\mathrm{momentum}$ times $\mathrm{position}$ would not be equal to $\mathrm{position}$ times $\mathrm{momentum}$, but that is the way it really is if you think of them as operators instead of numbers. This is common in the quantum world because matrices generically do not commute. For the simple set of qubit observables given in equation (II.2.2), you can verify that they do not commute with another indeed: for example $ZX - XZ = 2iY$.

To illustrate this *non-commutativity* we have in Figure II.2.5 depicted a sequence of two $90°$ rotations in opposite order: on the left we rotate the book first around the z-axis and then around the x-axis, and on the right we do it in the opposite order. At the bottom one sees that the resulting orientations of the book clearly differ, meaning that for the operations on the state of the book b one has that $R_z R_x \neq R_x R_z$. For the case of a particle it turns out that the position and momentum observables X and P do not commute: one finds that $XP - PX = i\hbar$. This non-commutativity of observables has dramatic consequences and lies at the root of many of the at first sight *inconvenient truths* that quantum theory revealed about the basic workings of nature.

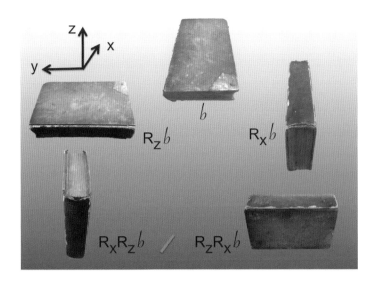

Figure II.2.5: *Non-commuting rotations.* We illustrate non-communativity of the 90^0 clockwise rotations R_z and R_x around the z- and x-axes respectively. The order in which they are applied (to the book) does matter and clearly leads to a different final state.

The labelling of quantum states. Consider a $N \times N$ matrix observable, in the generic case it will have N different real eigenvalues, with orthogonal eigenvectors. In general, it may happen that two or more eigenvalues coincide, in which case there will be more than a single (independent) eigenvector corresponding to a given eigenvalue. We say that the spectrum of the observable A is *degenerate*. In that case the eigenvalue a_i labels not just a particular state but rather some subspace $\mathcal{V}_i^a$ of the Hilbert space. In fact states can be simultaneous eigenstates of other observables. The previously mentioned state may also be an eigenvector with value b_j for the observable B, and we may label that state by the element of the combined sample space and write $|\Psi\rangle = |a_i, b_j, \dots\rangle$.

In general there will be many different sets consisting of a maximal number of independent, but compatible observables and these can be used to label a particular set of basis states (a frame) of the system. Observables A and B

for which a joint set of eigenstates can be chosen, necessarily commute and are therefore by definition *compatible*. What makes quantum theory so special is that this is often not the case, so that we continuously have to deal with observables A and B that are *incompatible*. For such incompatible observables Heisenberg's uncertainty relations impose quantessential restrictions, to which we will turn shorty.

Quantum setting. We conclude that there are four aspects in which the quantum setting significantly differs from the classical one:

(i) the set of admissible values for a dynamical variable may differ, in particular it may be a discrete set in which case the values would be quantized whereas in the classical case the values would be continuous;

(ii) a quantum variable may not have a classical analogue at all, such as a particle having an intrinsic rotational degree of freedom called 'spin', and most importantly;

(iii) in a given state of a quantum system generally *incompatible observables cannot be simultaneously assigned a definite value*. The non-zero spread in observed values in a given state is then governed by Heisenberg's uncertainty principle to be discussed later;

(iv) certain classical dynamical variables which involve products of incompatible variables will not have an unambiguous or unique quantum analog. There may be ordering ambiguities.

At first it seems inconceivable that such a vile theory has become one of the crown jewels of a rigorous science like Physics! It is remarkable that a theory can host this very anti-intuitive notion of incompatibility without becoming inconsistent. This notion of incompatibility has profound repercussions on what this theory can possibly mean and these matters will of course be discussed extensively in the forthcoming chapters.

Projection operators

Closely related to the notion of the state vector and a basis $\{|i\rangle\}$ is the concept of a projector. A *projector* is an operator P that may act on vectors in a vector space like $\mathcal{H}$ and it projects the vectors along a particular axis, or in general on some subspace of $\mathcal{H}$. By virtue of this defining property applying a projector P twice on any vector gives the same result as applying it once: $P^2 = P$. Note that $\mathbf{1} - P$ is also a projection operator as it also squares to itself. We can rewrite this as $P(\mathbf{1} - P) = 0$ which amounts to saying that P and $\mathbf{1} - P$ project on orthogonal subspaces of $\mathcal{H}$. So given a projection operator one can make an orthogonal decomposition of the Hilbert space. On vectors in the first subspace the projector act as the unit operator, and on the vectors in the orthogonal complement it acts like the zero operator. This observation is highly relevant if one wants to assign properties to a quantum state. A projector P assigns a truth value to a state, but only if the state vector sits entirely in the subspace on which P projects, or its orthogonal complement. Clearly if the state vector has components in both, you cannot say it has the property nor can you say that it has not. But in that case there are other projection operators that do a better job, because there are always subspaces which contain that state vector or to which that vector is orthogonal. The notion of projectors plays an important role in the theory of quantum measurement as we will see in the next section.

Elementary projectors. One easily verifies that the projector P_j which projects on the axis corresponding to the basis vector $|j\rangle$ is given by:

$$P_j = |j\rangle\langle j|, \qquad (\text{II.2.8})$$

and indeed its square equals itself and applying it to a state vector and using (II.2.6) yields:

$$P_j |\Psi\rangle = \Sigma_i \alpha_i |j\rangle\langle j|i\rangle = \alpha_j|j\rangle,$$

which is exactly the component along the j-axis, i.e. $\langle j|\Psi\rangle\,|j\rangle$.

Note that any sum over a subset of P_i is also a projection operator (because they mutually commute), and so is $|\Psi\rangle\langle\Psi|$ for any state $|\Psi\rangle$.

Consider 'bracketing' an elementary projector in some state:

$$p_i = \langle\Psi| P_i |\Psi\rangle = |\langle i|\Psi\rangle|^2| = |\alpha_i|^2, \qquad (\text{II.2.9})$$

it yields the component along the basis vector squared. This is the probability p_i of finding the particle in the state $|i\rangle$ in an appropriate measurement. The normalization condition (II.1.9) is nothing but the statement that the total probability of finding the system in some state equals one, as it should.

Completeness. One now can also understand that the set of elementary projection operators satisfies the so-called *completeness relation*, which amounts to the statement that

$$\sum_i |i\rangle\langle i| = \mathbf{1}. \qquad (\text{II.2.10})$$

This means that it works as the identity operator: acting on any state vector $|\psi\rangle$ it gives back the same state. The completeness relation is also referred to as the *projective decomposition of the identity operator*, since it is the operator equivalent of the statement that any state vector can be decomposed in its components with respect to some frame.

Observables and projectors. From the orthonormality relations of eigenvectors $\{|a_j\rangle\}$ of an observable A, and the properties of the corresponding elementary projectors P_j, one may show that we can actually write the operator A as:

$$A = \sum_j a_j P_j.$$

Needless to say that all projection operators are observables (as $P = P^\dagger$), but not the other way around!

Projectors on subspaces of $\mathcal{H}$. It is not hard to see that along these lines we can construct projectors that project

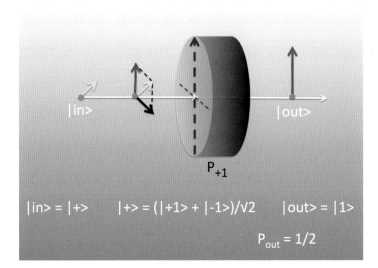

|in⟩

P₊₁

|out⟩

|in⟩ = |+⟩ |+⟩ = (|+1⟩ + |-1⟩)/√2 |out⟩ = |1⟩

$P_{out} = 1/2$

Figure II.2.6: *A photon polarizer.* A polarizer projects the photon onto a particular polarization state. There is a calculable probability for the photon to come through, after which it is fully polarized in the selected direction.

on a subspace of the Hilbert space, by adding up some subset Γ of elementary projectors:

$$P_\Gamma = \sum_{j \in \Gamma} P_j \, .$$

Such operators play an important role in the assignment of quantum properties to states in Hilbert space.

Photon polarizers are projectors. Photons can be projected on certain subspaces of the full Hilbert space, and these operations are quite familiar and dear to all of us. We can use a *color filter* to project on a certain subspace of wavelengths or frequencies. For example, you want to filter out the UV component of the light if you are high up in the mountains. But in the present context of qubits we should rather think of a *polarizer* which projects the polarization vector on a particular axis. As we have indicated in Figure II.2.6 the polarizer P_{+1} does actually more than just projecting the state, it projects the in-state $|+\rangle$ on the chosen $|+1\rangle$ *direction* of the polarizer, but then renormal-

izes the state to a vector of length one, so the outstate is $|+1\rangle$. The magnitude of the incoming component tells you the probability that the photon will be transmitted, so $p_{out} = (1/\sqrt{2})^2 = 1/2$. And that is what your fancy polaroid shades are really about. It is indeed a projector in the sense that if we let the photons that come through some polarizer, and subsequently let them go through an identical polarizer then all the photons will get through. If one rotates the second polarizer by 90 degrees, then that projects on the orthogonal subspace, and a photon that gets through the first polarizer will be blocked by the second. To check this you need two Ray-Bans, or if you are blessed with the curiosity of a true scientist you would happily break the one and only one you have in two pieces of course.

Note that for a large number of photons the result reproduces the classical result, if one identifies the reduction in the light intensity due to the polarizer with the ratio of the number of outgoing and the number of incoming photons. In the classical Maxwell theory, the light intensity is given by the square of the electric field. The classical field $\mathbf{E}$ is literally projected, giving the factor $1/\sqrt{2}$ in the magnitude of the projected component. And its square does give the reduction factor $1/2$., the same as in the quantum case. But again, for a single photon there is no classical description, and to explain the single photon experimental results one has to go quantum.

Raising and lowering operators

Let me try to make you more familiar with thinking about dynamical variables as operators or matrices by demonstrating a different use of the algebra of observables as operators on states. You may think of a system having some basic operator Q with its associated eigenvalues and eigenstates. We also require that the system has some ground state that we for the moment assume to be a unique lowest state $|0\rangle$ with $Q|0\rangle = q_0|0\rangle$. Then we may search for operators $A^\pm$ that satisfy the relation:

$$[Q, A^\pm] = \pm q A^\pm. \qquad (\text{II.2.11})$$

Writing this expression out we obtain the following property of the state $A^\pm|\psi_n\rangle$,

$$Q(A^\pm|\psi_n\rangle) = (q_n \pm q)(A^\pm|\psi_n\rangle).$$

This means that starting with an eigenstate of Q, the operators $A^\pm$ create again an eigenstate of Q with a higher (lower) eigenvalue. Such *raising* and *lowering* operators are extremely useful because they would in principle allow you to create the excited states from the ground state; they allow you to move through the spectrum of Q eigenstates and are therefore also called *laddering* or *step* operators. Clearly the raising operators can be written in an explicit form as:

$$A^+ = \Sigma_n |n+1\rangle\langle n|. \qquad (\text{II.2.12})$$

Such a setup works only if the eigenvalues q_n are evenly spaced, in other words if $q_n = q_0 + nq$, but this is quite often the case.

Let us see how this works out for the example of the Hamiltonian $H_1 = Z$ of the previous subsection. The step operators are now the following linear combinations:

$$Z_+ = |1\rangle\langle -1| \Leftrightarrow Z_+ = \begin{pmatrix} 0 & 1 \\ 0 & 0 \end{pmatrix}, \qquad (\text{II.2.13})$$

and

$$Z_- = (Z_+)^\dagger = |-1\rangle\langle 1| \Leftrightarrow Z_- = \begin{pmatrix} 0 & 0 \\ 1 & 0 \end{pmatrix}. \qquad (\text{II.2.14})$$

They are not hermitian but, as advertised, they satisfy indeed the commutation relations (II.5.21) with $q = 2$, and they further more satisfy:

$$[Z_+, Z_-] = Z,$$

which is just the Hamiltonian.

Now check that they step us through the spectrum of states. The ground state is in this case the state $|-1\rangle$ with lowest eigenvalue -1. Acting with the raising operator Z_+ yields:

$$Z_+|-1\rangle = |+1\rangle \Leftrightarrow \begin{pmatrix} 0 & 1 \\ 0 & 0 \end{pmatrix}\begin{pmatrix} 0 \\ 1 \end{pmatrix} = \begin{pmatrix} 1 \\ 0 \end{pmatrix},$$

with eigenvalue $+1$. You may want to check that the raising operator applied to the highest eigenstate $|+1\rangle$ yields zero and a similar statement holds about applying the lowering operator and the lowest energy or ground state.

We may turn the argument around and say that a lowering operator can be used to find the ground state $|\psi_0\rangle$ (up to some constant phase factor), by *requiring* $A_-|\psi_0\rangle = 0$ in the present case:

$$\begin{pmatrix} 0 & 0 \\ 1 & 0 \end{pmatrix}\begin{pmatrix} \alpha \\ \beta \end{pmatrix} = \begin{pmatrix} 0 \\ \alpha \end{pmatrix} = \alpha\begin{pmatrix} 0 \\ 1 \end{pmatrix} \quad \Rightarrow \quad \alpha = 0,$$

from which follows that $|\psi_0\rangle = |-1\rangle$, up to the phase factor α.

The action of the step operators on the states is summarized in simple spectral diagram in Figure II.2.7. Note that the figure is also supposed to imply the fact that

$$Z_\pm|\pm 1\rangle = 0,$$

where the '0" on the right-hand side is the zero vector in the vector space. This zero does not represent a physical state as it has norm zero. The spectrum is bounded: it has a so-called highest and lowest weight state.

State operators. These operators and the pictures that represent their actions are quite useful in situations that are more complicated than qubits. What they allow you to do, is to give a different symbolic representation of the general qubit state (II.1.2), as we can write:

$$|\psi\rangle = (\alpha + \beta Z_+)|-1\rangle = \hat{\psi}_+|-1\rangle, \qquad (\text{II.2.15})$$

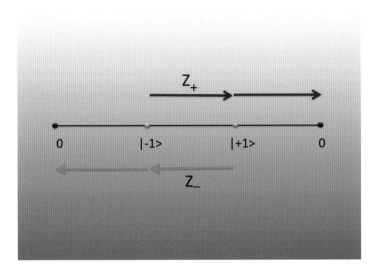

Figure II.2.7: *Step operators.* The action of the step operators $Z_\pm$ on the basis states $|\pm\rangle$. It is also implied that $Z_\pm|\pm 1\rangle = 0$, where 0 is the zero vector, which is not a physical state.

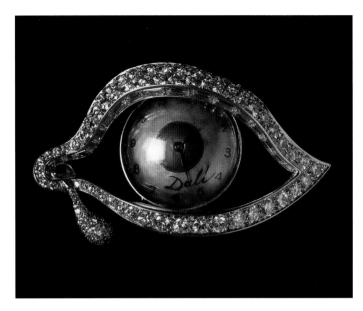

Figure II.2.8: Truth is in the eye of the beholder. *Time's eye* (1949) by Salvador Dali. (©Salvador Dalí, Fundación Gala-Salvador Dalí)

or alternatively:

$$|\psi\rangle = (\alpha Z_- + \beta)|+1\rangle = \hat{\psi}_-|+1\rangle. \qquad \text{(II.2.16)}$$

What this equation shows is that there is a correspondence between states and operators, if we know either a 'lowest weight' or a 'highest weight' reference state $|0\rangle_\pm$, defined by the conditions,

$$Z_-|0\rangle_- = 0 \text{ or } Z_+|0\rangle_+ = 0,$$

which, as we saw, yielded that the lowest or ground state is $|0\rangle_- = |-1\rangle$. What we learn is that there is an equivalence between specifying a state vector $|\psi\rangle$, and an operator $\hat{\psi}$ that acts on a given ground state $|0\rangle$. It is this perspective which turns out to be essential for understanding the spectrum of quantum particles and fields.

Quantum measurement

Physics as a science is deeply empirical. Theories have to be thoroughly tested by experiments and have to be adapted or refuted if they fail to be confirmed. Experiments involve measurements in which the features of the proposed theory are observed by some means. This means that quantum theory also features the subtle, if not exotic, concepts like the linear superposition principle and the possibility of entangled states. The basic theoretical features were hard to put to test at the time when the theory was formulated, because the experimental techniques were not sophisticated enough to reach the necessary degree of precision. The story of quantum measurement therefore has a rich history. The first dramatic pseudo experimental developments consisted of the well-known 'gedanken' or 'thought' experiments devised by none less than Einstein and Schrödinger themselves. Schrödinger's cat addressed the problematic side of the outrageous idea that a cat could be in a state that is a linear combination of a 'dead' and an 'alive' state, and we discussed it in the previous chapter on page 32. The other is the EPR paradox, addressing the problematic aspect of non locality as a direct consequence of having spatially separated particles in an entangled state. This led to the view that quantum theory would be an incomplete theory to which 'hidden variables' would have to be added to make it local and causally consistent. It took fierce debates like the Einstein–Bohr debate, and it caused a search for alternative interpretations or even theories like the 'hidden variable' theory of David Bohm and the 'many worlds' interpretation proposed by Hugh Everett in 1958.

Our strategy in this book is that using our knowledge of states and observables as discussed so far, we present the commonly adopted (called orthodox by some) Copenhagen interpretation of measurement in this chapter, primarily because it has never been falsified, quite the opposite. Indeed it has been vindicated by numerous extremely refined recent experiments. Yet, not everybody is quite comfortable with the situation and we will get to some of the paradoxes and their (experimental) resolutions into more detail in Chapter II.4.

The question of quantum measurement has two parts to it: part one answers the question: given that the system is in a state $|\psi\rangle$ what can we say about the measurement outcome of some observable A. And the second part answers the question: how does a measurement affect the state $|\psi\rangle$? We will see that in quantum theory object and subject are, strictly speaking, no longer separable.

Probabilism. The interpretation of the wavefunction is at first sight quite bizarre: it is a measure for where the particle may be found if one is to make a measurement. More precisely, its square gives the probability density of finding the particle at position x at time t. Expressed in a compact formula it reads simply: $P(x,t) = |\Psi(x,t)|^2$. Probability? What? Didn't we completely specify the state and now at

once we start talking about the odds of finding the particle somewhere. Is that all we can do? Can't we do better? Good question, so, let me quote what Richard Feynman said on this remarkable quantum state of affairs in part three of his famous Lectures on Physics.

> We would like to emphasize an important difference between classical and quantum mechanics. We have been talking about the probability that the electron will arrive in a given circumstance. We have implied that in an experimental arrangement (even in the best possible one) it would be impossible to predict exactly what would happen. We can only predict the odds! This would mean, if it were true, that physics has given up on the problem of trying to predict exactly what will happen in a given circumstance. Yes! Physics has given up. We do not know how to predict what would happen in a given circumstance, and we believe now that it is impossible – that the only thing that can be predicted is the probability of different events. It must be recognized that this is a retrenchment in our earlier ideal of understanding nature.
>
> *Richard Feynman, Lectures on Physics, Part III*

This quote characterizes the dramatic change of perspective on our capability to 'understand' the fundamental properties of nature. It was in fact the Austrian physicist Max Born who forcefully argued for this probabilistic interpretation of quantum mechanics, and he received the Nobel prize in 1935 for this work. This interpretation is usually referred to as the *Kopenhagener Deutung*, or *Copenhagen interpretation*, of quantum mechanics.

Classical versus quantum measurements. Measurement in classical physics is conceptually rather trivial: One simply observes the classical state variables with a finite precision and thereby approximates the variable as a real number with a finite number of digits. The accuracy of measurements is limited only by background noise and the precision of the measuring instrument. The crucial assumption is that one can make any such measurement without changing the state of the system. This implies that the order in which one makes measurements is irrelevant, and therefore there is no restriction on which variables could be measured 'simultaneously.'

In the quantum setup we describe a particle with a wavefunction which may be spread out over all of space. The fact that the wavefunction is spread over all of space, however, does not mean that the particle is at many places simultaneously, or that we could observe it in different places at the same time. It does not even mean that the particle is actually in some definite place and that we only happen to just not know *where* it is. The particle state is a probability amplitude, referring not to the probability where the particle actually *is* but to where it might be found upon making a position measurement. As we will see it basically doesn't make sense to talk about *where* the particle is before we observe it. In general the wavefunction tells us that the particle *is*, rather than where it is.

Indeed, that situation is quite different from the proposition that we know someone is in a room behind a closed door, and we do not know where in the room this person exactly is, because in that case we know for sure that the person will be definitely somewhere and we may assign a certain probability distribution as to where she is. That distribution however reflects *our* ignorance, *our* not-knowing the exact state. It describes our lack of knowledge as observer, not the actual state this person is in.

In quantum theory a given extended wavefunction specifies the state of the particle *completely*, and knowledge of that state does not allow us to deduce where the particle is; its position is just not determined, in that state *it has no position a priori* and it therefore makes no (quantum) sense to talk about it! The fundamental difference between a possible classical probability which reflects our lack of knowledge about the system, and the inescapable

 Leaving a trace. A misleading aspect of measurement theory is that the term measurement suggests that it is necessary to have an experimenter who is handling some intricate device to collect data. This is not the case. As a matter of principle, it only matters that the system interacted with something, somewhere, at some time, and that that interaction affected the state of the system. The interaction may have left a trace somewhere, an indelible mark, without any experimenter caring about it or even being aware of it. In that sense the notion of measurement is much more abstract, and less anthropocentric than you might have thought. It is like 'forensic science,' where one is searching for traces of past interactions call it of 'measurements' – that took place a long time ago: finger prints, car keys, or sunglasses left on a table, or phone calls, and photographs left on a remote server. A measurement is anything that leaves some discernible trace somewhere, at some instant in time.

So if I engage into an interaction with a particle, its behavior may have been influenced by previous interactions I have no knowledge about, and that may in turn lead to unexpected outcomes in my experiment. Something I better be aware of. It is the hidden constraints that often present an invisible yet fatal flaw. We return to these questions in Chapter II.4. □

uncertainty that occurs even if we know the state exactly is that the quantum probability refers to an intrinsic property of the system and not to the state of knowledge that an observer like you or me might or might not have about that system. Yet, at the same time, the state limits fundamentally what an observer could possibly get to know about the system. As a consequence the measurement process in quantum mechanics is not at all trivial.

Another notable difference with classical mechanics is that in many instances the set of observable states is discrete, with quantized values for the physical variable. It is this property that has given the theory of quantum mechanics its name.

Maybe the most profound difference is that quantum measurement typically causes a radical alteration of the state vector. Before the measurement of an observable we can only describe the possible outcomes in terms of probabilities, whereas after the measurement the outcome is known with certainty, and the wavefunction is irrevocably altered to reflect this. In the Copenhagen interpretation of quantum mechanics the wavefunction is said to 'collapse' when a measurement is made.

In spite of the fact that quantum mechanics makes spectacularly successful predictions, the fact that quantum measurements are inherently probabilistic and can 'instantly' alter the state of the system in such a disruptive manner has caused a great deal of confusion and controversy. In fact, one can argue that historically the field of quantum computation emerged from thinking carefully about the measurement problem.

No cloning!

If measuring a quantum state changes it, you may wonder whether it is not a smart idea to copy such a state, before making the measurement. Take one and make two identical ones out of it by using a quantum Xerox machine. The answer is simply that this just cannot be done. Quantum copying is a no-go! This exceptional feature create the possibility of a novel type of 'quantum security:' Information that cannot be copied without destroying it. This makes the no-cloning principle a blessing in disguise.

What I am trying to tell you is that reading a quantum book will change it in unpredictable ways. You might actually want to avoid trouble with the librarian by copying the quantum book before reading it. But even this precautionary measure is obstructed by a quantum *no cloning theorem*, which was first formulated by William Wootters and Wojciech Zurek and by Dennis Dieks in 1982.

Suppose I have one particle in a particular state, and I want to bring another particle into exactly the same state. Then I have to look at the state of particle one in order to know what state to bring particle two in. But, by doing so, I have to affect the state of particle one. The best I can do in general is to bring particle two in the state particle one was in before, but then particle one is no longer in that state. This remarkable property can be shown to hold rigorously: quantum states cannot be copied, but they may be transferred from one system to another. And thinking in terms of securing information and beating our National Security Agencies with respect to protecting our privacy, this no-cloning may turn out to be a blessing in disguise. And it is.

More precisely, the no-cloning theorem amounts to the statement that for an arbitrary state $|\psi_1\rangle$ on one qubit and some particular state $|\phi\rangle$ on another, there is no quantum device $[A]$ that transforms $|\phi\rangle \otimes |\psi_1\rangle \rightarrow |\psi_1\rangle \otimes |\psi_1\rangle$, i.e. that transforms $|\phi\rangle$ into $|\psi_1\rangle$, while leaving the old $|\psi_1\rangle$ unaffected. If U_A is the unitary operator representing A, this can be rewritten $|\psi_1\rangle|\psi_1\rangle = U_A|\phi\rangle|\psi_1\rangle$. For a true cloning device this property has to hold for any other state $|\psi_2\rangle$ as well, and we must also have $|\psi_2\rangle|\psi_2\rangle = U_A|\phi\rangle|\psi_2\rangle$. It is not hard to demonstrate that the existence of such a device leads to a contradiction. Since $\langle\phi|\phi\rangle = 1$ and $U_A^\dagger U_A = 1$, the existence of a device that can clone both ψ_1 and ψ_2 would imply that

$$
\begin{aligned}
\langle\psi_1|\psi_2\rangle &= (\langle\psi_1|\langle\phi|)\,(|\phi\rangle|\psi_2\rangle)) \\
&= (\langle\psi_1|\langle\phi|U_A^\dagger)\,(U_A|\phi\rangle|\psi_2\rangle)) \\
&= (\langle\psi_1|\langle\psi_1|)(|\psi_2\rangle|\psi_2\rangle)) = \langle\psi_1|\psi_2\rangle^2\,.
\end{aligned}
$$

The property $\langle\psi_1|\psi_2\rangle = \langle\psi_1|\psi_2\rangle^2$ only holds if ψ_1 and ψ_2 are either orthogonal or aligned meaning that either $\langle\psi_1|\psi_2\rangle = 0$ or 1. It does not hold for arbitrary values of ψ_1 and ψ_2, so there can be no such general purpose cloning device. In fact, in view of the uncertainty of quantum measurements, the no-cloning theorem does not come as a surprise. If it were possible to clone wavefunctions, it would be possible to circumvent the uncertainty of quantum measurements by making a large number of copies of a wavefunction, measuring different properties of each copy, and reconstructing the exact state of the original wavefunction.

The probabilistic outcome of measurements

In the formalism of quantum mechanics the possible measurement outcomes of an observable quantity A are given by the eigenvalues of the matrix A. For example, the three Pauli matrices, defined in equation (II.2.2), all have the same two eigenvalues $\lambda_\pm = \pm 1$. This means that the possible outcomes of a measurement of the spin *in any direction* can only be plus or minus one. This is fundamentally different from a spinning object in classical physics, which can spin at any possible rate in any direction. The observed value of any component of a classical spin in this picture could be any real number between -1 and $+1$. This confirms that quantum mechanics is counter-intuitive and subtle indeed.

If a quantum system is in an eigenstate of an observable, then the outcome of measurements of that observable is 100% certain. For example, imagine we have a qubit in the state with $\alpha = 1$ and $\beta = 0$, so that $|\psi\rangle = |+1\rangle$. It is then in the eigenstate of Z with eigenvalue $z = +1$ and the measurement of Z will always yield that value. This is depicted in Figure II.2.9(a), and is reflected in the mathematical machinery of quantum mechanics by the fact that for the spin or polarization operator in the z–direction, $A = Z$,

the eigenvector with eigenvalue $\lambda_+ = +1$ is $|+1\rangle$ and the eigenvector with $\lambda_- = -1$ is $|-1\rangle$. In contrast, if we make measurements in another direction, e.g. $A = X$, the outcomes become probabilistic. The outcome is still $+1$ or -1, but there are calculable probabilities for each value to occur. So the take-away message here is that it is not the values of possible outcomes that change, only the probability by which they will occur. Quantum theory is dealing with 'certain uncertainties', so to say. This is depicted in Figure II.2.9(d). The eigenvectors of X are:

$$|+\rangle = \sqrt{\frac{1}{2}}(|+1\rangle + |-1\rangle) \quad \text{and} \quad |-\rangle = \sqrt{\frac{1}{2}}(|1\rangle - |-1\rangle).$$

In general the probability of finding the system in a given state through a measurement is computed by first writing the given state $|\psi\rangle$ as a linear combination of the eigenstates $|a_k\rangle$ of the matrix A corresponding to the observable, i.e.

$$|\psi\rangle = \sum_k \beta_k|a_k\rangle \text{ with } \beta_k = \langle a_k|\psi\rangle.$$

The notation $\langle a_k|\psi\rangle$ means that the component β_k is indeed equal to the projection of the state vector $|\psi\rangle$ on the eigenvector $|a_k\rangle$. The probability of measuring the system in the state corresponding to eigenvalue a_k is then given by

$$p_k = |\beta_k|^2 = |\langle a_k|\psi\rangle|^2. \qquad (II.2.17)$$

As we discussed briefly before, this is why the coefficients β_k in the expansion of the state $|\psi\rangle$ in a set of eigenstates of some observable are called *probability amplitudes*, amplitudes because it is only after squaring them that one obtains the probabilities for a certain measurement outcome. And the normalization condition on the state vector is just the statement that the total probability to find the system in one of the allowed states, equals one. The other two pictures of Figure II.2.9 give smilar distributions for an incoming $|+\rangle$ state. In Figure II.2.10 we given the corresponding distributions of electrons hitting the screen perpendicular to the beam. This is what one sees preparing the beam in the incoming state and then measuring its polarization along some given axis.

So, what constitutes a measurement? I have been somewhat cavalier in talking about the notion of a measurement, while showing you nice and clean figures of some idealized experiments. Indeed at this stage, where we for example talk about spin polarization measurements, we have a situation in mind where we distinguish three stages in a measurement experiment.

(i) A preparatory stage, where we prepare the particle(s) so that the spin is in the desired state. For example we have electrons coming in and by using a Stern–Gerlach device (this will be explained in the next chapter) we can split the beam into two with opposite polarizations along an axis one may choose. This way one may prepare a beam of spins in some definite and identical polarization state up to an overall phase.

(ii) A first stage of the measurement, where we let the prepared beam sequentially interact with some other devices, which make up the experiment.

(iii) The second and final stage of the measurement, where we actually have a 'screen' or other counting device. So, in the end we measure a probability distribution that can be compared with a theoretical prediction, and potentially falsify our theory.

The purist may say that only the very last stage constitutes the measurement, so where the distribution over the sample spaces of some pre-chosen set of observables is obtained by projecting the outcoming particle states.

The projection postulate

In classical physics, science started from the belief – or should one say, from the illusion? – that we could describe the world, or least parts of the world, without any reference to ourselves.

Werner Heisenberg

Apart from the probabilistic nature of measurement outcomes, a second remarkable aspect of quantum measurement is the fact that the act of making a measurement will generically change the state of the system. It is disruptive and will cause what is known as a '*collapse of the wavefunction*.' The mechanism is also known as the *projection postulate*, which was formulated by John von Neumann in the early days of quantum mechanics. This postulate is at this point an extra and in fact ad hoc postulate. Ad hoc, because the measurement process itself is just a quantum process and therefore should be completely described within the framework of the theory. The outcome should be 'calculable' from first principles and cannot be decreed by an additional postulate. In the end it is to be decided by ever more precise measurements whether or to what extent the postulate really holds and correctly represents all possible choices. But even then, the postulate including its range of validity should be 'proven' from first principles.

This being said, the reason this is so hard is because a typical realistic measurement device is a macroscopic, classical machine. So what I just said will be extremely complicated, because you have to model the effective interaction between quantum and classical degrees of freedom, basically by going all the way down to the quantum level in describing the apparatus.

In an operational sense the projection postulate so far has been confirmed by basically all experiments dedicated to test it. It is this 'success' which causes that the terminology and related picture of the measurement process persist in the mindset of most quantum practitioners .

Over the last few decades, physicists like to distinguish socalled *strong* and *weak* measurements. Let us comment on them subsequently.

Strong measurements. The strong measurements are the most common ones. One observes a particular eigenvalue as we discussed, and the system makes then a transition exactly to the corresponding eigenstate. This type of measurement does confirm the postulate by definition.

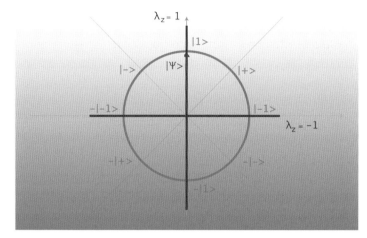

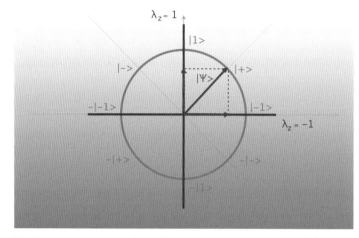

(a) Measurement spin polarization along z-axis, of the state $|\psi\rangle = |1\rangle$. Outcome: probability $p_z(+1) = 1$ and $p_z(-1) = 0$.

(b) Measurement spin polarization along z-axis, of the state $|\psi\rangle = |+\rangle$. Outcome: $p_z(+1) = p_z(-1) = 1/2$.

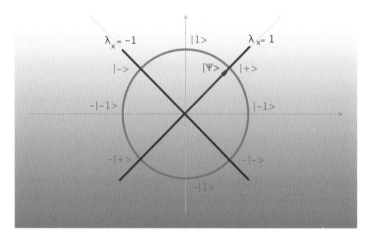

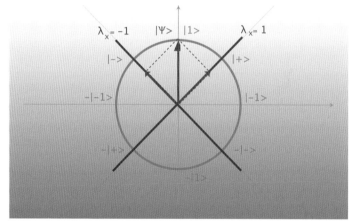

(c) Measurement spin polarization along x-axis, of the state $|\psi\rangle = |+\rangle$. Outcome: $p_x(+1) = 1$ and $p_x(-1) = 0$.

(d) Measurement spin polarization along x-axis, of the state $|\psi\rangle = |1\rangle$. Outcome $p_x(+1) = p_x(-1) = 1/2$.

Figure II.2.9: *Spin polarizations.* Graphical representation of spin polarization along different axes. The projections of the red state vector $|\psi\rangle$ along the axes of the measurement frames gives the probability amplitude for the outcome to be plus or minus one.

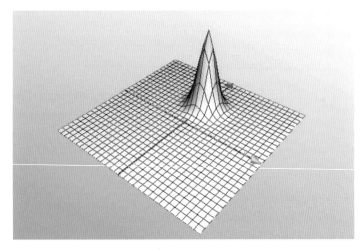

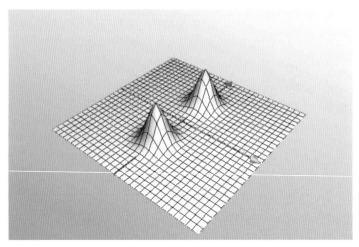

(a) Measurement spin polarization along z-axis, of the state $|\psi\rangle = |1\rangle$. Outcome: probability $p_z(+1) = 1$ and $p_z(-1) = 0$.

(b) Measurement spin polarization along z-axis, of the state $|\psi\rangle = |+\rangle$. Outcome: $p_z(+1) = p_z(-1) = 1/2$.

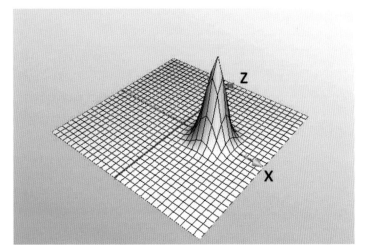

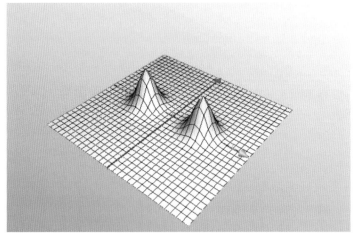

(c) Measurement spin polarization along x-axis, of the state $|\psi\rangle = |+\rangle$. Outcome: $p_x(+1) = 1$ and $p_x(-1) = 0$.

(d) Measurement spin polarization along x-axis, of the state $|\psi\rangle = |1\rangle$. Outcome $p_x(+1) = p_x(-1) = 1/2$.

Figure II.2.10: *Spin polarization measurements*. We have visualized the probability distributions discussed in the previous figure, in counts on a $z - x$ screen. The incoming beam is coming down along the y-axis after passing through a polarizing beamsplitter. The width of the distribution is supposed to reflect the width of the beams.

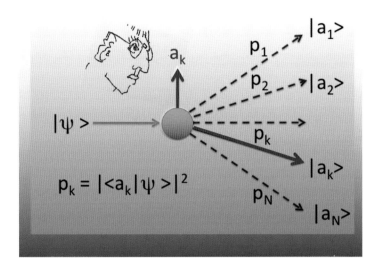

Figure II.2.11: *Projective measurement.* For the incoming state $|\psi\rangle$ there is a probability p_k, equal to the projection of the state on the eigenvector squared, to observe the (eigen)value a_k.

What happens is depicted schematically in Figure II.2.11. We start with a system in some state $|\psi\rangle$ and we make a measurement of the observable A and find a value a_k, then the act of making the measurement changes the state $|\psi\rangle$ to the state $|a_k\rangle$, the eigenstate of A with observed eigenvalue a_k. What this means is that if we would act with A again immediately after, we would measure that same eigenvalue with 100% probability, and that seems like a reasonable thing to expect.

Weak measurements. Fortunately, one is of course free to invent whatever smart measurement schemes one wants to pursue, in order to – in a more subtle way – extract more information than the projection postulate would allow you to. This has lead to an interesting debate within the physics community about so-called *weak measurements* and *weak values*.

The idea is to make measurements where the interaction with the system is sufficiently weak so that it does not affect the incoming state. Yet, there is the possibility to ob-

serve a 'weak value' which would tell us 'something extra' about the state of system. As the state hasn't changed after the weak measurement, a strong measurement of another incompatible observable, made right after the weak one would not be affected. You should think of this as the subtle changes in the screen patterns of Figure II.2.12, like a small displacement in one of the peaks.

We have seen that a projective measurement with its collapse of the wavefunction amounts to a major disruption of the system, and here we consider the possibility to perturb the system in a subtle way, meaning weakly. These weak measurements may tell us something about the state of the system without really making a complete projection. In Figure II.2.12 we have depicted a scheme proposed by Aharonov, Albert and Vaidman, and show what happens to the particle distributions after we do such a weak measurement. We have incoming particles in a state $|\psi\rangle = (|+\rangle + \sqrt{2}|-\rangle)/\sqrt{3}$. In Figure II.2.12(a) we have the incoming beam and do no polarization measurement. In the second Figure II.2.12(b) we measure the polarization along the x-axis, and we see the expected splitting, with outcome $p_x(+1) = 1/3$ and $p_x(-1) = 2/3$. In Figure II.2.12(c) we start with an incomplete polarization measurement along the z-direction, which means that we apply a weak field so that the beam does not really split. This amounts to a small perturbation of the incoming beam. However, if directly after the weak measurement, we measure the x-polarization of the perturbed beam we observe a small displacement of the weak peak in the z direction as indicated in Figure II.2.12(d). The projection along the x-axis, however, takes place as usual, but one has succeeded in getting some extra information on the 'incompatible' z-polarization. It is this tiny shift in the z direction which amounts to the measurement of a *weak value*.

So here we have an example that illustrates the subtlety of the notion of measurement, the clue being that we have concocted a setup where we go beyond a simple projective measurement. It underscores that all interactions in some

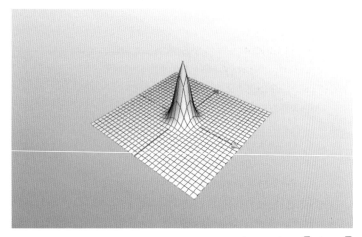

(a) Measurement spin polarization of the state $|\psi\rangle = (|+\rangle + \sqrt{2}|-\rangle)/\sqrt{3}$. Polarizers are turned off.

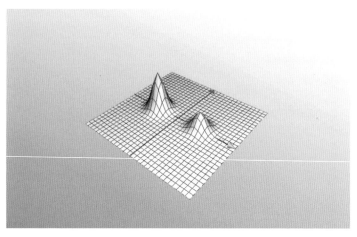

(b) Measurement spin polarization along x-axis, of the state. Outcome: $p_x(+1) = 1/3, p_x(-1) = 2/3$.

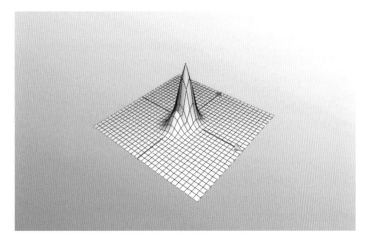

(c) A weak measurement of the spin polarization along z-axis, of the same state, yields a perturbed state.

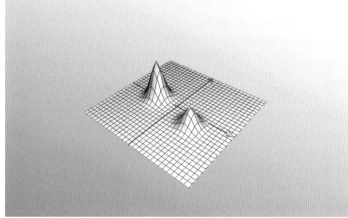

(d) Measurement spin polarization along x-axis, of the perturbed state. Outcome $p_x(+1) = 2/3$ and $p_x(-1) = 1/3$. However the small peak is slightly shifted.

Figure II.2.12: *A weak spin measurement.* The incoming beam is coming down along the y-axis after passing through a z- and/or x-polarizing beamsplitter. The width of the distributions reflects the width of the beams. The results are explained in the text.

Figure II.2.13: *Logic and syntax.* In search of semantics?

way could be called a measurement, if you are willing to stretch the semantics of the term measurement.

Quantum grammar: Logic and Syntax

In the classical situation we speak of the phase space *of a system, to be contrasted with the* Hilbert space *for quantum systems. The fundamentally different structure of these two spaces has profound consequences for the logical and deductive structure of these theories. Whereas in the classical case properties of the system generally can be associated with subspaces of the total phase space, one has on the quantum level to distinguish the space of observables from the Hilbert space, and choose from possible consistent* frameworks *which are more restrictive. Within a framework certain* **properties** *can be unambiguously assigned, and deductive logic can be applied. This is illustrated for the cases of a qubit and a particle.*

Compatible observables allow for joint eigenstates and thus for those states one may assign a point in the joint sample space. A maximal subset of independent observables that are mutually compatible defines a *consistent framework* $\mathcal{F}$ to describe the system with. With the framework comes a sampling space $\mathcal{S}$ which is a kind of quantum equivalent of the classical phase space. So for the qubit example this is clear. A consistent framework could correspond to the Z observable, and we may describe all states of the qubit, as (normalized) linear combinations of the basis states $|\pm 1\rangle$ which are the eigenvectors of the Z observable as it makes up the framework.

The framework for a quantum system is not unique, and the choice of framework depends on what question one wants to address and what aspect of the system one wants to study. If you make position measurements you use the Z-framework, and if you make momentum measurements you choose the X-framework. Let me emphasize however that a quantessence here is that there are observables which are not compatible with the framework. Logically speaking what this implies is that the observables incompatible with the particular framework you are using cannot be assigned a *meaning*. They are *meaningless* in that framework because there is no logical way one can decide whether a property referring to the values of incompatible observables is true or not. Henceforth quantum theory has well-defined observables that have the unusual feature that they cannot be part of a logically sound deductive argument within a given framework. Let us take a closer look at this statement and find out what this means for a classical particle and its quantum descendent.

Collapse of the wavefunction. In figure (a) below we give a graphic impression of what is called 'the collapse of the wavefunction.' If you think of the wavefunction as a probability amplitude, it makes actually a lot of sense, because you would expect that repeating the same measurement immediately after you have made the observation a_k would give exactly the same outcome with 100% certainty. But that can only be the case if the state has changed to the corresponding eigenstate $|a_k\rangle$ as decreed by the projection postulate. So the term 'collapse of the wavefunction' suggests that there is a violent physical action at a distance going on if we make a measurement, but that is totally misleading. The wavefunction which indeed encodes all there is to know about the state of the system represents a probability amplitude, and making a measurement can drastically change the probability of future measurement outcomes.

This is a familiar phenomenon. If I know that you are somewhere in town, I may have a rather uniform probability distribution for where you are that stretches all the way to the outskirts of the city. If you then suddenly happen to walk into my office, my probability distribution will indeed instantaneously collapse to some narrow spike that peaks right in front of my desk. But that doesn't mean that something is physically changing on the outskirts of town, nor will you be affected.

The quantessential difference between the quantum case and you is of course that the distribution I had in my mind about you was certainly *not* all there was to know about the system called 'you!'. It had more to say about my state of ignorance than about you. The measurement did not affect you nor places where you could have been. Apparently in quantum theory the strict separation of object and

subject that reigns in classical physics is no longer valid: no longer any neutral observers, no peeking, or looking without touching.

In the classical context, the separation of object and subject is based on the assumption that it is in principle possible to make the effect of the measurement on the system arbitrarily small. This is no longer true in quantum theory.

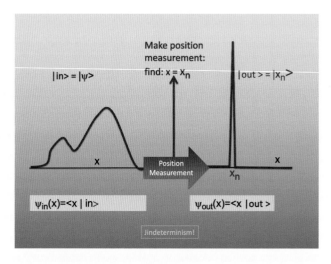

(a): *Collapse of the wavefunction.* A state $|\psi\rangle$ comes in and a measurement of the observable A is made. This yields with a probability p_n the outcome $x_n \in x$, and the state $|\psi\rangle$ instantly 'collapses' to the state $|x_n\rangle$.

Sure enough, given a particular state there may be an appropriately chosen measurement that does not change the state, but in general it does change the state. So imagine how strange it would be if, after you read that quantum book, it changed. Never a dull moment, but alas nobody could guarantee you that the book would still make sense after you read it. A recipe for great applications in social media I think.□

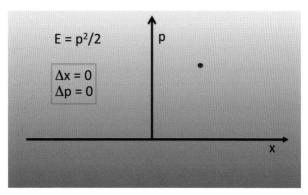

(b) Classically the state of a particle in one dimension is defined by its position x and momentum p, which define a point in its phase space $\mathcal{F}_{\mathrm{ph}}$.

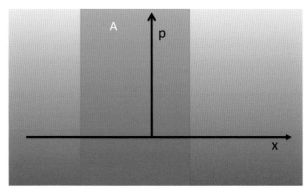

(c) The region corresponding to the proposition A: $x_0 < x < x_1$ is shaded blue. It is true for a state if the point representing that state is in the blue region.

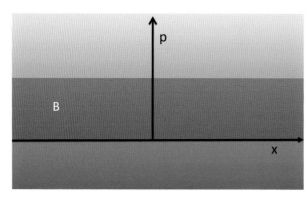

(d) The proposition B: $0 < p < p_1$ is true for all points in the dark red shaded region.

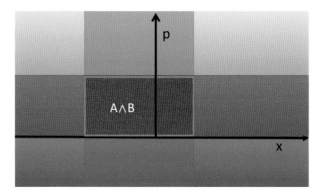

(e) The conjunction 'and' denoted as $A \wedge B$ corresponds to the bright red region.

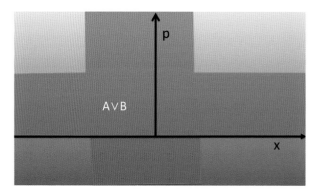

(f) The conjunction 'or' denoted as $A \vee B$ corresponds to the green region.

Figure II.2.14: *Propositions in classical physics.* Propositions about the the position x and momentum p of a particle in one dimension and their conjunctions.

The case of a classical particle

Position and momentum are the basic observables that label the dynamical state of a particle which corresponds to a point in the phase space of the particle as illustrated in Figure II.2.14(b). These are basic because in the Newtonian 'framework' one has to specify the momentum and position at some initial time. Then the states at any other time would be determined provided we know the force acting on the particle. The fact that the momentum and position variables are basic also implies that other dynamical variables like energy can be expressed in them.

We can make propositions involving properties of particular states of the particle and find a yes/no answer to whether that proposition is true or false. Not only can we answer questions about the elementary properties but also about conjunctions of those. For example, we may ask whether a state has the property A: $x_0 \leq x \leq x_1$. Then for all points x, p in phase space in the blue shaded region of Figure II.2.14(c) the answer is yes, and outside that region it would be no.

So we can assign a truth value '1' or '0' to the proposition A accordingly. Similarly we may ask for the p value to satisfy $0 \leq p \leq p_1$ and define it as proposition B, and then we get the picture of Figure II.2.14(d). Now we can ask for combined properties of x and p. For example, if may ask whether the property $A \wedge B$ (A **and** B) is true or not. The truth value of this conjunction can be calculated, and for the case at hand it equals the product of the truth values of A and B. This assignment requires of course that $AB = BA$, which means that the point has to be located in the bright red shaded rectangle as indicated in Figure II.2.14(e), the region that is the intersection of the shaded regions in the two previous figures.

Similarly, one may ask whether $x_0 \leq x \leq x_1$ **or** $0 \leq p \leq p_1$ is valid, which means that we ask whether the property

Table II.2.1: Truth table for the propositions made in Figure II.2.14

A	B	A∧ B	A∨ B
0	0	0	0
1	0	0	1
0	1	0	1
1	1	1	1

$A \vee B$ is true or not. This proposition is in the picture represented as the union of the shaded areas, which is the green shaded area in Figure II.2.14(f). Formally the truth value can be calculated by the formula $A + B - AB$. The figures can be summarized in a conventional truth table as shown above, exactly as they are used in elementary (propositional) logic. So to find the properties of the classical particle, the physicists infer these from the rules of a simple deductive logical scheme that is mathematically represented by a Boolean algebra with variables that can only take two values, zero (false) or one (true).

The case of a quantum particle

Let us now sketch what happens to the particle in the quantum arena. There is again a basic set of quantum observables 'X' and 'P'. And again one may ask at any moment what the value of any of the observables is and verify by measurement whether the proposition is true or false.

Sampling spaces. Here we first have to address the question of what the *sampling spaces* for these observables are. Let us allow two possibilities for the space in which the particle moves: it could be infinite and correspond to a straight line or it could be finite, say, a circle. The possible outcomes of position measurements would of course correspond to points in these spaces, meaning that the sam-

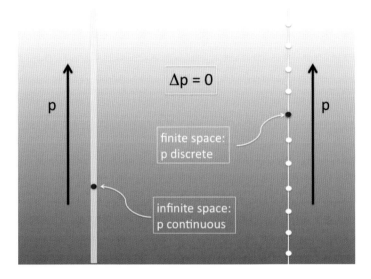

Figure II.2.15: *Sample space of momentum.* The sample space $\mathcal{S}_{\mathrm{p}}$ for the momentum observable in the quantum case depends on the topology of the (continuous) configuration space $\mathcal{X}$ in which the particle moves.

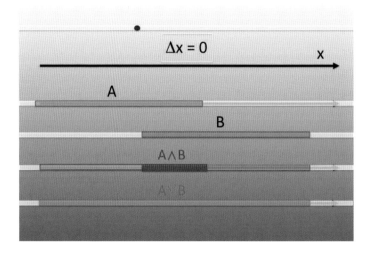

Figure II.2.16: *Sample space of position.* The sample space for the position observable is the real line. We indicated two possible propositions A and B, and their conjunctions.

ple space $\mathcal{S}_{\mathrm{x}} \simeq \mathcal{X}$. However, the sample space for the momentum observable turns out to depend on the topology of the underlying configuration space.

If the particle lives on the real line and $\mathcal{X} \simeq \mathbb{R}$, then the possible values for the momentum variable are continuous just like the position variable, $\mathcal{S}_{\mathrm{p}} \simeq \mathbb{R}$.

On the other hand, if the configuration space would be a circle $\mathcal{X} \simeq S^1$, then, as Bohr told us, the spectrum of the momentum becomes discrete and would in fact correspond to the set of integers denoted by $\mathcal{S}_{\mathrm{p}} \simeq \mathbb{Z}$. We will treat the case of a particle on a circle in detail in the Chapter II.5. We have indicated the two possibilities in Figure II.2.15.

There is a third possibility here, that at first may strike you as utterly pointless but turns out to be quantessential and should not be overlooked. Imagine that the position space itself is *discrete and infinite*, like a one-dimensional lattice $\mathbb{Z}$, then, one should expect to find that the sample space for the momentum becomes a circle, $\mathcal{S}_{\mathrm{p}} \simeq S^1$.

The momentum in that case becomes an angular variable $0 \leq \theta \leq 2\pi$.

Going yet one step further, we can also ask what happens if the position space is *discrete and finite*, for example cyclic like the corners of a polygon, then interestingly enough the sample space of the analogue of a momentum observable associated with the particle hopping from one state to another would also becomes periodic and discrete. We have already run into the simplest example of this, a space with two points being just a classical bit, or classical Ising spin, which as we saw on a quantum level gives rise to the qubit or quantum spin. For that case it turned out that the position observable Z had two eigenvalues ± 1, and the same was true for the 'momentum operator' X. As you see, we have managed to wrap a whole lot of quantessence in a qubit, and will continue to do so. This concludes our discussion of a first crucial difference between the classical and quantum sampling spaces of a 'particle'.

Incompatible observables. The second difference is far more dramatic. It turns out that the position and momentum observables are incompatible, which means that a consistent framework for the quantum particle can only be based on either the momentum observable *or* on the position observable.[6] So, in going from classical phase space to the quantum space one can chose the momentum sample space indicated in Figure II.2.15 or for example the position space of Figure II.2.16, and we 'loose' the orthogonal dimension. The amputation of half the number of dimensions is quite an operation and I can imagine that you, following our discourse, may suffer from a kind of 'phantom pain' like experience. This loss implies a quantessential restriction on what can be considered 'a meaningful statement' about properties of the system, and at the same time creates ample room for void statements and 'fake news.'

What we just said also means that the quantum extension of our deductive logic gets severely restrained. Clearly if we compare the possible properties of a classical particle illustrated in Figure II.2.14 to the possible properties of a quantum particle given in Figure II.2.16, these are radically different. *Most importantly we cannot assign properties to the* P *and* X *observables simultaneously*, and hence cannot carry over the classical picture at all. What is left on the quantum level is that we may assign properties and ask for their conjunctions as long as they refer to one of the two observables, and this is illustrated in Figure II.2.16 where we did define two propositions A and B pertaining to the position variable and their logical conjunctions $A \wedge B$ and $A \vee B$. In conclusion, we note once more that because quantum operators in general do not commute, axes prominently present in the classical picture may be completely absent on the quantum level. This does not mean that the 'lost' observable X or P has taken the value zero and we have left out the corresponding axes. No,

it says that a variable which is not part of the framework has no meaning let alone a value, and the axis is just not there!

We will run into these kind of situations repeatedly, where before making any strong statements on the properties of a state of a quantum system, we have to be explicit about the framework we are using. In quantum theory we apparently have one complete, consistent and rigorous mathematical formalism that supports many logically distinct frameworks. This may remind you of special relativity where one also distinguishes many reference frames which are relativistically equivalent, as they can be transformed into each other by a Lorentz transformation. But to make an argument you better do not mix up statements that hold in different frames. And here we are finding many frameworks which are quantum (or unitarily) equivalent but making a physical argument, you better stick to one if you want to keep your physics straight.

This may at first sight look strange and unfamiliar and a heavy load of reader unfriendly jargon, but at the same time it is a precise, concise and explicit statement of what states, dynamical variables and measurements in quantum theory are about. And it is this core structure of the theory that we want to extensively explore in the remainder of this volume. This exposition has hopefully made you feel more comfortable with it, because from the underlying mathematical structure lots of quantessential properties can be derived. These quantessential properties, which to the classical mind may appear exotic to say the least, are falsifiable at least in principle, and have turned quantum physics into a full-fledged scientific theory. The construction of this solid mathematical framework was largely the brilliant work of the second generation of outstanding quantum physicists, like Werner Heisenberg, Erwin Schrödinger, Paul Dirac, Max Born and John von Neumann to mention a few.

---

[6]In fact one may choose any linear combination of the two, but for the moment we choose this simple restriction.

The case of a quantum bit

Philosophers talk about an *ontology* in which the quantum reality could be understood and categorized. What are its basic entities, what are their measurable properties and what are the rules governing them? One likes to understand what the propositions or properties are that are either true or false. And as we have seen in quantum theory the rules about observables appear to be rather bizarre, and therefore it is illuminating to study their logical structure in more detail.

Projection operators. It is convenient to go back to some of the statements we made on page 58 of the previous section. Suppose we have some Hilbert space $\mathcal{H}$ and a suitable set of observables that are mutually commutative and their common eigenvectors $\{|i\rangle\}$ span $\mathcal{H}$. Or we could construct a single observable which would be non-degenerate and therefore satisfy

$$A|i\rangle = a_i|i\rangle ,$$

with all its eigenvalues a_i being different. Then we could consider the *elementary projectors*:

$$P_i = |i\rangle\langle i| ,$$

which satisfy:

$$\Sigma_i \, P_i = \mathbf{1} ,$$

and therefore we can introduce its *logical negation* $\neg P_i = \mathbf{1} - \Sigma_{j\neq i} \, P_j$, which is of course also a projection operator that projects states on the subspace orthogonal to $|i\rangle$. These projectors all commute; furthermore the observable A can in this basis simply be expressed as

$$A = \Sigma_i a_i |i\rangle\langle i| ,$$

with the eigenvalues as coefficients. The Hamiltonian operator for example can be written as:

$$H = \Sigma_n E_n |\psi_n\rangle\langle\psi_n| . \qquad (\text{II.2.18})$$

Let us verify some of the equations above for the Pauli matrices. The projection operators would correspond to the matrices:

$$P_1 = |1\rangle\langle 1| = \begin{pmatrix} 1 & 0 \\ 0 & 0 \end{pmatrix}, \ P_{-1} = |-1\rangle\langle -1| = \begin{pmatrix} 0 & 0 \\ 0 & 1 \end{pmatrix} .$$

$$(\text{II.2.19})$$

These operators commute and indeed $P_1 + P_{-1} = \mathbf{1}$. The observable Z can be expanded in the projection operators as $Z = P_1 - P_{-1}$. Just for completeness we also give the expressions related to the observable X:

$$P_+ = |+\rangle\langle +| = \frac{1}{2}\begin{pmatrix} 1 & 1 \\ 1 & 1 \end{pmatrix}, \ P_- = |-\rangle\langle -| = \frac{1}{2}\begin{pmatrix} 1 & -1 \\ -1 & 1 \end{pmatrix} ,$$

and similar properties hold.

With these projectors we may now associate properties or propositions that may be true or false in the sense that if we measure A and obtain some particular outcome a_k, stipulating that P_k is 1 (true), and all other P_i are 0 (false):

$$\begin{aligned} P_k|k\rangle &= 1 \, |k\rangle \\ \neg P_k|k\rangle &= (\mathbf{1} - \Sigma_{j\neq k} P_j) \, |k\rangle = 0 . \end{aligned}$$

You may verify this outcome from the examples above.

Non-commuting projectors. So far so good, but what happens if we want to define elementary conjunctions between properties, say we want to ask whether P *or* Q ($P \vee Q$) is true. From Table II.2.1 one learns that such a proposition would correspond to the truth value of the projector PQ or QP. The logical proposition P *and* Q, ($P \wedge Q$) has truth value $P + Q - PQ$, and also involves the product. But now we run into a problem because the product of two projectors is again a projector only if they commute. So in quantum mechanics neither PQ nor QP can in general be true or untrue, and this poses a fundamental problem from an ontological point of view.

Consider in the qubit example above, for instance the proposition $P_1 \vee P_+$. This would have to correspond to the product operator

$$P_{1+} = P_1 P_+ = \frac{1}{2}\begin{pmatrix} 1 & 1 \\ 0 & 0 \end{pmatrix} \text{ or } P_{+1} = P_+ P_1 = \frac{1}{2}\begin{pmatrix} 1 & 0 \\ 1 & 0 \end{pmatrix},$$

but these are different and moreover neither of them is a projection operator ($P_{1+}^2 \neq P_{1+}$) to which truth values could be assigned. In the language used before we say that Z and X are indeed incompatible observables.

The choice of a framework. We can now avoid some of this by demanding that we only use a set of mutually commuting projectors or a set of compatible observables, linked to a given basis defined by some generic observable. Such a framework does indeed limit the number of properties that can be assigned to the system. But adopting such a framework one can use ordinary deductive logic concerning the restricted set of properties of the system.

And conversely a state can only have or not have a property a_i if we work in a framework where we can assign a truth value to its associated projector P_i. So, other non-commuting observables simply have no meaning in such a framework. And we have to think of such states in terms of a probability amplitude over the sample space connected to the framework one happens to be working with. There are many inequivalent such sets and it depends on what aspects of the theory one wants to study which one to choose. This observation suggests the use of the notion of a *single framework*, as a set in which to describe quantum states and also the propositions about the system which are meaningful in that framework. This defines an additional *syntactic rule* which forbids employing incompatible frameworks into a single description of the properties of the system. This is central to what is sometimes referred to as the *new quantum logic*.

In this single framework setting of quantum mechanics we return as closely as possible to a classical description of states with definite properties and statistical distributions over sample space. Describing the dynamics in such a single framework makes the quantum time evolution into some quite ordinary stochastic process as we will point out later.

Certain uncertainties

> Nothing [in quantum theory]... was more startling than Heisenberg's uncertainty principle, which denied the possibility of simultaneously measuring certain properties of motion. The uncertainty principle introduced us to quantum fluctuations, revealing empty space to be in fact a cauldron of activity.
>
> *John Archibald Wheeler,*
> *Geons, Black Holes & Quantum Foam* (1998)

Early on in the development of quantum theory it was Werner Heisenberg who proved his fundamental uncertainty relations stating the impossibility of simultaneously measuring certain variables that characterize the state with arbitrary precision. There is a fundamental limit to the accuracy of quantum measurements set by Planck's constant. These relations, more than anything else, express the profound difference between classical and quantum systems. We discuss the position-momentum uncertainty relation for a particle state, and work out the detailed example for a qubit.

Momentum versus position. Accepting that the state is completely specified by a wavefunction that will only tell you the probability amplitude for finding certain outcomes for any given observable another question remains: what does the wavefunction say about the momentum of the particle? There is no mention of momentum, it doesn't seem to play any role whatsoever in the definition of the state. This seems perfectly alright in view of what we have been talking about in the previous section on compatible observables and frameworks. All true, but could I not per-

Figure II.2.17: *Pointillism.* Detail (bottom) of the pointillist painting *'A Sunday Afternoon on the Island of La Grande Jatte'* (top) by the French painter Georges Seurat. Painted some years before the moment when Planck made his groundbreaking quantum hypothesis, this work showed how a closer look may reveal a quantum structure.(Source: Wikimedia.)

fectly well decide to go out and just measure it, couldn't I? Yes, you certainly can and you would indeed get a definite answer. But the story is the same as with the position measurement. Say, if you prepare a particle in a certain state described by some wavefunction $\psi_0(x)$ and you measure

a value for the momentum $p = p_0$. Then you could repeat the whole procedure and somehow again prepare the particle in exactly the same initial state and then once more measure its momentum, what would you find? Well, the statement is that in general you would get another outcome $p_1 \neq p_0$. How vague can a theory be? Well, in a sense that's precisely what quantum theory is about, it tells you exactly how vague outcomes of measurements are.

Certain uncertainties. Probabilities imply uncertainties in outcome, but the magnitude of those uncertainties are precisely determined. We have to deal with 'certain uncertainties' so to speak. In fact there are strong bounds on the uncertainties of different observable quantities. You might for example try to circumvent the quantum uncertainties by being smart. If you say, I measure the position of a particle so that it is well localized in position space, and then immediately after I measure the momentum so that I can also localize the particle in momentum space. By doing this, am I not arbitrarily close to the state in classical physics where we could assign a precise position and momentum to a particle at any instant? The stupefying answer is: certainly not!

The Heisenberg uncertainty principle

The quantessential message on the differences between classical and quantum observables is very clearly, concisely and quantitatively encoded in what are called the Heisenberg uncertainty relations. For the case at hand he derived that for any state of a particle the following relation holds for the uncertainties in position Δx and momentum Δp of the particle *in that state*:

$$\Delta x \, \Delta p \geq \frac{h}{4\pi},$$

where the spread is just the width of the respective probability distributions. It relates measurement outcomes for the same state in different frameworks! What Heisenberg proved was exactly that there is a lower bound on the product of those widths. It shows unequivocally that the situation, generally assumed in classical physics, where both widths can be taken to zero in principle (assuming ideal measurement apparatus etc.) is not possible in quantum theory as a matter of principle.

If we drop a marble in a bowl, it will after some oscillations settle down in the minimal energy state which means that it will be at rest at the bottom of the bowl. Momentum zero and position fixed exactly: no uncertainties. Classically yes, but because of the uncertainty relations, or the particle-wave duality for that matter, this cannot be the quantum story. A quantum marble cannot settle down in a state where it is at rest at the bottom of the quantum bowl, because then its position and momentum would be exactly known, there would be no uncertainty, and that is not an allowed state. The lowest energy state of the quantum marble in a quantum bowl turns out to be one where the uncertainties in position and momentum are about equal and saturate the lower bound of the uncertainty relation. It gets as close to the classical ideal as possible you could say, but the truth is that the lowest energy state of the particle does not specify where it exactly is nor what its momentum precisely is.

As we will see later, there exist Heisenberg uncertainty relations between any pair of observables A and B, only if a non-trivial (non-zero) bound only occurs for an incompatible (non-commuting) pair. What does this have to do with my expose about frameworks? Surprisingly little in fact. The uncertainty relations link the variance in outcomes of measurements of a pair of observables in any given state. So given a state $|\psi\rangle$ of a particle, one can imagine making many independent measurements of say the position x of the particle in that state. This of course does not mean that you make a simple sequence of measurements on a single particle, because a measurement will *change*, what do I say, will *collapse* the state! So you have to prepare

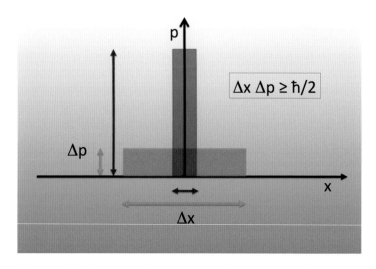

Figure II.2.18: *Heisenberg's uncertainty relation.* The uncertainty relations for position and momentum define the minimal area in classical phase space corresponding to possible states with uncertainties Δx and Δp.

'identical' particles in identical states and then make repeated measurements of the observables in question. You may start with position to obtain an average or expectation value $\bar{x}$ and some variance Δx. Subsequently, one could make independent momentum measurements producing a distribution of outcomes with an average $\bar{p}$ and variance Δp. Heisenberg's fundamental relation says that the product of these variances or 'uncertainties' is larger than or equal to $\hbar/2 = h/4\pi$. So we do not compare individual measurement outcomes but distributions thereof. In Figure II.2.18 we show that the product of uncertainties in a given state corresponds to a certain rectangular area in the (classical) phase space, the shape of the rectangle depends on the state but its area has to be larger than the minimal area indicated in the figure. The conclusion therefore is that in the quantum world there can be no states in which both position and momentum take on precise values! It is a profound statement concerning probabilities of measurement outcomes of different variables in any given state, but that in itself has no bearing on the logical struc-

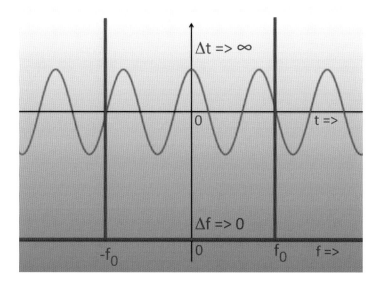

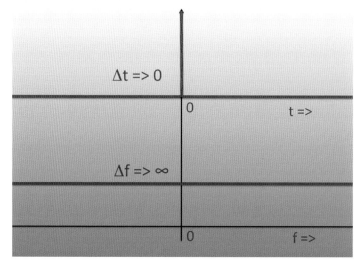

Figure II.2.19: *Time-frequency duality.* Representation of a sound signal as a periodic function of pressure (in red) in time: $P(t) = \cos \omega t$, or as a function of frequency $P(\omega)$ with two narrow peaks around $\omega/2\pi = \pm f_0$. A periodic signal is not localized in time with $\Delta t \to \infty$, but is very localized in frequency, $\Delta f \to 0$.

Figure II.2.20: *Time-frequency duality.* The 'clap in hands' signal is very much localized in time, $\Delta t \to 0$ and spread out very widely in the frequency domain, $\Delta f \to \infty$.

ture of the quantum world we were discussing in the previous section, though it is of course consistent with it.

Non-trivial uncertainty relations exist for all pairs of *incompatable* or non-commuting observables, because these cannot be measured simultaneously, or stated more precisely: if the system has a definite value for the one variable, it is not possible to assign a value for the other. One can choose either one to quantify or describe *any* state of the system but not both. We conclude that quantum states are thus described by a maximal number of mutually compatible observables that define a framework. And indeed not all choices of sets of compatible observables are equally convenient or practical, that depends on what you want to know about the system.

A sound analogy

In this subsection we take one further step trying to understand what incompatible observables, and the uncertainty relations they obey, mean. Surprisingly enough, there are uncertainty relation look-alikes in the classical physics of waves that may take some of the mystery away. Let us for example think about sound. Sound is a pressure wave that passes. At some point in space we hear a sound signal and ask how we would characterize it. One way is to plot the pressure variations in real time, and another way is to represent the signal in the frequency domain as a superposition of sounds of different frequencies with different amplitudes. These pictures would look quite different but contain the same information and are just different representations of the same signal.

Let us first look at (or listen to) a pure tone like the 'a'. A truly pure 'a' of 441 hertz is represented in time by a pure sine or cosine wave of a fixed wavelength which has that single frequency of 441 Hz. But for a cosine to be pure it has to last a very, very long time (compared to the inverse frequency), as I indicated with the red curve in Figure II.2.19. So, a pure tone is very much extended in the time domain, but if you look in the frequency domain it is extremely narrow because the signal has only a single frequency (in fact $f = \pm f_0$) as you see in the narrow peaked blue curve in the same figure. Now, in Figure II.2.20, the opposite happens when I clap loudly my hands once, or shoot a gun, then the signal is extremely short in the time domain, but in the frequency domain it is very wide.[7] If I clap my hands or bang a hammer on the table and I ask you what the pitch was of the sound you heard, you will answer that you could not determine any pitch because the sound lasted for too short a time. If you were to fire a revolver next to a piano and keep the right pedal down then all the strings will resonate showing that basically all the frequencies were present in the sound of the shot: an overdose of pitch rather than no pitch. The upshot of this exercise is that indeed duration and frequency are dual to each other. The more accurate the frequency (i.e. the smaller Δf) in a signal, the longer it has to last (i.e. the larger Δt) and vice versa. In other words one expects a relation like $\Delta f \Delta t \geq \mathrm{constant}$ to hold. This is true and by the way the constant is $1/4\pi$. The lesson here is that you can't have it all: you cannot have the cake and eat it. The physics in this example is quite comprehensible and much what we experience in daily life, yet we encounter a situation where we cannot ask for a signal that is precisely localized in time and also has a well-defined pitch. These two physical quantities are in that sense incompatible, and this duality is intimately linked to the wave character of the phenomenon.

Let us switch now to electromagnetic waves which are

made up of many photons. Remember that photons obey the Planck-Einstein relation $E = h\nu$, so we can replace the frequency ν by the energy and obtain an energy-time relation $\Delta E \Delta t \geq \hbar/2$, and that is indeed exactly an instance of Heisenberg's uncertainty relations. The interpretation is that we cannot measure both variables with arbitrary precision simultaneously.

Heisenberg's derivation

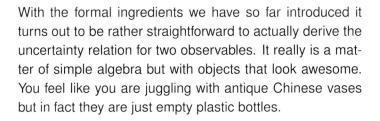

With the formal ingredients we have so far introduced it turns out to be rather straightforward to actually derive the uncertainty relation for two observables. It really is a matter of simple algebra but with objects that look awesome. You feel like you are juggling with antique Chinese vases but in fact they are just empty plastic bottles.

Let us consider two observables A and B, in particular we study two vectors $(A-a)|\psi\rangle$ and $(B-b)|\psi\rangle$ where $a = \langle A \rangle$ and $b = \langle B \rangle$ are real numbers. The variance (the mean square deviation) of an operator A in a state $|\psi\rangle$ is defined in terms of expectation values as (see the *Math Excursion* on Probability and statistics in Volume III):

$$(\Delta A)^2 \equiv\, <(A-a)^2> \,=\, <A^2-2aA+a^2> \,=\, <A^2> -a^2.$$

The variance is a measure for the width of the distribution. Note that if $|\psi\rangle$ is an eigenstate of A, meaning that $A|\psi\rangle = a|\psi\rangle$, then $\Delta A = 0$. Now there is a famous inequality for vectors called the Schwarz inequality. It says that if you have two vectors and their inner product, then the product of their lengths squared is always larger or equal than their inner product squared. In the familiar Euclidean setting we would have $|\mathbf{v} \cdot \mathbf{w}|^2 = |\mathbf{v}|^2|\mathbf{w}|^2 \cos^2 \theta \leqslant |\mathbf{v}|^2|\mathbf{w}|^2$, which holds because the cosine squared is smaller than one. Applied to our vectors above this yields the statement that

$$\langle |A - a|^2 \rangle \, \langle |B - b|^2 \rangle \geq |\langle (A - a)(B - b) \rangle|^2.$$

---

[7]The two figures are not entirely symmetric because I choose to clap at time $t = 0$, the exactly dual situation would be obtained by choosing $\omega = 0$ in the first figure then the cosine function would become constant, $\cos 0 = 1$, and the two peaks move on top of each other as $f_0 = 0$.

Note that on the right-hand side $\langle (A-a)(B-b) \rangle$ is just some complex number, let us call this number z. Then the absolute value squared is

$$|z|^2 = z^* z = (\mathcal{R}e\, z)^2 + (\mathcal{I}m\, z)^2,$$

and clearly $|z|^2 \geq (\mathcal{I}m\, z)^2$, where

$$(\mathcal{I}m\, z) = \frac{1}{2i}(z - z^*) = \frac{1}{2i}\langle [A, B] \rangle.$$

The commutator is the only term that survives because $z^* = \langle (A-a)(B-b) \rangle^* = \langle (B-b)(A-a) \rangle$ and all other terms cancel out.

Putting the results of the above equations together, we arrive at the desired result, the celebrated *Heisenberg's uncertainty relation* in its general form:

$$\Delta A\, \Delta B \geq \frac{1}{2} | < i[A, B] > |. \tag{II.2.20}$$

Note that if A and B are hermitian then also $i[A, B]$ is, which makes its expectation value real. We obtain a nonzero lower bound for the product of uncertainties in the case the operators A and B do not commute. An immediate consequence of the relation is that in any state the uncertainty in the measurement value for two such incompatible variables can never be zero for both. There is a complementarity: the more precise you know observable A the less precise you know the value B. It is the golden rule for giving and taking: you can't have it all. ∎

Qubit uncertainties

After this derivation of the precise form (II.2.20) of the uncertainty relations it is interesting to see how these relations play out for the simple case of qubits.

We are going to check the qubit uncertainties in the cases we considered before. If we take as two incompatible observables $A = Z$ and $B = X$, then the relation would

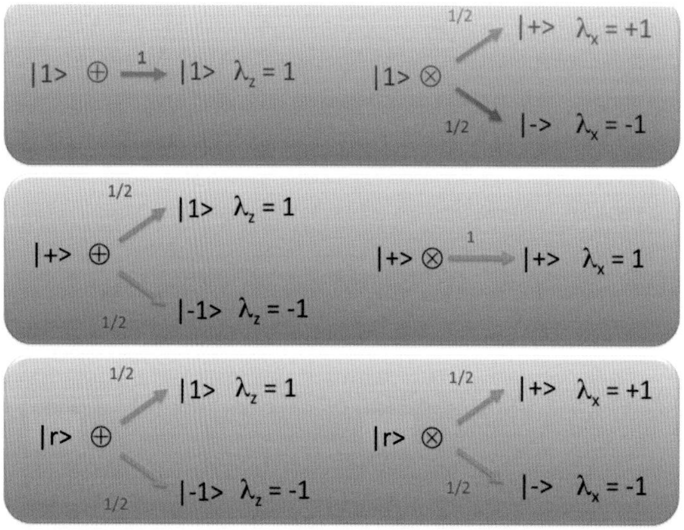

Figure II.2.21: *Spin uncertainties.* Uncertainty in spin measurements of Z and X denoted by $\oplus$ and $\otimes$ respectively, for the states $|1\rangle$ and $|+\rangle$ respectively. The blue numbers are the probabilities for the various outcomes. We see that where one of the spin measurements has minimal uncertainty ($\Delta = 0$), the other is maximal ($\Delta = 1$). Had we chosen an eigenstate $|r\rangle$ of Y then the uncertainty in both X and Z would have been maximal, and the uncertainty relation would again be satisfied.

read

$$\Delta Z\, \Delta X \geq \frac{1}{2} | \langle\, i[Z, X]\, \rangle | = |\langle \psi | Y | \psi \rangle |. \tag{II.2.21}$$

Let us then choose for the states $|\psi\rangle$ subsequently (i) $|1\rangle$, (ii) $|+\rangle$, and (iii) the eigenstate of Y with eigenvalue $+1$, denoted by $|r\rangle$. We recall that $Z^2 = X^2 = 1$ and also that $|\langle\, A\, \rangle|$ equals either 1 or 0 for our A depending on whether $|\psi\rangle$ is an eigenstate of A or not. This makes the calculation relatively simple for example for the left-hand side we obtain:

$$(\Delta A)^2 = \langle A^2 \rangle - (\langle A \rangle)^2$$
$$= \begin{cases} 1 - 1^2 = 0 \text{ (if eigenstate)} \\ 1 - 0^2 = 1 \text{ (if not eigenstate)} \end{cases},$$

and for the right-hand side:

$$|\langle \psi | Y | \psi \rangle| = \begin{cases} 1 \text{ (if eigenstate)} \\ 0 \text{ (if not eigenstate)} \end{cases}.$$

So, for the subsequent cases we end up with the following inequalities (i) $0 \cdot 1 \geq 0$, case (ii) $1 \cdot 0 \geq 0$ and case (iii) $1 \cdot 1 \geq 1$, and we happily agree that in all cases the uncertainty relation is satisfied and moreover saturates the lower bound. In Figure II.2.21 we give the various measurement outcomes with their probabilities for the Z and X observables for the three states $|1\rangle$, $|+\rangle$ and $|r\rangle$.

 Ground state energy. For a quantum particle the lowest energy state will, even if it is weakly localized, always have some extra *zero point energy* associated with it. Adding up all the zero point energies of all particles means that what we call the 'vacuum' must be full of energy. Can't we get it out and do something useful with it is a question that regularly comes up. No presumably not. All physical observables like spectral lines and so on are related with energy differences, and you are free to choose the ground state level as it has no observable effect.

Having said that, you could of course scratch your head, and modestly point out to me that there is a notable exception, and that is Einstein's theory of general relativity, where the vacuum energy does indeed cause physical effects, even of cosmic importance. The shocking news has been that indeed the energy balance in our universe is dominated by the vacuum contribution, which amounts to some 70 percent. But it remains a complete mystery why that number is what it is. Yet, this vacuum energy is like a cosmological constant and it has a mind-blowing property that it anti-gravitates and exerts an outward gravitational pressure that makes the universe expand, and will keep the universe expanding forever as we discussed briefly in Chapter I.2. So, there are instances that much ado about nothing is quite OK, especially if one understands nothing about that nothing. □

From these the variances on the left-hand side of (II.2.21) can immediately be read.

Let me make a final comment. Let us go back to the discussion of 'bit dynamics' at the beginning of Chapter II.1. There we stated that Z could be interpreted as a 'position' operator giving the ± 1 eigenvalue for the spin-up (down) state. In that context the X operator 'generated' translations (hopping in z) and as such acted like a 'momentum' operator. And once more we see that the two operators do not commute and hence satisfy non-trivial uncertainty relations. By the way, these uncertainties imply that quantum computers will provide an array of potential answers, from which the correct one has to be selected somehow.

The breakdown of classical determinism

The uncertainty relations imply strict limits on the predictability in physics. This unpredictability implies the breakdown of classical determinism. A surprising and profound philosophical sacrifice in the realm of our material universe.

The uncertainty relations of quantum theory go further: they imply that if we know the particle has a small uncertainty in position because we just measured its position, then it is in a state where the uncertainty in momentum will be relatively large. If you were to ask me to tell you where the particle would be some time after, then it would be hard to point at a specific point. I do know its starting position precisely, but I don't know its momentum, and thus it is hard to say where it goes and with what momentum. We see that the quantum postulates, concisely expressed in the uncertainty relations, imply the breakdown of classical predictability and determinism. This is one more truly quantessential feature of the underlying reality.

Humankind's limited abilities to observe have through our

common experiences precipitated in what we call deep intuitions about how the world works. And such intuitions tend to shape our judgements and expectations. One thing that has become inescapably clear is that quantum theory has shown such intuitions to be essentially mistaken in an essential way, a sobering thought indeed. That one more illustrates the power of the invisible. At this point I should remind you of the wonderful quote from the Feynman's which I included in the preface to Volume I on page xiv.

This fundamental indeterminacy in nature has lead to numerous speculations on the far-reaching consequences it might have, varying from metaphysical hocus-pocus like floating tables to explanations of the human free will.

Why does classical physics exist anyway?

After all this classical physics bashing, you might ask: how come classical physics is doing so extremely well in ordinary life, if it is so fundamentally wrong? How can that be?

A golf ball. Let us consider a golf ball. If I neglect its internal structure, should I not treat it as a quantum particle and if I do so just reproduce the classical answer? Yes, you better do so, otherwise quantum theory would be in conflict with direct observations. Suppose you would make an extremely accurate measurement and measure its momentum in four decimal places so $\Delta p = 10^{-4}$ kg m s^{-1}, then substituting this into the uncertainty relation you would find that the uncertainty in position would be a mesmerizingly tiny $\Delta x \geq h/4\pi\Delta p \simeq .5 \times 10^{-30}$ m. But wait, that is the realm where string theorists wander. You will agree that nobody is ever going to make a measurement of position with such 30-decimal places accuracy, let alone of a golf ball! Think of an ultimate machine like the Large Hadron Collider at CERN, where physicists are able to localize par-

ticles 'only' up to about 10^{-18} meters at present. Physicists may have their ways, but to verify the uncertainty relations by playing golf in the LHC is not of them. So, what then saves the day for classical physics or if you prefer, what saves quantum physics? That is the dazzling smallness of Planck's constant if you express it in our anthropocentric system of units, made up of meters, seconds and kilograms. That is why the basic need for quantum theory, i.e. the failure of classical theory manifests itself at first only on small scales, and it is also for that reason that it took so long for the quantum world to be discovered.

An electron. To appreciate the point just made, let us replace the golf ball by an electron with a mass of about 10^{-30} kg. Then we could easily measure its momentum with an uncertainty of 10^{-30} kg m s^{-1}, leaving a position uncertainty of about one tenth of a millimeter. So, indeed in an atom with a typical size of 10^{-10} m – one-tenth of a nanometer – this uncertainty matters and therefore we should treat the electron quantum mechanically. This observation by the way implies that we should no longer think of electrons as well-localized particles orbiting the nucleus. Indeed the way the atom is usually depicted (see Figure I.3.6) is a severe misrepresentation inherited from our classical intuition. Rather we should represent the electron as a standing wave pattern of the probability wave in the tiny volume of atomic size. Atoms are not like tiny solar systems, but rather like tiny *quantum bongos!* In fact knowing the size of the atom to be about $\Delta x \sim 10^{-10}$ m one may use the uncertainty relations to estimate the minimal momentum as $p \sim \Delta p = h/(4\pi\Delta x) \simeq 10^{24}$ kg m/s, which corresponds to an electron energy of 10^{-19} Joule $\simeq 1$ eV. And 1 electron Volt is indeed the order of magnitude of atomic energy levels. It can't be much less and you could even say that this is one of the reasons that matter is actually stable.

The emergence of classical physics. The macroscopic world which obeys by definition the classical laws of physics is a world consisting of emergent phenomena, and the classical laws are therefore only approximately true. The world we perceive is an incredibly coarse-grained version of a well-shielded microscopic reality. Our world has an incredible amount of entropy exactly because there is so much information hidden within, and science is exactly the systematic uncovering of that information and making it accessible. It is a gigantic hacking operation, a gigantic striptease of mother nature in which she slowly confides to us her deepest secrets. There are many *why*-questions one may ask on the macroscopic level that can be answered only after they have been turned into *how*-questions on the underlying quantum level. In other words, classical physics is the emergent macroscopic manifestation of an underlying quantum world. The *quantessence* comprises of the unescapable laws underlying classical reality. This exemplifies the profound gain of progressing insight in the long run. The process of scientific progress is seldomly gradual and smooth, and rather proceeds unpredictably, with sudden shocks. In evolutionary biology Jay Gould introduced the notion of *punctuated equilibrium*, which clearly echoes in the picture of long periods of 'normal' science, broken up by scientific revolutions, radical turning points in our thinking leading to paradigm shifts, as described by Thomas Kuhn in his book on *Scientific Revolutions*. I may add that important novel cultural dimensions have opened up, as a result of this process of progressing insight in science as I have argued in my book *In praise of science*.

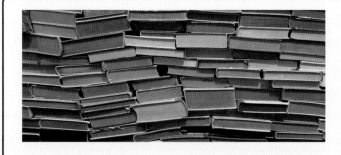

Further reading on quantum measurement:

— *Quantum Theory*
  D. Bohm
  Dover Publications Inc (1989)

— *Quantum Measurement Theory and its Applications*
  Kurt Jacobs
  Cambridge University Press (2017)

Table II.2.2: **Key quantum principles introduced in this chapter on observables.**

	Keyword	Description
(ii)	**Observables**	A physical variable a or observable is represented by a hermitian operator or matrix A. To the system as a whole corresponds a set (algebra) of observables $\mathcal{O} = \{A, B, \ldots\}$.
(iii)	**Eigenvalues**	The observable A has a set of real eigenvalues $\{a_i\}$ which make up the sample space or spectrum S_a of possible measurement outcomes for A.
(iv)	**Eigenvectors**	To each eigenvalue a_i corresponds an eigenvector $|a_i\rangle$, or a subspace $\mathcal{V}_i^a$.
(v)	**Preferred frames**	In the non-degenerate case, the eigenvalues of A are all different, their number equals the dimension of the Hilbert space, and the set of normalized eigenvectors $\{|a_i\rangle\}$ forms an orthonormal basis for $\mathcal{H}$.
(vi)	**Superposition**	Any state $|\psi\rangle$ has a linear expansion in the basis of any framework. $|\psi\rangle = \sum_i \beta_i |a_i\rangle$.
(vii)	**(In)compatibility**	Observables are compatible if (and only if) they mutually commute so that common eigenvectors can be chosen. Observables that do not commute are by definition incompatible.
(viii)	**Frameworks**	A maximal number of independent compatible observables forms a framework $\mathcal{F}$. A complete orthonormal set of joint eigenvectors of a framework forms a basis for the Hilbert space $\mathcal{H}$.
(ix)	**Measurement outcomes**	When making a measurement of an observable A on a state $|\psi\rangle$ there is a probability $p_k = |\langle a_k|\psi\rangle|^2$ of obtaining the result a_k.
(x)	**Projective measurement**	Upon measuring the value a_i in a strong or projective measurement of A, the state $|\psi\rangle$ 'collapses' to the eigenstate $|a_i\rangle$ of A. This statement is referred to as the *projection postulate* of Von Neumann.

Chapter II.3

Interference

We have seen that a quantum particle like an electron has wave-like features and that an electromagnetic wave has particle-like properties as we may consider such a wave as a collective of photons. This naturally raises the question how quantum particles really exhibit these wave-like properties. In this chapter we focus on the question of whether particles can show interference effects like waves do. The answer to this question is affirmative, as is demonstrated by the famous double slit experiments of various kinds. In this chapter we consider classical as well as quantum wave phenomena.

Classical wave theory and optics

Classical geometric optics treats light as straight rays that can be deflected or reflected by different media. The strict geometrical picture consisting of straight light rays can be augmented by the wave-type constructions based on Huygens' principle, which states that any point on a wavefront can be considered as a source of secondary spherical waves. It is not only the laws and patterns of geometric optics like reflection and refraction (breaking) of light at interfaces between different media that can then be explained, but also more subtle effects like diffraction (bending).

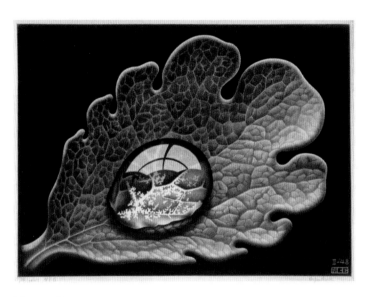

Figure II.3.1: *Dew drop*. In this lithograph of M.C. Escher, the reflection of light causes the image of the windows of the observer's room. The refraction or breaking of light at water-air interface yields the enlarged image of the underlying veins of the leaf. (© 2023 The M.C. Escher Company.)

Basics of wave theory

Characteristics of waves. Let us recall some basics of classical wave theory. A propagating wave can in general be characterized by:

(i) a periodic wave pattern of subsequent *maxima and minima*. The height of the maxima is called the *amplitude* of the wave. The curves connecting adjacent maxima are

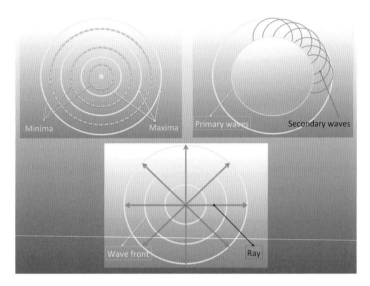

Figure II.3.2: *Wave patterns and propagation.* We show the wave pattern corresponding to propagating wavefronts from a single point-like source, to illustrate the some basic wave concepts.

called *wavefronts*; for the case of plane waves these are parallel straight lines or planes, while for a single source these are circular or spherical as illustrated in Figure II.3.2.

 (ii) a pattern of *rays*, which are lines perpendicular to the wave fronts. So from a point source the rays are straight lines pointing radially out.

(iii) a *wavelength* λ, which is defined as the distance between two subsequent wavefronts measured along a ray. Often one uses the *wavenumber* k defined by $k = 2\pi/\lambda$, instead of the wavelength.

(iv) a *speed* v, which is the speed at which the wavefronts propagate. For light and other electromagnetic forms of radiation propagating in vacuum, this is the universal speed of light c. In physical media (like glass) with electrodynamic properties different from the vacuum, however, the velocity of light will be less than its universal value in vacuum. The speed of light in media may generally depend on the wavelength (or frequency).

(v) a *frequency* f refers to the frequency by which every point in the wave oscillates.

(vi) we distinguish *longitudinal* and *transversal* waves where the medium oscillates parallel to the direction of propagation (sound), or orthogonal (light).

(vii) a *polarization*. Transversal waves can be (linearly) *polarized*, meaning that there is a single orthogonal axis along which the field oscillates.

Typical sizes and scales. For water waves the wavelength may vary from micrometers to many miles. For sound audible by the ear, in air at room temperature, the frequency f varies from $20\,\text{Hz}$ to $20.000\,\text{Hz}$; and with the sound velocity $v = 343\,\text{m/s}$, the wavelength would vary between $1.7\,\text{cm}$ and $17\,\text{m}$. For visible light the typical wavelength is thousands of angströms ($\sim 10^{-7}\,\text{m}$). It is easier to remember for microwaves, because the wavelength you correctly guess to be of the order of micrometers. For quantum particle waves the scale is set by the De Broglie wavelength $\lambda = \hbar/p$, typically about 10^{-10} meters or 1 angström.

Fundamental wave relations. There is a fundamental relation between the velocity, frequency and wavelength of a wave given by $v = \lambda f$. Mostly when talking about waves one assumes these are described by a linear theory. In such situations the linear superposition principle holds, so to understand the wave phenomena caused by independent sources one can simply add the wave patterns produced by the sources individually. On the one hand this applies in general to wave phenomena, as long as the oscillations are small because then the linear approximation holds well, but on the other hand we know that the Maxwell equations describing the electromagnetic waves are linear, and so are the Schrödinger and Dirac equations.

The physics of waves in a medium is interesting, because a wave carries a certain amount of energy and momentum. This, however, does not imply that matter somehow moves along with the wave. Think of a wave of water, you drop a stone in the pond which excites the water surface, locally perturbing the equilibrium situation. It is the deformation

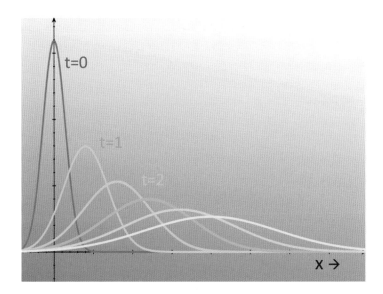

Figure II.3.3: *Dispersion of a wavepacket.* Depicted is a Gaussian shaped wavepacket in x–space at $t = 0$ and after five equal time intervals. The packet disperses (broadens) in time because different components travel at a different speed.

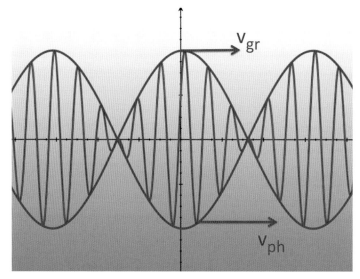

Figure II.3.4: *Group and phase velocity.* We have depicted a superposition of two linear waves with different frequencies and momenta. The combined result shows an *enveloping wave* in blue moving with the group velocity v_{gr}, and the actual superposition in red moving faster with phase velocity v_{ph}.

energy of the (elastic) medium that causes the perturbation (along with some characteristic derformation energy density) to spread as a wave pattern. As the total energy of the perturbation is conserved (if we assume assume that there is no dissipation), the amplitude of the circular wave has to decrease in time because the circumference of the wavefront increases. Anyway, for this transversal wave the position of a water molecule stays fixed as it only oscillates up and down. In the case of sound, the air molecules swing forth and back, but also in that case there is no material streaming along with the wave.

With light waves the situation is different though, because the lightwave is made up of photons, all moving with the same speed of light. The classical wave does not correspond to a single photon, rather it is a strange coherent superposition of different states with a different number of photons in them. They may all have the same frequency, but the various terms can involve quite arbitrary phases. As a matter of fact what this means is that the number of photons corresponding to a 'classical' wave is really not defined. This is not meant in a statistical sense but in a more fundamental way. To speak in the spirit of the previous chapter, their number is not defined, or better indefinite, because the corresponding 'number operator' is incompatible (does not commute) with the quantum operator that creates the classical wave configuration from the vacuum. In other words an electromagnetic wave is not in an eigenstate of the photon-number operator.

Dispersion. We have mentioned the fact that waves of different wavelength or frequency may travel at different speeds: this phenomenon is called *dispersion*. The most well known is the dispersion of light in glass for example, giving rise to separation of colors when light passes through a prism, as in Figure II.3.8. Dispersion means that the velocity and frequency depend on the wavelength or the wavenumber. It is usually specified by giving the functional relation between the angular frequency $\omega \equiv 2\pi f$

and the wavenumber k, so by specifying $\omega = \omega(k)$. And we have seen that electromagnetic waves satisfy the linear dispersion relation $\omega = ck$, while for the De Broglie matter waves we have a quadratic dispersion because $E = p^2/2m$ with $p = \hbar k$ and $E = \hbar\omega$ yields: $\omega = \hbar k^2/2m$.

Broadening. The effect of dispersion manifests itself if we consider the time evolution of a *wavepacket*, which is just some linear superposition of components with different wavelengths. In Figure II.3.3 we see an initial packet that has some shape which is spatially localized with a certain width. One will find that such a packet will broaden or spread out (disperse) during its propagation, because the momentum components that make up the packet move at different speeds.

Group velocity. The next question that comes to mind is what the velocity of this wave packet is. After all it is made up of different components that move with different velocities. The basic answer to this question is illustrated in Figure II.3.4, for the simple case where we have shown the linear superposition of two waves with different frequencies and wave numbers, the combination can be rewritten as a product of a difference and sum wave with frequencies $\omega_{\pm} = (\omega_1 \pm \omega_2)/2$ and wave numbers $k_{\pm} = (k_1 \pm k_2)/2$. What we obtain is that the actual superposition, which is the wave pattern in red, propagates 'inside' the slowly moving enveloping wave in blue. You could say that the red wave with frequency ω_+ and wavenumber k_+ has a frequency modulated by the blue wave with ω_- and wavenumber k_-. The red wave moves with the phase velocity $v_{ph} = \omega_+/k_+$, whereas the envelope moves with the group velocity $v_{gr} = \omega_-/k_-$.

Dissipation. Dissipation refers to the loss of energy of a system, for example to the environment, or by producing heat internally due to friction. For waves, dissipation is often caused by inelasticity (viscosity) of the medium. Dissipation causes the signal to die out. Note that dispersion is not a dissipative phenomenon; it just is a consequence

Figure II.3.5: *Three views.* This picture offers three perspectives on yours truly, from a *direct, to the point*, a *reflective* and a *refractive* point of view. This can be achieved by just looking at a glass of wine!

of the fact that different components of the wave packet move with different velocities.

Reflection, transmission, breaking and diffraction

Huygens' principle. To find out how the wavefront of a propagating wave moves forward, one may consider every point on the front as a source from which secondary waves emanate. The envelope of the secondary wavefronts defines the new wavefront. This is illustrated in the top right picture of Figure II.3.2. Huygens' principle is a powerful tool to explain all kinds of generic wave phenomena, like reflection, refraction, diffraction and interference. A nice example of reflection and refraction on which the working of lenses is based is provided by M.C. Escher's lithograph *The dew droplet* in Figure II.3.1.

Reflection. Light can be reflected off a surface, like in the reflection of an ordinary mirror. The law of reflection in

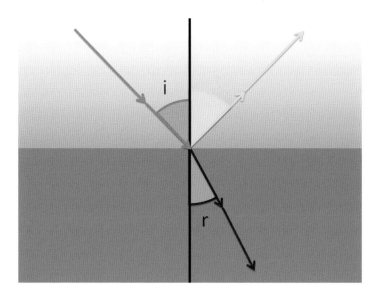

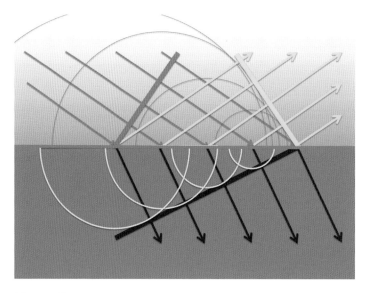

Figure II.3.6: *Reflection and refraction.* The picture illustrates reflection and refraction at an interface between two media. From the vacuum to any medium the angle with the normal to the interface of the refracted ray r is smaller than the angle i of the incoming beam.

Figure II.3.7: *Huygens' principle.* The construction for the reflected and refracted beams (thin lines) and wavefronts (fat lines) using Huygens' principle, assuming you know the ratio of velocities in the two media, or breaking index.

geometric optics reads simply:

$$i = t \,,$$

or in words the angle i of the incoming beam (with the normal on the surface) is equal the angle t of the reflected beam. This is illustrated in fig II.3.6.

Refraction or breaking. The law for breaking of light at an interface between two media with relative breaking index n is given by Snellius' law which is also illustrated in the same figure:

$$\frac{\sin i}{\sin r} = n \,,$$

where n is given by the ratio of the speed of lights in medium 1 and medium 2:

$$n = \frac{c_1(f)}{c_2(f)} \,.$$

The proof of both laws can be given using Huygens' principle as we depicted in Figure II.3.7. We use the principle at

the points where the incoming rays hit the layer between the two media, where the new front can be constructed using the same radii in the same medium (reflection), or reduced radii (because of the reduced speed of light) in the dense medium.

Note that whereas in vacuum the velocity of light is universal and therefore does not depend on the frequency or wavelength (color), this is no longer true in other media. As a consequence the angle of refraction will be different for different colors, as was so beautifully demonstrated by Newton by letting a sun ray pass through a prism (see Figure II.3.8).

Bragg diffraction and reflection.

William Henry Bragg and his son Lawrence Bragg proposed in 1913 a nice explanation of the reflection lines observed in X-rays of crystals. The key idea of their model was that X-rays would scatter of the individual atoms in

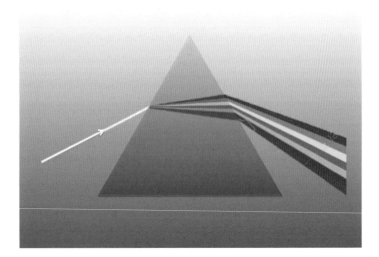

Figure II.3.8: *Color decomposition of white light through a prism.* The refraction of white light by passing through a prism. The propagation speed of light of different colors (frequencies) is different in glass and leads to different amounts of refraction.

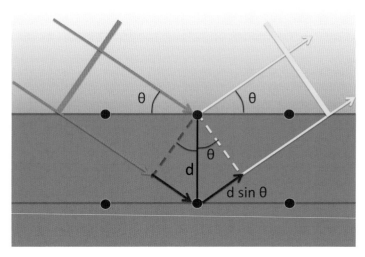

Figure II.3.9: *Bragg reflection.* The crystal consists of equally spaced layers. Two rays from the top two layers are drawn, the path difference between the incoming and outgoing wavefronts of the two paths equals $2\mathrm{d}\sin\theta$, this should equal an integer times the wavelength λ.

subsequent layers of the crystal. The layers in a crystal are equally spaced with a distance d, a distance that is typically about $10^{-10}\,\mathrm{m}$. Requiring radiation with a wavelength comparable to d yields that we need high frequency X-rays indeed. The question then was to derive the condition for constructive interference of incident and reflected waves. Assuming a monochromatic wave incident under an angle θ with the surface of the crystal, the condition follows from Huygens' principle, as is schematically depicted in Figure II.3.9. The path length between the two rays scattering from the two top layers should be proportional to an integer m times the wavelength to obtain constructive interference. The integer m is called the *diffraction order*. This leads to the Bragg formula:

$$2\mathrm{d}\sin\theta = \mathrm{n}m\lambda\,.$$

This formula is general as long as the particles in the beam are scattered in a spherical fashion from each individual atom in the lattice. In that sense the formula can also be applied to matter waves, in other words, to the scattering

of electrons or neutrons from crystal surfaces. By looking at different plane orientations this principle turns into a powerful technique to determine the spatial structure of crystals.

Beamsplitters and polarization

In classical optics it was Newton who in his *Opticks*, published in 1704, introduced the prism to split a beam of light into its different light components (see Figure II.3.8), while Huygens in his monumental *Traité de la lumière*, published in 1690, emphasized the importance of double breaking by 'Icelandic crystal' or calcite, and explained it to a certain extent with his wave theory of light.

These explanations were all based on the idea that different components of 'ordinary' light have different velocities

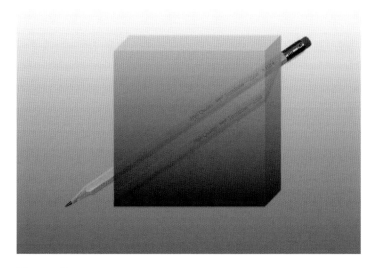

Figure II.3.10: *Icelandic crystal.* Double refraction of light by an Icelandic crystal or calcite.

in various media, and therefore have a different amount of refraction at interfaces between various media. And this is indeed a fundamental ingredient of all beam splitting devices. We should be aware that in the early theories of light that arose in the Enlightenment era through the works of Descartes and later of Huygens and Newton, many properties of light were discovered and these led to the great dispute between the latter two about the particle versus wave-like nature of light. The property of polarization was not really discussed, and understanding the transversal wave nature of light had to wait untill Maxwell identified light as an electromagnetic waves two centuries later.

However it is remarkable to see how tantalizing close Huygens came to discovering the nature of polarization exactly because of his particular emphasis on the phenomenon of bi or double refraction exhibited by light passing through an *Icelandic crystal*, which we have depicted in Figure II.3.10. This phenomenon occurs basically in all transparent anisotropic media. In his treatise he remarks:

Before finishing the treatise on this Crystal, I will add one more marvellous phenomenon which I discovered after having written all the foregoing. For though I have not been able till now to find its cause, I do not for that reason wish to desist from describing it, in order to give opportunity to others to investigate it. It seems that it will be necessary to make still further suppositions besides those which I have made; but these will not for all that cease to keep their probability after having been confirmed by so many tests.

He then goes on to describe how he studied the properties of light subsequently passing through two crystals and makes the observation that the double refraction does not take place at the second crystal, as is clear from his illustration (see Figure II.3.11). He even goes as far as to observe that the properties of the second refraction depends on the orientation of the crystal. And his humble conclusion reads:

It seems that one is obliged to conclude that the waves of light, after having passed through the first crystal, acquire a certain form or disposition in virtue of which, when meeting the texture of the second crystal, in certain positions, they can move the two different kinds of matter which serve for the two species of refraction; and when meeting the second crystal in another position are able to move only one of these kinds of matter. But to tell how this occurs, I have hitherto found nothing which satisfies me.

In the following we discuss various cases of how the splitting of a beam, dependent on the polarization state of the particles can be achieved. First we discuss some beam splitters for photons. Next we discuss the case of spin one half particles like electrons, protons and neutrons in a magnetic polarization device like the Stern–Gerlach setup. We also introduce some other devices from which more

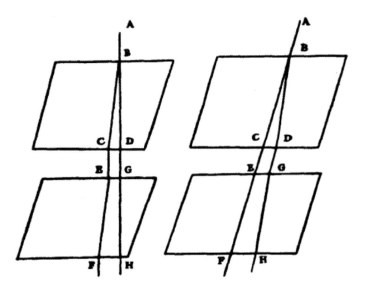

Figure II.3.11: *'A marvelous phenomenon.'* Double refraction of light does not occur in the second crystal. Illustration taken from Huygens' *Treatise on light*.

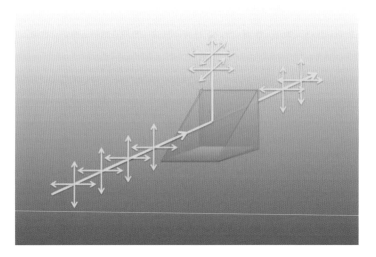

Figure II.3.12: *A half mirror.* A half-silvered mirror reflects half the number of photons in a beam, the other half is transmitted. It is a beam splitter (BS) that is insensitive to the polarization state of the incoming photons.

elaborate interference experiments can be assembled. Together, they form part of the toolkit for many famous experiments that demonstrated how different quantum theory really is, where particles can interfere with themselves, or where certain forms of non-locality (which are strictly forbidden in the classical realm) pertaining to entangled states of particles can be unambiguously demonstrated. This will be our focus in the remainder of this chapter.

Photon polarization: optical beamsplitters

In modern (quantum) optics using monochromatic lasers, many quite stunning experiments have been performed, demonstrating the paradoxical but quantessential features of light and in particular its polarization. In the previous chapter we have already discussed various filters: polarizers on page 59, and wave plates on page 56 through which the polarization states can be selected and/or ma-

nipulated. Now we extend the toolset with some beam-splitters much in analogy with the Icelandic crystal. These devices play a crucial role in experiments where properties like particle interference and entanglement can be put to the test.

Clearly, by splitting a beam one obtains two beams which are strictly in phase and therefore offer interesting experimental possibilities.

A first splitting device would be the *half-mirror*, where half the number of photons in the beam gets reflected while the other half gets transmitted. As such this mirror is insensitive to the polarization state of the photons, as we have indicated in Figure II.3.12.

It is also possible to coat the interface with particular chemicals in which case we obtain a *polarizing beam splitter* as depicted in Figure II.3.13; if the incoming beam is unpolarized, the reflected photons are horizontally polarized, while the transmitted ones are vertically polarized. We obviously can rotate the polarizing cube around the incoming

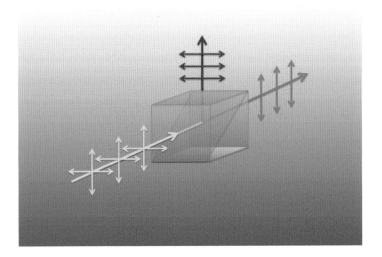

Figure II.3.13: *A polarizing beam splitter (PBS).* This component is sensitive to the polarization state of the photons: the reflected ones are horizontally polarized, the transmitted ones vertically.

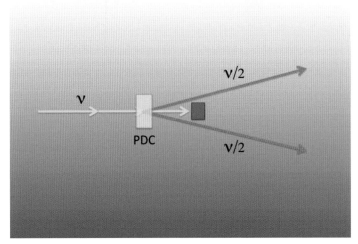

Figure II.3.14: *Two photons out of one.* A parametric down converter (PDC) is a nonlinear crystal where incoming photons may be converted down to two photons with half the energy or frequency. These secondary beams leave the crystal under a small angle with the primary beam. The polarizations of the secondary pair are entangled and can be chosen to be either parallel or orthogonal.

photon momentum vector, generating a split between two other linear polarizations. This device acts much like the anisotropic crystals causing double diffraction like the ones Huygens mentioned. It is also similar to the Stern–Gerlach device to split a beam of spin-$1/2$ particles to which we turn shortly.

A final device we want to mention is what is called a *parametric down converter*. It is a nonlinear crystal that splits an incoming monochromatic beam of a given frequency f; it splits a fraction of the incoming photons into two photons with half the frequency (or energy). These secondary photons leave the crystal under a small angle with the incoming beam as we have indicated in Figure II.3.14. As we will discuss later, the remarkable property of these secondary pairs is that their polarization states are entangled. Depending on the type of crystal this maybe parallel or orthogonal entanglement, where one speaks of type I or type II down conversion.

Spin polarization: the Stern-Gerlach device

We have illustrated this means of polarizing the spin for various choices of the state $|\psi\rangle$ and observable A being the spin polarization, in the Figures II.2.9. Let us comment on their content. The green circle is the space of normalized quantum states; normally this would be a three-sphere but we have chosen the section where the coefficients α and β are real, so we are left with an ordinary circle in R^2. We consider two real observables being Z and X and combinations thereof, those have always eigenstates that are lying on the circle. In the diagrams in the figure we see pairs of blue axes. These axes are in the direction of the eigenvectors of A and labeled by their eigenvalue. The blue axes together represent thus the *measurement frame* corresponding to A. Now there are five things to observe: (i) the blue axes have a direction but are not oriented, ex-

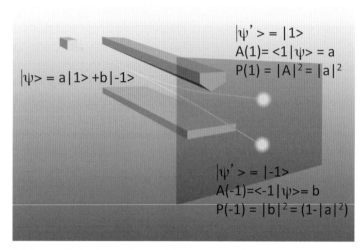

(a) Stern–Gerlach experiment: Measurement of spin polarization along
z-axis, of a state |ψ⟩. Outcome can only be +1 or −1 in units ℏ/2 with
probabilities depending on the particular state |ψ⟩. The measurement
outcome affects the state of the outgoing particle.

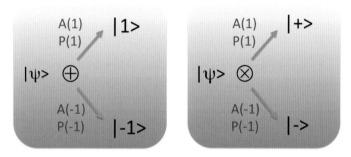

(b) Measurement spin polarization (c) Measurement spin polarization
along z-axis, of a state |ψ⟩.   along x-axis, of a state |ψ⟩.

Figure II.3.15: *The Stern–Gerlach experiment.* (a): Sending
the electron beam through an inhomogeneous magnetic field
will split the beam. (b) and (c): Symbolic representation of the Z
and X polarizing beam splitters that we will use later on.

pressing the fact that the opposite points $\pm|\psi\rangle$ have the
same probabilities. They are indistinguishable by measurement. In other words they only differ by a phase, which
in this case a real phase, which can only be -1;

(ii) perhaps it is also surprising that the frames correspond-

ing to Z and X are *not* orthogonal, rather they only make
an angle of 45°, half the expected angle. If we were to
turn the polarizer in the $minus\,z$ direction, thus rotating in
real space the polarizer in the plane by 180°, would interchange the eigenvalues and consequently interchange
the axes of the measurement frame, which is equivalent to
rotating in *state* space by half the angle, in this case 90°.
Saying it yet differently: we have chosen the up and down
state vectors of the spin as orthogonal unit vectors. This
means that if we rotate the device by φ in ordinary x, y, z-
space, then the polarization plane will only rotate by $\varphi/2$
degrees in spinor space, which in the Hilbert space for this
system means a rotation by 90°. That explains why the
choice of observable involves fixing two orthogonal axes
in state space; it is really a choice of frame rather than se-
lecting a particular direction.

(iii) Once the measurement has been made, one axis of
the frame has been singled out, and the wavefunction 'collapses' to a normalized state along that axis. If in the example of Figure II.2.9(d) above, we happen to measure the
X eigenvalue $+1$, then the state collapses along the corresponding axis, meaning that we move from the state in
Figure II.2.9(d) to the state in Figure II.2.9(c).

This picture indeed allows us to make the projections on
the axes which give the probability amplitudes while the
measurement outcome labels the axis, and they also tell
you what the collapsed state looks like.

Indeed this graphical representation captures some quantessential features of the measurement process. We will
make use of it repeatedly later on.

(iv) The analysis we just presented underscores the subtle
meaning of the 'state vector' or wavefunction. Indeed it is
important to always keep in mind that it is as much defining
a state as it is a probability amplitude, which means a way
of encoding probabilities of measurement outcomes of any
given observable.

(v) Bearing the previous points in mind there is an additional remark to be made at this point. Did we make a
measurement or not necessarily? When we put a screen

Barbie's choice. Let us now rephrase the measurement process in the language of the Barbie on the globe, the representation of spin space we introduced in the figure on page 51 . The geometry is now somewhat different: we first have the spin in a certain state, which means that the Barbie is located at some point on the 2-sphere and pointing her nose in a certain direction of the tangent plane at her location.

Making a measurement amounts to choosing an orientation in the X, Y, Z space, which we can mark as a line through the center and intersecting the unit sphere into two antipodal points on the sphere. The intersection of the positive direction with the sphere corresponds to the positive eigenvalue eigenstate, and the negative intersection corresponds to the negative eigenvalue eigenstate. Indeed the choice of observable determines the eigenstates up to a phase factor. So, staying within the narrative, choosing the orientation of the detector corresponds to installing two inspectors at the corresponding antipodal points on the sphere. These inspectors do not look in any specific direction, they just search around and try to spot the Barbie. Once they have spotted her they both call to her (the sphere is of course transparent – a crystal three-sphere...) and order her to report immediately at their place. Barbie doesn't quite know who of the two to choose, but she makes a choice, it doesn't matter who Barbie chooses as long as the probabilities are in accordance with her little quantum calculation. The inspectors go home and leave her on the spot she happened to choose. That's the state she ends up in, and that was what the measurement was.■

and record the electron hitting the screen we surely have made a measurement of its spin. But you may also imagine an experiment where we do not register (or measure) it explicitly, but think of the experiment as a way to select the initial spin state for some other experiment that makes use of the upper or lower beam. Then it is clear that the Stern Gerlach devise is used as a preparatory device to select an incoming spin state.

And that naturally accommodates the fact that the state alters after a measurement, because the information we gather from the measurement may drastically affect the probabilities. It is not that we as observers play a role, because we may or may not look at the results, it is the interaction that has or has not taken place between the apparatus and the system, which matters.

Interference: double slit experiments

An important property of waves is that if we combine two of them their amplitudes are added together and we get interference: in places where the waves are in phase the combined wave gets a maximal amplitude and where they are out of phase they will compensate resulting in a reduced amplitude.

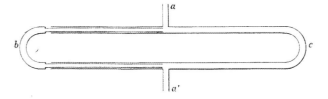

Figure II.3.16: *Interference.* A 'sound' interference experiment, due to Georg Hermann Quincke, which demonstrates the interference of sound waves. Image from a 19th century high school book on physics.

The interference of sound. A simple demonstration of classical interference can be given with the sound experi-

Figure II.3.17: *Two pointsources emitting waves*. The two sources are 4 wavelengths apart and are in phase.

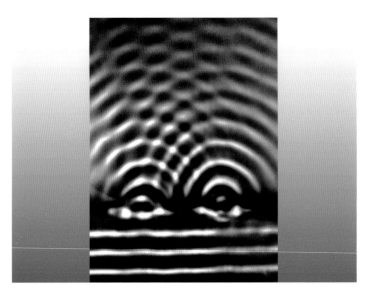

Figure II.3.18: *Water waves*. Two slits act as sources emitting water waves that interfere. This illustrates the geometric constructions displayed in the following figures.

ment devised in the nineteenth century by Georg Hermann Quincke as shown in Figure II.3.16. In the modern guise a tone is generated with small loudspeaker at the point a on top, the sound (air pressure) wave splits and propagates through both the left and right tubes. They come together again at the point a' at the bottom, where the two waves interfere. The difference in length between the left and right paths can be adjusted so as to obtain constructive or destructive interference. In the latter case a microphone positioned at a' would not register any sound. The crucial thing is that the total signal at the microphone is built up from the various amplitudes along the two independent paths and in that sense this is really a kind of double slit experiment.

Wave interference from two point sources. Figure II.3.17 shows two point sources emitting circular waves which are in phase. The two individual wave patterns overlap and will therefore interfere, meaning that at certain points the signals will amplify each other and in other points they will cancel. A new pattern of maxima and minima will develop. In Figure II.3.18 we show the pattern of water waves

generated by two point sources that oscillate in phase (almost). The pattern is obtained by literally adding up the amplitudes of the two individual spherical patterns coming from the two slits which act as point sources, incoming are the plain waves from below and this makes that the two sources oscillate in phase. So this is indeed a double slit experiment and we see that the resulting pattern has a number of striking features. We roughly see rays of outward moving waves with indeed an amplitude that varies depending on the angle.

In Figure II.3.19 we give the theoretical reconstruction of the situation combining the two previous figures. In the top half of this figure we could mark the points by the path difference from the two sources (which equals an integer times the wavelength) and then connect the points with equal differences, as we did in Figure II.3.20. What we obtain are the orange colored hyperbolic rays along which the maximal amplitude oscillations propagate upwards. In between we could have drawn the zero amplitude node lines connecting points where the difference is

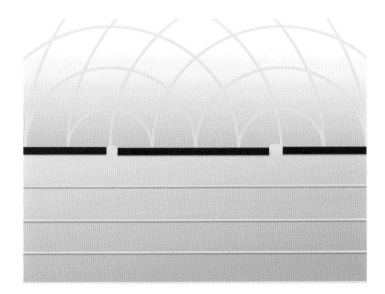

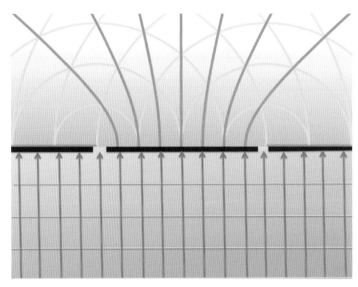

Figure II.3.19: *Double slit interference.* The slits act as sources emitting semicircular waves that will interfere. Compare the pattern with the water wave interference pattern of the previous figure.

Figure II.3.20: *Rays.* The orange maximal amplitude rays connect points that have distances to the sources which differ by a certain integer times the wavelength.

a half-integral multiple of the wavelength. The pattern of rays that emerges is not entirely obvious, because there is no such thing as 'adding' rays; you add the wave patterns and then construct the resulting ray pattern.

Once we have the pattern of rays we could also draw the new wavefront picture. These correspond to the blue elliptic curves in Figure II.3.21. Note that indeed the rays and wave fronts are orthogonal in any point where they meet. Rays and wavefronts always form what is called two orthogonal families of curves. What you will see is that these wave fronts move outward. So what is the picture along any one of these wave fronts? It crosses a fixed number of maximal amplitude and node rays and these rays stay fixed in time. Therefore we would encounter a one-dimensional *standing wave pattern* along the wave front, and that is what is nable nable in the water wave picture II.3.18.

The interference of light. In Figure II.3.22 we have depicted the classical experiment of Young in which he showed

the interference of the light going through the two slits. It only occurs if both slits are open. If only one slit is open, one gets a single maximum comparable to that of classical particles. The result was fully consistent with Huygens' principle of light propagation following from the wave nature of light. Comparing this experiment with the previous one on sound waves it is clear the sound measurement only corresponds to a single point on the detection screen for the light. Moving the trombone arm on the left of Quincke's device corresponds with moving the light detector up and down the screen, which is necessary to probe the minima and maxima of the interference pattern.

The non-interference of marbles (classical particles). In Figure II.3.23 we see a source shooting particles (say, marbles) in all forward directions. Most get absorbed by the screen but if they are directed to one of the two slits, the particles can get through. If we count the number of particles hitting the detector screen, we typically get a distribution with two single maxima as indicated in Figure II.3.23. This is exactly what one would expect: there is no inter-

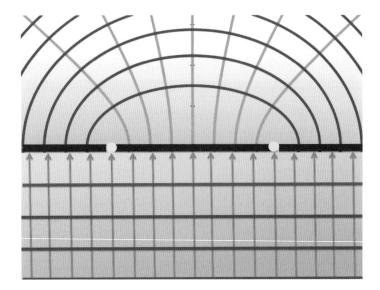

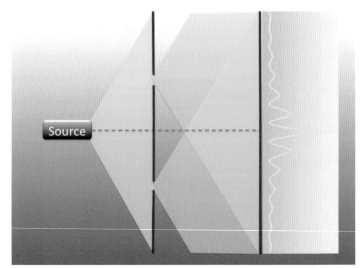

Figure II.3.21: *Wave pattern.* If we draw the elliptical curves orthogonal to the rays, we do not get the familiar wave fronts where the phase difference is constant. Along the curves one obtains a standing wave with varying amplitude and wavelength.

Figure II.3.22: *Young's experiment.* The double slit experiment for light as performed by Young to demonstrate the wave character of light, thereby confirming Huygens' theory of light. On the right the varying intensity of the light on the screen due to the interference.

ference of marbles, let alone that a marble would interfere with itself.

The self-interference of a quantum particle. In Figure II.3.24 we have sketched what happens with a beam of quantum particles such as electrons or protons or neutrons when they hit a screen with two narrow slits. The quantessence is that it does not repeat the pattern of the classical particles of Figure II.3.23 but rather that of light depicted in Figure II.3.22. This fundamental experiment demonstrates the wavelike nature of particles in the quantum domain. The most remarkable, really quantessential aspect of this behavior is that the phenomenon is *not* a consequence of different particles in the beam interfering with each other. This would make it a collective phenomenon, but no, the truly remarkable fact is that if you shoot the electrons one by one, then the interference pattern would slowly build up as is shown in Figure II.3.25. This implies that each electron somehow interferes with itself, and one has to conclude that each electron has 'knowl-

edge' of the probability distribution as a whole.

This is indeed the case in quantum physics, as the wavefunction of the particle is exactly the probability amplitude for finding it in any place at any time. Alternatively you may say that in quantum theory you could calculate the probability for distinct paths from the beginning to any endpoint on the screen separately, then the total amplitude from the beginning to that given endpoint is the sum of those amplitudes. It is the linear superposition principle in a different guise. Let us go one step further and assume that the state $\psi_1(x)$ describes the wavefunction for the configuration with only the left slit open, and $\psi_2(x)$ with only the right slit. The (normalized) wavefunction for the experiment with both slits open would then correspond to $\psi(x) = (\psi_1(x) + \psi_2(x))/\sqrt{2}$, as we just have to add the amplitudes. The probability of finding the particle on a screen behind the slits is then not the same as the sum of the probabilities of the individual left and right slit experi-

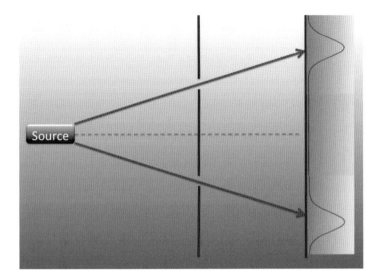

Figure II.3.23: *Marbles don't interfere.* In the double slit experiment with classical particles, the number density of particles hitting the detector screen has two separate maxima and there is no interference.

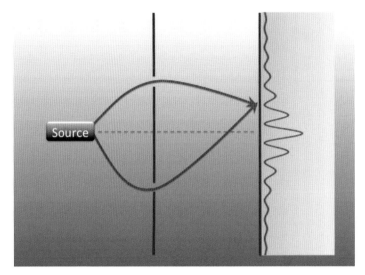

Figure II.3.24: *Electrons are not like marbles.* The double slit experiment showing two conceivable paths that a quantum particle like the electron may have taken. The variation in the intensity pattern on the screen demonstrates the wave nature of quantum particles.

ments, because squaring the total amplitude, yields

$$p(x) = \frac{1}{2}(p_1(x) + p_2(x)) + I(x) \, ,$$

where the interference term $I(x)$ is defined as

$$I(x) = \frac{1}{2}\left(\psi_1^*(x)\psi_2(x) + \psi_1(x)\psi_2^*(x)\right) \, . \qquad \text{(II.3.1)}$$

This is basically the one-particle *quantum interference* effect, a direct consequence of the particle-wave duality in quantum physics.

In talking about quantum interference we should appreciate that a single particle is described by a wave pattern that may or may not be considered to be composed of different components, and therefore a particle can 'interfere with itself' because of the linear superposition principle. And that is what makes quantum interference a truly quantessential phenomenon.

At this point there is an additional remark I would like to make. The question whether or not an interference pattern

for the quantum particle will appear depends in a subtle way on what the experimental setup is. For example, look at the experiment of Figure II.3.26, where we have introduced a source which emits pairs of entangled particles; and particle 2 goes to the left and may or may not be detected, while particle 1 goes to the right in the direction of the double slit. The question is whether or not we will see an interference pattern as in Figure II.3.24. The answer is, that whether we will or will not see interference depends on the state of particle 2, *irrespective* of whether we actually measure particle 2! It is the mere *possibility* of identifying the path that particle 1 has taken that destroys the interference pattern. The state of the entangled particles is basically,

$$|\psi\rangle = \frac{1}{\sqrt{2}}(|\text{red}_1\rangle|\text{red}_2\rangle + |\text{green}_1\rangle|\text{green}_2\rangle) \, . \qquad \text{(II.3.2)}$$

The interference term for particle 1 would come from the red-green cross term appearing in $\langle\psi|\psi\rangle$ evaluated along

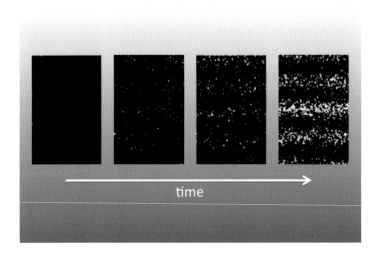

Figure II.3.25: *How particles make a wave pattern.* Buildup of the interference pattern of Figure II.3.24, from the successive hits of single particles (like electrons) on the screen.

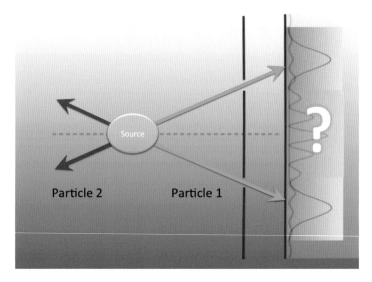

Figure II.3.26: *'Which path' information.* No interference of particle 1 (moving to the right) if it is entangled with particle 2 and thus a path identification would be possible *in principle* by measurement of particle 2.

the screen:

$$I_{rg} = |\langle red_1 | green_1 \rangle| \, |\langle red_2 | green_2 \rangle|,$$

and this term containing the self interference of particle 1 in the first factor will vanish if the second factor for particle 2 vanishes because the $|red_2\rangle$ and $|green_2\rangle$ states are orthogonal. Orthogonality here means that they have no overlap: $\langle red_2 | x \rangle \langle x | green_2 \rangle = 0$ for all x. If they are not, (some) interference will result, but as you see this really depends on the actual setup of the experiment. As entanglement with the environment can easily take place, sufficient care has to be taken if one wants to demonstrate quantum interference effects. Physicists have gone one step further by investigating the effect of *erasing* the tracking information of particle 2, and they have shown that if you succeed in constructing a quantum eraser in your setup, the interference pattern will emerge. These in-between cases have been investigated in many different types of experiments. We will discuss one such experiment for photons shortly.

It is the non-commutativity of observables that gives rise to the intricacies in the quantum theory of measurement. The predictions of quantum mechanics are intrinsically probabilistic yet the theory is essentially different from classical probability theory. On the one hand it is clear that a given operator defines a probability measure on Hilbert space; however as the operators are non-commuting (like matrices) one is dealing with a non-commutative probability theory, and complementary measures.

A basic interference experiment

We have illustrated the schematic of a typical quantum interference experiment in Figure II.3.27 which compares two different states and their superposition in the familiar spin or qubit system.

In the top figure (a) we have a beam incoming identically prepared spins that goes through a polarizer in the x di-

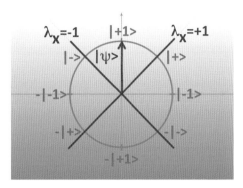

(a) X polarizer and beamsplitter.

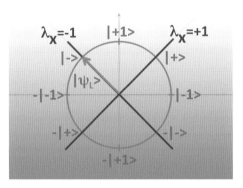

(b) $X = -1$ polarized in left channel.

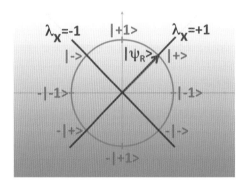

(c) $X = +1$ polarized in right channel.

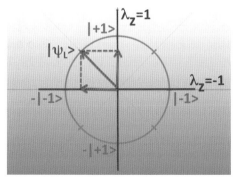

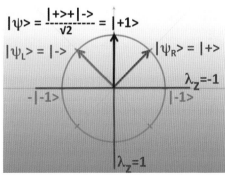

(d) *Experiment 1:* Measurement Z after blocking right channel: $p(+1) = p(-1) = \frac{1}{2}$.

(e) *Experiment 3:* Measurement Z of left-right interference: $p(+1) = 1$ and $p(-1) = 0$.

(f) *Experiment 2:* Measurement Z after blocking left channel: $p(+1) = p(-1) = \frac{1}{2}$.

Figure II.3.27: *Three experiments.* Schematic of a typical quantum interference experiment. Adding the red amplitudes of left (d) and right (f) gives the purple amplitude of (e). The corresponding probabilities *do not* add.

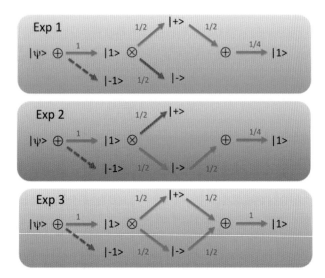

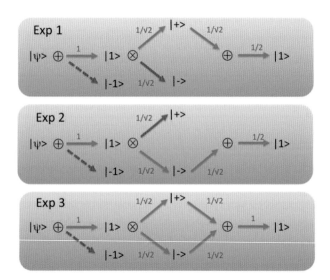

Figure II.3.28: *Adding probabilities.* A different schematic view of the three interference experiments of Figure II.3.27 using the symbolic notation of Figure II.3.15. Adding the final probabilities of the first and second experiment does not give the probability of the third experiment.

Figure II.3.29: *Adding probability amplitudes.* The same schematic view of the three interference experiments as the previous Figure II.3.28. In this figure we give the probability amplitudes and now one finds that adding the total amplitudes of the first and second experiment *does* give the amplitude of the third experiment.

rection and is split into a left and right channel with opposite polarizations as shown in the two middle row figures (b) and (c). It is important to bear in mind that what we say next applies to each particle individually. The beam is just there to allow us to do a series of repeated measurements in each setup. In the bottom row we have depicted the probabilities for three distinct experimental setups, all measuring the Z polarization indicated by the blue frame. In figure (d) we give the situation if the right channel were blocked where we have $|\psi\rangle = |\psi_L\rangle = |-\rangle$ corresponding to the purple state vector, yielding equal probabilities to measure plus or minus one: $p_L(+1) = p_L(-1) = \frac{1}{2}$. Similarly in Figure (f) on the right we have blocked the left channel, giving $|\psi\rangle = |\psi_R\rangle = |+\rangle$, corresponding to the red state vector in the figure, and we obtain once more $p_R(+1) = p_R(-1) = \frac{1}{2}$. Finally in the middle experiment of figure (e) we have both channels interfere. Adding the probability amplitudes in red of (d) and (f) yields the amplitudes in purple of (e). Now we have to consider the (normalized)

superposition $|\psi\rangle = \frac{1}{\sqrt{2}}(|\psi_L\rangle + |\psi_R\rangle) = |1\rangle$ corresponding to the purple arrow in figure (e), so that the probability distribution becomes $p(+1) = 1$ and $p(-1) = 0$. This is notably different from the sum of the probabilities of cases (d) and (f) which would give $\tilde{p}(\pm 1) \equiv \frac{1}{2}(p_L(\pm 1) + p_R(\pm 1))$ yielding once more $\tilde{p}(+1) = \tilde{p}(-1) = \frac{1}{2}$. The differences between $\tilde{p}(\pm 1)$ and $p(\pm 1)$ are indeed due to the interference terms $I(+1) = +\frac{1}{2}$ and $I(-1) = -\frac{1}{2}$.

In Figures II.3.28 and II.3.29 we present an alternative visualization of the same three experiments using the symbols $\oplus$ and $\otimes$ introduced in Figure II.3.15 for the polarisor settings. The left three panels give the probabilities and one sees that they don't add up, while in the right three panels we give the amplitudes and one sees that they do add up. Confirming our expectations for the interference of the spin polarizations.

A delayed choice experiment

A modern and clean quantum incarnation of the canonical double slit experiment is the interference experiment using a so-called Mach–Zender interferometer. In such a device the self-interference of quantum particles/waves, and in particular photons, can be beautifully demonstrated. This setup is also called a *'delayed choice experiment'* after a *gedanken* proposal of John Archibald Wheeler, or a *'which-way experiment'*. The delayed choice refers to the fact that the decision which experiment one is going to do is taken *after* the incoming particles have gone through the first polarizer thereby having chosen one of the two paths or both. In this clever setup the device randomly chooses between:

(i) a 'which way' experiment where one identifies the path which the particle has chosen and thus no interference will take place, or

(ii) a mode where the information on 'which way' is erased and one expects interference.

In Figure II.3.30 I have sketched the schematic of such an experiment[1] by the French group of Alain Aspect, who has pioneered this type of experiments. It consists of two components, first an input part on the left where the polarizations get split. Next the photon travels over a considerable distance of maybe 50 meters (but recently distance of kilometers have been achieved). Finally the photon enters the output part (on the right) where one measures whether the photon has interfered with itself or not. The two components are space-like separated,[2] so that there can be no causal relation between the decision taken in the output part and preparation of the photon in the input part.

Single photons enter the interferometer on the left where they go through a polarizing beamsplitter. The horizon-

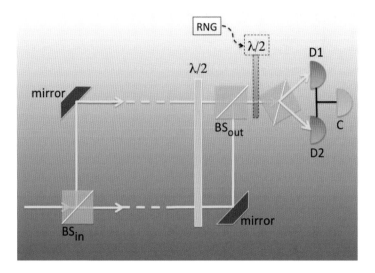

Figure II.3.30: *Delayed choice.* A Mach–Zender quantum interference device, involving two polarizing beamsplitters of the type shown in Figure II.3.13, which demonstrates the quantum interference of photons.

tally polarized component goes up and the vertically polarized goes straight through. Reflection by the mirrors does not change the polarization. Then the signal travels some distance. The $\lambda/2$ plate with its axis under 45°, flips the horizontal and vertical polarizations. This is necessary to allow for the beams to be joined by the second beamsplitter. They traverse the reversed path, so in fact the second splitter acts like a 'joiner'. By tilting the 'joiner' one can also introduce a phase difference φ between the vertical and horizontal component, where the vertical amplitude becomes $e^{i\varphi/2}$ and the horizontal $e^{-i\varphi/2}$. The further encounter depends on the random number generator (RNG) which decides on whether or not to effectively insert another $\lambda/2$ wave plate.

Let us first assume the plate is *not* inserted, then the photon reaches another beam splitting prism that sends the horizontal polarization up to detector D_1 and the vertical polarization down to detector D_2. Furthermore, there is a device that determines whether the detectors 1 and 2 fire

---

[1]V.Jacques et al., Science, Vol 315 (2007).

[2]Space-like separated means that the output component is outside the future and past light cones of the input component.

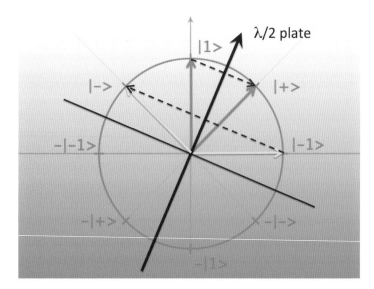

Figure II.3.31: *The $\lambda/2$ wave plate.* Effect of the $\lambda/2$ wave with its principle axis under $22.5°$ with the vertical line. The component orthogonal to the principal axis changes sign (phase= -1). The result is that $|v\rangle = |1\rangle \rightarrow |+\rangle$ and $|h\rangle = |-1\rangle \rightarrow |-\rangle$.

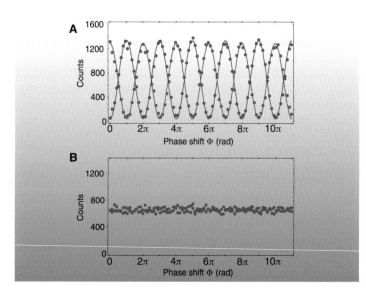

Figure II.3.32: *Single photon interference.* The counts in the detectors D_2 (red) and D_1 (blue), with and without interference. The top graph gives the count with the wave plate in the output channel and the bottom graph without. Taken from V. Jacques et al., Science, (2007).

simultaneously. So the beauty of the setup is of course that all the counts in the detectors are recorded as well as the random time series for the presence of the second plate, and then *a posteriori* one calculates what has happened. Clearly in this mode, the polarization of the photon entering the prism carries the information about which path the photon has taken. The D_1 detects only the photons that came along the lower path, and D_2 detects only the photons that took the upper path. And indeed no interference is observed as is clear from the lower graph in Figure II.3.32. The amplitudes do not add up, and the probabilities are 1/2 and independent of the phase φ. The punchline here is that the whole setup in this mode just 'measures' which path the photon has taken. And knowing that path the photon is just a particle and no interference is to be expected.

In the other mode of the interferometer, an additional $\lambda/2$ wave plate with its axis under an angle of $22.5°$ is inserted. This has the effect that the polarizations are flipped as Fig-

ure II.3.31 illustrates, so that Figure II.3.31 so that $|1\rangle \rightarrow |+\rangle$ and $|-1\rangle \rightarrow |-\rangle$. The important thing is that when the photon enters the final prism the components of different paths will mix again, the amplitudes will add and interference will occur. This is of course assuming the photon took both paths, which is what quantum theory predicts.

So the vertical and horizontal amplitudes become:

$$\alpha_v = \frac{1}{2}(e^{i\varphi/2} + e^{-i\varphi/2}) = \cos\frac{\varphi}{2}$$
$$\alpha_h = \frac{1}{2}(e^{i\varphi/2} - e^{-i\varphi/2}) = i\sin\frac{\varphi}{2}.$$

Thus, the probability for counts in D_2 becomes $\cos^2(\varphi/2) = \frac{1}{2}(1+\cos\varphi)$ and that for counts in D_1 equals $\sin^2(\varphi/2) = \frac{1}{2}(1-\cos\varphi)$. And this prediction is beautifully confirmed by the data plotted in the top graph of Figure II.3.32. A single photon interferes with itself, something more quant-essential is hard to imagine.

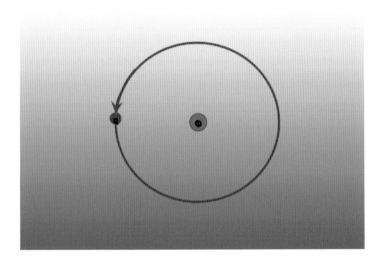

Figure II.3.33: *The Aharonov–Bohm phase factor.* If a charge q encircles a magnetic flux Φ, the quantum state of the particle will acquire a phase factor $W = \exp iq\Phi/\hbar c$.

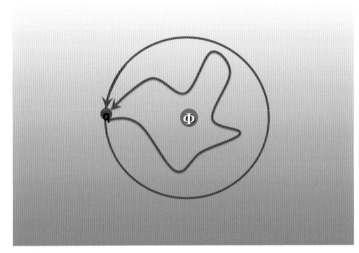

Figure II.3.34: *Path-independence.* The phase factor does not change under deformations of the path, as long as the region in between the paths is free of magnetic fields.

The Aharonov-Bohm phase.

Relative phase factors are all-important in quantum theory and lead to quantessential observable phenomena.

One important example that comes back in many guises is called the *Aharonov–Bohm phase-factor*. The corresponding effect is caused by inserting magnetic flux filament in the one electron double-slit interference experiment. The extra phase that results is due to the line integral of the gauge potential **A** along a closed loop, which we introduced already in the section on classical electrodynamics of Volume I in equation (I.1.52) and Figure I.1.27.

Let us recall that if we are in a medium where there is some electromagnetic potential and I have a charge q which I move along a path γ from $\mathbf{x}_0$ to $\mathbf{x}_1$, then the state vector or the wavefunction for that matter will be transformed by

a phase factor:

$$\psi(\mathbf{x}_1) = W(\gamma; \mathbf{x}_1, \mathbf{x}_0)\, \psi(\mathbf{x}_0), \qquad \text{(II.3.3a)}$$

$$W(\gamma; \mathbf{x}_1, \mathbf{x}_0) = \exp\left(i\frac{q}{\hbar c}\int_{\mathbf{x}_0}^{\mathbf{x}_1} \mathbf{A}\cdot \mathbf{dl}\right). \qquad \text{(II.3.3b)}$$

Here in the integral you take at every point along the path the component of the vector potential directed along the path. The outcome will in general depend on which path you choose. This phase factor is an interesting object, and we should pause for a moment to understand it better.

Firstly note that it is what we call 'non-local,' and under a gauge transformation $U(\mathbf{x})$ it transforms like

$$W(\gamma; \mathbf{x}_1, \mathbf{x}_0) \rightarrow U(\mathbf{x}_1)W(\mathbf{x}_1, \mathbf{x}_0)U^\dagger(\mathbf{x}_0).$$

If we close the loop, then the phase-factor becomes gauge invariant, because we get $U^\dagger(\mathbf{x}_0)U(\mathbf{x}_0) = U^{-1}U = 1$, the transformations act at the same point and therefore cancel out.

What does this non-local gauge invariant quantity mean? To understand that we go back to classical electrodynamics, and you have the simple property called Stokes' law, which tells us that if you calculate the line integral of A around a closed loop γ, then you get the magnetic flux through (any) two-dimensional surface bounded by the loop. So this means that the loop operator W_γ 'measures' the magnetic flux:

$$W_\gamma(q, \Phi) = e^{iq\Phi/\hbar c},$$

which is indeed a gauge invariant quantity, as it should be. Let us now go to a two-dimensional situation to simplify the picture, and imagine we have a well-defined narrow magnetic flux tube piercing through the surface as in Figure II.3.33. If we adiabatically move a charge around the flux Φ the state will change according to,

$$|q, \Phi\rangle \rightarrow W_\gamma(q, \Phi)|q, \Phi\rangle.$$

In Figure II.3.34 we show the effect of deforming the contour or loop doesn't affect the outcome as long as we do not cross magnetic flux lines. In field free regions you can deform the loop arbitrarily. Also, if you first go one way around the flux and you subsequently go back around some other loop encircling the flux in the opposite way, the net effect will be zero.

The beauty of this story is that one can directly measure this gauge invariant phase factor W in a one particle quantum interference experiment. It is called the Aharonov–Bohm effect, after the two theorists who proposed it in 1959 with reference to earlier work by Ehrenberg and Siday.[3] The setup of the experiment is given in Figure II.3.35. The gauge and path independent extra phase factor W_γ appears as a relative phase factor between the ψ_1 and ψ_2 factors in the interference term defined in equation (II.3.1), causing the observed shift of the interference pattern shown in the figure.

------

[3]And maybe this credential ambiguity explains why there was no Nobel prize awarded for this fundamental effect.

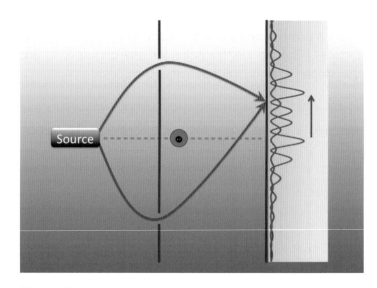

Figure II.3.35: *Path-independence.* The presence of a magnetic flux filament between the slits causes an extra phase difference between the two paths. This leads to a shift of the interference pattern from 'red' to 'blue' as indicated.

Phase shift due to magnetic flux.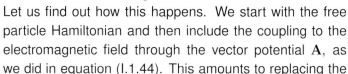
Let us find out how this happens. We start with the free particle Hamiltonian and then include the coupling to the electromagnetic field through the vector potential $\mathbf{A}$, as we did in equation (I.1.44). This amounts to replacing the derivatives ∇ by covariant ones $\mathbf{D} \equiv \nabla + iq\mathbf{A}/\hbar c$:

$$H = -\frac{\hbar^2}{2m}\nabla^2 \quad \rightarrow H = -\frac{\hbar^2}{2m}\mathbf{D}^2.$$

Suppose we have solved the problem with $\mathbf{A} = 0$ corresponding to $\psi_1(\mathbf{x})$ and $\psi_2(\mathbf{x})$. We want to find out what changes if we take $\mathbf{A} \neq 0$. Consider the covariant derivative working on any function, then we have the following equality:

$$\mathbf{D}\psi^A(\mathbf{x}) = \nabla\left(\exp\left(i\frac{q}{\hbar c}\int_{x_0}^{x_1}\mathbf{A}\,d\mathbf{x}\right)\psi^A(\mathbf{x})\right),$$

The only way the coupling to the $\mathbf{A}$ field manifests itself is through the phase factor W. In other words the solutions are linked as follows:

$$\psi_i^A(\mathbf{x}) = W^*(\gamma_i; \mathbf{x}, \mathbf{x}_0)\psi_i(\mathbf{x}) \quad ; \quad i = 1, 2.$$

The phase factor looks awkward in that there at once appears a point $\mathbf{x}_0$ and the line integral along a path γ_i from $\mathbf{x}_0$ to $\mathbf{x}_1$. But the identity holds for *any* choice of $\mathbf{x}_0$ and may depend on γ, as will become clear.

Now return to the interference term $I(\mathbf{x})$ defined by equation (II.3.1). One chooses for $\mathbf{x}_0$ the position of the source, and for ψ_1^A the path γ_1 has to be chosen to pass through the first slit and for ψ_2^A a path γ_2 through the second slit. Then the first term of $I(\mathbf{x})$ involves the product:

$$\psi_1^{A*}(\mathbf{x})\psi_2^A(\mathbf{x})$$
$$= W(\gamma_1,\mathbf{x},\mathbf{x}_0)W^*(\gamma_2;\mathbf{x},\mathbf{x}_0)e^{i(\beta_2(\mathbf{x})-\beta_1(\mathbf{x}))}\,|\psi_1(\mathbf{x})||\psi_2(\mathbf{x})|\,,$$

where the the the $\beta_i(\mathbf{x})$ are the phases of $A = 0$ solution. Note that $W^*(\gamma;\mathbf{x},\mathbf{x}_0) = W(\gamma;\mathbf{x}_0,\mathbf{x})$, in other words the conjugation reverses the path, but then the product of the two W factors yields a closed path through both slits encircling the magnetic flux giving the overall phase factor $W_\gamma(q,\Phi) = e^{iq\Phi/\hbar c}$. Putting it all together we obtain:

$$I(\mathbf{x}) = \cos\left(\frac{q\Phi}{\hbar c} + \beta(\mathbf{x})\right)|\psi_1(\mathbf{x})||\psi_2(\mathbf{x})|\,,$$

with $\beta(\mathbf{x}) \equiv \beta_2(\mathbf{x}) - \beta_1(\mathbf{x})$.

What this calculation shows is that the position dependent phase $\beta(\mathbf{x})$ corresponding to the $A = 0$ gets shifted by an amount proportional to the flux-charge product. This shift is constant; it does not depend on where you are, which means that the interference pattern generated by $\beta(\mathbf{x})$ gets shifted as a whole, as we have indicated in Figure II.3.35. We will return to these Aharonov–Bohm phases on page 182 of Chapter II.5, where we talk about exotic particle spin and statistics properties in two dimensions.

■

Why is this an important effect? This experiment shows a really interesting aspect of electrodynamics. The electrons in this experiment are shielded from the flux. They only travel through regions of space where both the electric

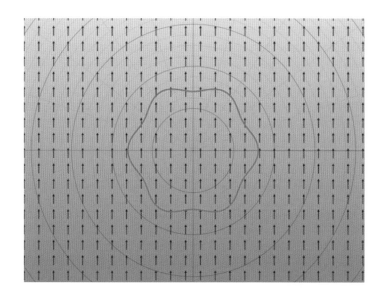

Figure II.3.36: *Super phase (A)*. Phase of the superconducting condensate. This is the ground state with the trivial constant phase equal one. This configuration has winding number $n = 0$.

and the magnetic fields $\mathbf{E}$ and $\mathbf{B}$ are strictly zero. The vector potential $\mathbf{A}$ is non-zero but it is a gauge dependent field and therefore not a local physical observable like the other fields. In fact locally it is a gauge transform of the vacuum, in other words locally the gauge potential can always be gauged to zero! And yet, there is an observable effect! The clue is that there is this subtle *nonlocal gauge invariant observable* which involves only the vector potential, namely the loop integral, its value if non-zero cannot be gauged away. This means that if you would like to transform the gauge field to zero everywhere that transformation would *not* be single valued and therefore not a proper gauge transformation. It is this gauge invariant observable that is measured in this quantessential experiment.

Flux quantization in a superconductor. Let me point out another crucial 'application' of this argument in the context of superconductors, in particular type II superconductors. The defining property of superconductors is that their resistance is zero. If you were to move a piece of superconducting material in a magnetic field, super currents would

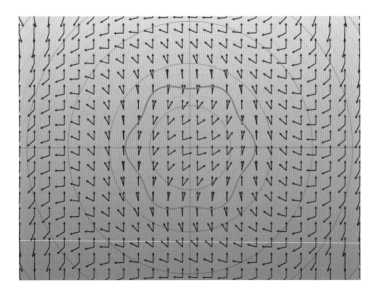

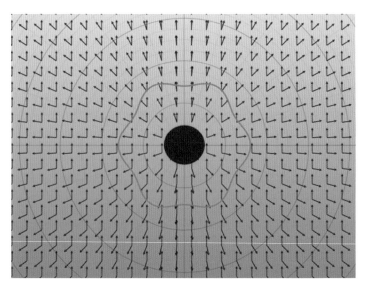

Figure II.3.37: *Super phase (B)*. Phase of the superconducting condensate. This is again the trivial ground state but where the phase has been changed by a local gauge transformation, but the winding number is still zero.

Figure II.3.38: *Super phase with flux (A)*. Phase of the super-conducting condensate with a magnetic fluxtube in the center in the so-called radial gauge. The phase rotates by 2π after encircling the flux once along a closed curve like the green one in the figure. The winding number of this configuration equals $n = 1$.

start running so as to expel the magnetic field lines out the superconductor. This is the *Meissner effect*. In the type II superconductors, it is possible for flux lines to enter the medium, but only if the amount of flux satisfies a certain flux quantization condition. The situation is very similar to what we are discussing here: there is a superconducting ground state that corresponds to a condensate of pairs of electrons. These *Cooper pairs* have charge $2e$, and the medium has no electromagnetic field except for the filaments. The condensate is static and effectively described by a complex scalar field $\psi(\mathbf{x})$ that is doubly charged and carries an electromagnetic phase factor. To say that the pairs are condensed means that in that case the field acquires a constant non-zero magnitude, and because it describes the ground state it is called a *vacuum expectation value*. We write $|\psi(\mathbf{x})| = 1$ and ψ is described by a pure phase factor with angle $\beta(\mathbf{x})$. In Figure II.3.36 we have plotted the local phase β of the condensate in the ground state. The gauge field is in this case globally gauged to zero and the corresponding phase is trivial, $\beta(\mathbf{x}) = 0$. In

Figure II.3.37 we have made a local ($\mathbf{x}$-dependent) gauge tranformation which changes $\beta \rightarrow \beta + \Lambda(\mathbf{x})$. If we follow the phase along a closed curve like the green one, the phase will change forth and back, but the net change after returning to the initial point remains zero. We say that *winding number* of the configuration is $n = 0$. This winding number is not just gauge invariant. It a topological invariant, which means that it cannot be changed by *any* smooth transformation of the gauge potential or the phase $\beta(\mathbf{x})$. If we follow that phase around a magnetic flux line, the state should certainly return to the same value. It should be single valued because it is macroscopic state describing the condensate of Cooper pairs. We discussed this briefly in Chapter II.1 when discussing the *Josephson effect*. The upshot is that only fluxes are admitted that are 'invisible' for the medium, or the condensate. In other words, we want the induced phase factor to be equal one, which implies:

$$\exp(i\frac{2e}{\hbar c}\Phi) = 1 \quad \Rightarrow \quad 2e\Phi = 2\pi n \hbar c ,$$

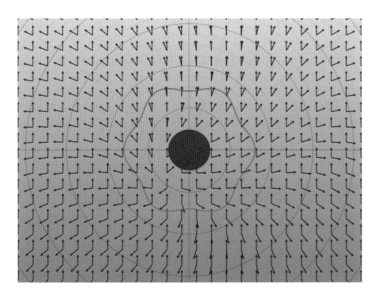

Figure II.3.39: *Super phase with flux (B).* Same physical situation as in the previous figure after a local gauge transformation, the winding number did not change.

The Berry phase

You may ask whether it is really possible to 'drag' a state vector along a closed loop like we described and whether the resulting phase change can be measured? The answer is affirmative. In this subsection we will discuss the *Berry phase* which is a substantial generalization of the Aharanov–Bohm phase, named after the British mathematical physicist Sir Michael Berry who discovered the possibility to measure holonomies in certain experimental setups with a well-chosen time or space dependent Hamiltonian.

which means that the flux is quantized according to:

$$\Phi = n\phi_0 \ \text{ with } \ \phi_0 = \frac{hc}{2e} ,$$

and ϕ_0 is called the fundamental flux quantum, which is expressed directly in fundamental constants. In the Figures II.3.38 and II.3.39 we show the phases of the condensate after a flux tube has entered. Moving along the green curve encircling the flux, the phase changes by 2π. This is clear in the radial gauge of the first figure but remains true after a gauge transformation has been applied.

This quantization rule is exactly what has been observed in type II superconductors. A flux tube has a negative surface energy and therefore an arbitrary flux likes to decay in individual minimally quantized filaments. These repel and therefore, if there is a strong magnetic field causing many tubes, these will form a lattice, a two-dimensional triangular crystal. If you keep turning up the magnetic field strength, the pairs will break up and therefore the superconductive state will break down at some critical value for the magnetic field.

The question is how to translate the rather abstract pictures of parallel transport into a suitable experimental setup. The idea behind Figure I.2.32 is clear: there is an 'agent' carrying the state vector, and by moving through space the frame changes and therefore the parallel transported vector appears to be rotated with respect to the initial local frame.

In the qubit or spin-one-half context you may think of the agent as an electron carrying a qubit (spin-one-half spinor) around. If we apply a magnetic field, the spin will align or anti-align with the external field as that minimizes the interaction energy. The ground state of the spin depends therefore on the orientation of the magnetic field. So to get the spin to move through its state space, we should move the electron in real space through an inhomogeneous magnetic field or we should fix its position and change the field. And by walking around along a closed loop in real spacetime we may find the state of the spin is rotated by some phase angle. In other words, due to the inhomogeneous magnetic field, a closed loop in space-time gets mapped onto a smooth path in state space that is not necessarily closed.

In fact Berry took the approach where he looked at a time-dependent Hamiltonian $H(t)$. We have said that the time evolution of a state is generated by the Hamiltonian. If the Hamiltonian is time=independent and the system is in an eigenstate of that Hamiltionian, then the time dependence is the time dependent phase factor $|\psi_n(t)\rangle = \exp(-iE_n(t - t_0)/\hbar)|\psi_n(t_0)$. The question is now what happens if the Hamiltonian becomes time dependent. You can think of the Hamiltonian having a set of parameters $\{c_i\}$. For example, if we consider the coupling of a spin to an external magnetic field, the parameters would correspond to choosing the direction and the strength of that external field. And the time-dependent Hamiltonian we are interested in would be one where we slowly vary these parameters: $H(t) = H(\{c_i(t)\})$. So the experiment is set up to see what happens if we make a round-trip through this paramater space or the space of Hamiltonians. The Hamiltonian moves between t_0 and t_f along a closed path in parameter space so that $H(t_0) = H(t_f)$. The choice of this path is of course made by the experimenter. In Figure II.3.40 we have depicted a time-dependent closed path (pink) through a two-dimensional coordinate space of Hamiltonians where $\mathbf{c}(t_0) = \mathbf{c}(t_f)$. The figure also shows the yellow path straight up, corresponding to the time independent Hamiltonian $H = H(t_0)$, leading to the aforementioned phase factor $\exp(-iE_n(t - t_0)/\hbar)$.

The expression for the phase factor. We assume that the Hamiltonian $H(t)$ has a time-dependent discrete spectrum:

$$H(t)|n(t)\rangle = E_n(t)|n(t)\rangle$$

If we now assume that we vary the Hamiltonian slowly so that the system smoothly (adiabatically) evolves in the state $|n(t)\rangle$, we can construct an approximate solution;

$$|\psi(t)\rangle = C_n(t) \exp\left(-\frac{i}{\hbar} \int_{t_0}^{t} E_n(t')\, |n(t)\rangle\, dt'\right),$$

and because $\psi(t)$ and $|n(t)\rangle$ are both normalized the coefficient $C_n(t)$ can only be a phase:

$$C_n(t) = \exp(i\gamma_n(t))$$

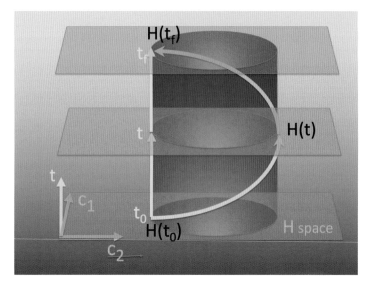

Figure II.3.40: *Berry phase.* A closed (circular) path in Hamiltonian space with coordinates $\mathbf{c} = (c_1, c_2)$. The system follows the pink curve in time such that $H(t_0) = H(t_f)$.

We can substitute this solution into the time-dependent Schrödinger equation,

$$i\hbar \frac{\partial}{\partial t} \psi(t) = H\psi(t)$$

to obtain an equation for the phase:

$$i \frac{\partial \gamma_n(t)}{\partial t} |n(t)\rangle = -\frac{\partial |n(t)\rangle}{\partial t}$$

which has the solution

$$\gamma_n(t) = i \int_{t_0}^{t} \langle n(t')| \frac{\partial |n(t')\rangle}{\partial t'}\, dt'$$

Berry connection and curvature. To give this phase a direct physical interpretation let us look at the integrand and ask what we mean by the state $|n(t)\rangle$. The time dependence is not the time dependence of n but rather of the state labeled by n. The time dependence all comes through the changing of the parameters $c_i(t)$. The appropriate notation is in fact to write $|n(t)\rangle = |n; \{c_i(t)\}\rangle =$

$|n; \mathbf{c}(t)\rangle$ where I combined the parameters into a vector, a position vector in parameter space. If I now take the time derivative of the state, I may rewrite that as follows:

$$\frac{\partial |n; \mathbf{c}(t)\rangle}{\partial t} = \boldsymbol{\nabla}_c |n; \mathbf{c}(t)\rangle \cdot \frac{\partial \mathbf{c}(t)}{\partial t},$$

where the nabla operator is the vector of $\partial / \partial c_i$ derivatives. In other words the gradient operator acting on functions of the parameter vector.

This turns the time integral for the phase into a loop integral on parameter space over a connection (or pseudo gauge potential) $\mathbf{C}(c)$ named after Berry:

$$\gamma_n = \oint \langle n; \mathbf{c} | \boldsymbol{\nabla}_c | n; \mathbf{c} \rangle \cdot d\mathbf{c} \equiv \oint \mathbf{C} \cdot d\mathbf{c}$$

In other words, the phase factor using Stokes' theorem can be expressed as a surface integral of the corresponding Berry curvature $\mathbf{F} = \boldsymbol{\nabla}_c \times \mathbf{C}$:

$$\gamma_n = \oint \mathbf{C} \cdot d\mathbf{c} = \int \mathbf{F} \cdot d\mathbf{S}_c .$$

There is a striking analogy with the Aharonov–Bohm case, but it is also clear that the Berry analysis is much more general.

Spin coupled to an external magnetic field.

To be more concrete about such an experiment, imagine a closed path $\mathbf{c}(t)$ in time parametrized by a parameter $0 \leq t \leq 1$ with $\mathbf{c}(0) = \mathbf{c}(1)$. The system is an electron spin coupled to a slowly varying external magnetic field $\mathbf{B}(t)$, with a Hamiltonian

$$H(t) = \mathbf{B}(t) \cdot \sigma,$$

a hermitean 2×2 matrix acting on the two-component electron spin.

Let first ask what the space of Hamiltonians looks like, which is asking for a natural parametrization of all magnetic fields.

The field $\mathbf{B}(t)$ has some direction and some magnitude. As shown in Figure II.3.43 we choose spherical coordinates in $\mathbf{B}$ space. So the direction is parametrized by the angular coordinates θ and φ, while the magnitude is given by the radial coordinate. If we only change the direction of the external field, the space of possible Hamiltonians would just correspond to the radial magnetic fields on a spherical surface of constant radius. Note that this looks like the field surrounding a magnetic monopole as we have drawn in Figure I.1.29.

The starting point with the Berry phase experiment is to choose the time path that gets mapped onto some closed curve $\mathbf{c}(t)$ in the space of Hamiltonians, thus on the two-sphere in this case.

The adiabatic change or 'dragging' of the state amounts to parallel transporting a frame (of the tangent plane) along the curve, like we discussed in Chapter I.2 in the section on geometry.

As we will show shortly, the result for the acquired phase will depend on the solid angle that the path $H(t)$ has covered on the sphere.[4] This means that the Berry phase is a purely geometric phase (in fact a holonomy) which depends on the geometry of the space of Hamiltonians, but also on the probe (in this case a spinor).

The idea is simple: at $t = 0$ we start at the North Pole with the Hamiltonian $H(0) = BZ$ and the energy eigenstates correspond $|\psi_n(0)\rangle = |\pm 1\rangle$. Next we start rotating the magnetic field and we assume that the initial eigen spinor just follows. In that sense it is fair to say that the Berry

---

[4]The path is oriented and the orientation decides whether to take the solid angle ω or $4\pi - \omega$, which with equation (II.3.4) amounts to $R_k(\theta) \rightarrow R_k(-\theta)$.

phase probes the Hamiltonian space but also the spin or qubit space which is a three-sphere S^3 as we know.

To work this out in more detail for an electron spin or a qubit for that matter we first look at how the rotations act on the spinors and then we find a convenient parametrization of the magnetic field space. ∎

Probing the geometry of state space

To better understand what I mean by 'probing the state space' of a qubit I propose we return to the 'Barbie on a globe' representation of the qubit, as we introduced it in Chapter II.2 on page 52. What you see there is that we represent the qubit as a vector or rather spinor bundle over a two-sphere, where a particular qubit state corresponds to a unique tangent vector at some point on that sphere. And the X, Y and Z operators are generating the 'motions' of the Barbie in that space.

Let us first visualize the actions discussed above in the Figure II.2. We see the Barbie standing on the North Pole, say looking West corresponding to the state $-|1\rangle$. Acting with Z does not affect her at all, but acting with X moves her to the state $-|-1\rangle$ which is the mirror image of the initial state through the origin of the tangent space.

To probe the space in more detail we have to construct operators that move the Barbie around on the sphere and make her perform pirouettes. What we need are rotations generated around various axes, and these correspond to exponentials of X, Y and Z.

Rotation of qubits. As we will explain in more detail in the *Math Excursion* on page 179 of Part III on groups, this amounts to going from the *Lie algebra* of infinitesimal transformations to the corresponding *Lie group* of finite transformations. Here we need the explicit relation for any of the Pauli matrices $\sigma_k = X$, Y or Z that we introduced in

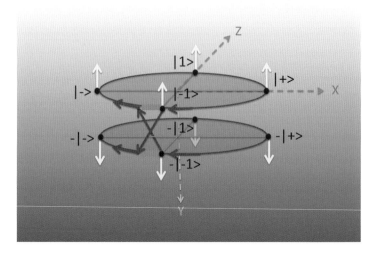

Figure II.3.41: *Effect of rotations around Y-axis on Barbie.* Rotating the Barbie state $|1\rangle$ around a large circle in the ZX-plane by angles $\theta = \pm n\pi/2$. The rotation angle in this representation equals θ. As she only passes through real states, the overall phase β, denoted by the white arrow, is either 0 or π. Rotating over an angle 2π any state goes to minus itself.

equation (A.34) of the chapter on *Math Excursions*:

$$R_k(\theta) \equiv \exp\left(i\frac{\theta}{2}\sigma_k\right) = \mathbf{1}\cos\frac{\theta}{2} + i\sigma_k\sin\frac{\theta}{2}, \quad \text{(II.3.4)}$$

which should be compared with its one-dimensional analogue, the Euler formula (A.28). At this point we recall some important observations we made before.

1. Since the spinor or qubit is a two-dimensional complex vector, the rotations are relatively simple two-by-two unitary matrices which can be given explicitly as you see.

2. These complex rotations form the group $SU(2)$.

3. The formula for $R_k(\theta)$ represents a rotation about the k-axis over an angle θ. That means to say that acting on an ordinary three-dimensional vector like $\mathbf{B}$, it rotates over an angle θ in real space. That is, under

a rotation $R_k(\theta)$,, the Hamiltonian will rotate as:

$$H \rightarrow H' = \mathbf{B} \cdot \sigma' = \mathbf{B} \cdot R_k \sigma R_k^{-1} \qquad (\text{II.3.5})$$

4. However, on the two-component complex state vector of a qubit the rotation acts like

$$|\psi\rangle \rightarrow |\psi\rangle' = R_k |\psi\rangle.$$

Note that it 'rotates' only over half that angle because of the factor $\theta/2$ in the formula (II.3.4).

5. This factor one-half has dramatic consequences. For example a rotation by $\theta = 2\pi$ around any axis produces in (II.3.4) just minus the unit matrix! So, under such a transformation the qubit state always goes to minus itself. One has to rotate by 4π before one gets back to the unit matrix. This is indeed a defining property for a *spinor*, to be contrasted with rotating an ordinary vector about an angle 2π, which always gives the same vector back. This minus sign for a spinor has a deep physical significance for particles carrying half-integer spin as we will explain later. It is one of those minus signs that does matter a great deal.

6. Note that under the rotations the norm of the state is preserved

$$\langle \psi' | \psi' \rangle = \langle \psi | \psi \rangle,$$

and this is what we expect as we are moving over a sphere, because by taking the complex conjugate vector the transformation is going to its hermitian conjugate, which means changing $i \rightarrow -i$ or $\theta \rightarrow -\theta$, what amounts to the same thing. This means that the conjugate rotates by the opposite amount, so that the net effect of the rotation on the inner product of vector with itself (or any other vector) always cancels.

To familiarize ourselves a bit with these rotations, let us first restrict our attention to real qubit state vectors as in-

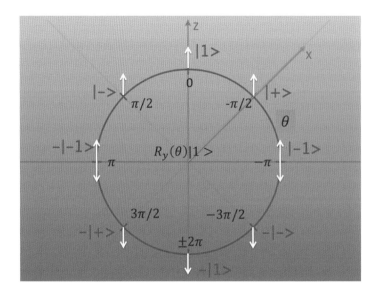

Figure II.3.42: *Effect of rotations on the real circle of qubit states.* Same situation as previous figure, but now we have plotted the states at half the angle θ from $-2\pi < \theta < 2\pi$. In the upper half-of the circle the overall phase β is for real states 0 and in the lower half it is π.

troduced in Figure II.1.7. These states form a real circle. The operators Z and X are qubit observables which have real eigenvectors. For Z those are $\pm|1\rangle$ and $\pm|-1\rangle$ respectively with eigenvalues $+1$ and -1. Similarly for X we have $\pm|+\rangle$ and $\pm|-\rangle$ also with eigenvalues $+1$ and -1 respectively. We may ask which operator would move you around in that subspace of real states, on that circle. Such moves correspond to rotations about the Y-axis, generated by Y and indeed, a rotation by an angle θ yields the real matrix:

$$R_y(\theta) = \cos\frac{\theta}{2} + iY\sin\frac{\theta}{2} = \begin{pmatrix} \cos\frac{\theta}{2} & \sin\frac{\theta}{2} \\ -\sin\frac{\theta}{2} & \cos\frac{\theta}{2} \end{pmatrix}, \qquad (\text{II.3.6})$$

which indeed corresponds to a rotation of the qubit state vector over an angle $\theta/2$. In other words, rotations about the Y in the $(|-1\rangle, |1\rangle)$ plane move a state around the circle.

So let us find out what the formula yields for rotations over multiples of π acting on the $|+1\rangle$ state, and then visualize the results in the two different representations of the qubit space corresponding to (i) the 'Barbie on the globe' picture, and (ii) the real circle of Figure II.1.7.

Using the formula (II.3.6) we obtain the following values for some $(-2\pi \le \theta \le 2\pi)$ rotations. For a transformation by $-\pi$ we find:

$$R_y(-\pi)|1\rangle \leftrightarrow \begin{pmatrix} 0 & -1 \\ 1 & 0 \end{pmatrix} \begin{pmatrix} 1 \\ 0 \end{pmatrix} = \begin{pmatrix} 0 \\ 1 \end{pmatrix} \leftrightarrow |-1\rangle,$$

and for the others:

$$R_y(\pm\frac{\pi}{2})|1\rangle = |\mp\rangle, \quad R_y(\mp\pi)|1\rangle = \mp|-1\rangle,$$

$$R_y(\pm\frac{3\pi}{2})|1\rangle = -|\pm\rangle, \quad R_y(\pm 2\pi)|1\rangle = -|1\rangle.$$

If we carry a spinor along a large circle over an angle of 2π we obtain from (II.3.6), just a (phase)factor minus one. We have illustrated the sequence of values just calculated in Figure II.3.41 which should be compared with the 'Barbie on the globe' figure on page 52. The rotations for increasing values of θ correspond to the Barbie moving by the same angle over the globe, anti-clockwise in the vertical plane. The states remain real for all θ and the only phase change that may occur is that it jumps from 1 to -1 or the other way around. This corresponds to a jump in the phase angle of $\beta = \pm\pi$ depicted by the white arrows either pointing up or down in the figures.

In Figure II.3.42, the same sequence is represented in the standard qubit decomposition that we introduced in Figure II.1.7, and we see indeed the phase jumping at odd-multiples of $\theta = \pm\pi$.

You may think of this as a *holonomy* effect, referring to the concept we introduced in Chapter I.2 while discussing parallel transport of vectors through curved space, which is exactly what we are doing here. If the Barbie parallel transports her spinor, it may pick up a phase factor equal minus one. So if she starts walking along a big circle on the sphere looking straight ahead, she will looking straight

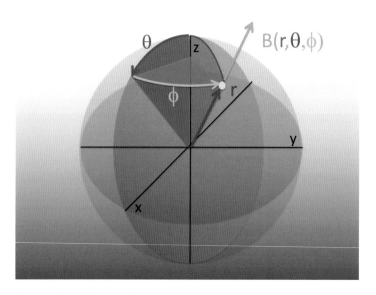

Figure II.3.43: *Radial magnetic field.* The Hamiltonian landscape.

back upon returning. What the Figures II.3.41 and II.3.42 show is that the Barbie at $\theta = \pm\pi$ suddenly turned her head by $180°$ ..

Magnetic field space. We choose that initially the field is in the positive z-direction $\mathbf{B}(0) = B\hat{z}$ and the spin to be in the aligned up $|1\rangle$ state, so, in the $n = 1$ energy eigenstate. We change the direction of the field slowly so that the spin stays aligned with the varying external field provided the changes are slow.

From the figure we learn what the x, y and z components of $\mathbf{B}$ are in terms of the angular variables:

$$B_x = B \sin\theta \cos\varphi \quad B_y = B \sin\theta \sin\varphi \quad B_z = B \cos\theta$$

And thus the Hamiltonian of equation (II.3.5) corresponding to a point on the sphere i (we set $B = |\mathbf{B}| = 1$) looks in matrix form like:

$$H(\mathbf{c}) = H(\theta, \varphi) = \begin{pmatrix} \cos\theta & e^{-i\varphi}\sin\theta \\ e^{i\varphi}\sin\theta & -\cos\theta \end{pmatrix}.$$

The two eigenstates with eigenvalues plus and minus one

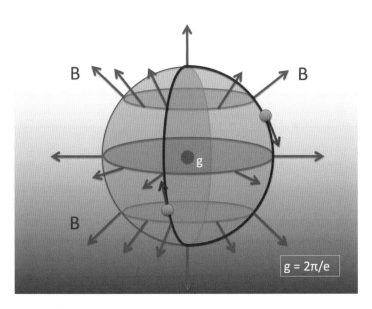

Figure II.3.44: *Magnetic field space.* The space of a magnetic field of constant magnitude can be represented as the field on a sphere around a magnetic monopole. Adiabatic transport of een spin-1/2 particle moving along a closed path (in red) in the radial magnetic field of a pole of strength $g = 2\pi\hbar/e$ centered at the origin (blue).

correspond to the spinors:

$$|1;\mathbf{c}\rangle = \begin{pmatrix} \cos\frac{\theta}{2} \\ e^{i\varphi}\sin\frac{\theta}{2} \end{pmatrix} \quad \text{and} \quad |-1;\mathbf{c}\rangle = \begin{pmatrix} -e^{-i\varphi}\sin\frac{\theta}{2} \\ \cos\frac{\theta}{2} \end{pmatrix}$$

The adiabatic process. The process of adiabatically moving over the sphere corresponds to making rotations around the proper axis and angles. So for example to move from the North Pole to the point (r, θ, φ) one may apply the transformation(s):

$$R_B = R_z(-\varphi)R_y(-\theta)R_z(\varphi) = \begin{pmatrix} \cos\frac{\theta}{2} & -e^{-i\varphi}\sin\frac{\theta}{2} \\ e^{i\varphi}\sin\frac{\theta}{2} & \cos\frac{\theta}{2} \end{pmatrix}.$$

One checks that:

$$H(\theta, \varphi) = R_B Z R_B^{-1} \quad \text{and} \quad |\pm 1;\mathbf{c}\rangle = R_b |\pm 1\rangle,$$

as it should be. ∎ ∎

The Berry connection.

Let now calculate the Berry connection which involves applying the ∇_c operator, but the c coordinates are just the ordinary three-dimensional spherical coordinates where the (angular) components are given by $\nabla_\theta = \partial/\partial\theta$ and $\nabla_\phi = \sin^{-1}\theta\partial/\partial\varphi$. The Berry connection is then:

$$\mathbf{C}(\theta, \varphi) \equiv \langle n;\mathbf{c}|\nabla_c|n;\mathbf{c}\rangle = \frac{1-\cos\theta}{2\sin\theta}\,\hat{\varphi}.$$

This connection is exactly the gauge potential written down by Dirac in his famous 1931 monopole paper, and indeed its curl give the field of a magnetic monopole with magnetic charge $eg/\hbar c = 2\pi$. The total magnetic flux through the sphere is 2π, which is half the solid angle of the total sphere being 4π. And thus is the resulting phase after closing the loop equal to the magnetic flux going through the loop. It is nice to see how nice this subject of the Berry phase connects with matters that we discussed in early chapters of Volume I.

Some explicit examples. Let us now consider some specific paths and see how this works. In the first example we start at the North Pole meaning to say that $H = Z$ and $|\psi(t = 0)\rangle = |1\rangle$. Then we parallel transport vector along a geodesic generated by rotating around X-axis over an angle $\theta = -\pi$ and bring it back along a geodesic generated by rotating around the Y-axis by $\theta = \pi$. The path corresponds to the red two-angle indicated in Figure II.3.44. This means that the Hamiltonian between $t = 0$ and $t = \frac{1}{2}$ smoothly rotates in the YZ-plane from $Z = H(0)$ to $Y = H(\frac{1}{2})$. From formula (II.3.4) we see that:

$$R_k(\pm\pi) = \pm i\sigma_k.$$

So the overall (unitary) transformation of the state vector corresponds to:

$$U = iY(-iX) = -iZ.$$

So the net effect on the state $|1\rangle$ after coming back home is that it is rotated by an angle $\theta = -\pi/2$ around the z-axis. So the loop integral would give a magnetic flux of

$\pi/2$ which is $1/4$ of the total flux of 2π, which in turn is consistent with the fact that the loop covered $1/4$ of the total solid angle of the sphere.

So what is the interference effect on the probabilities measured, if we start with $|\psi_1\rangle$ and end up at $|\psi_2\rangle = -iZ|\psi_1\rangle$? The expression is given by the following equation for any outcome of a measurement:

$$I(a_i) = \gamma(\langle\psi_1|P_i^A|\psi_2\rangle + \langle\psi_2|P_i^A|\psi_1\rangle)$$

The outcome is the expectation value of an expression involving U and P_i^A:

$$I(a_i) = \gamma\langle\psi_1|\left(P_i^A U + U^\dagger P_i^A\right)|\psi_1\rangle.$$

We obtain that in the case at hand by choosing $P = P_\pm^Z$ the result is zero for all $|\psi_1\rangle$. However for $P_\pm^Y$ we find $\langle\psi_1|Y|\psi_1\rangle$ which of course may or may not be observable dependent on the choice of the initial state.

Another example would be as sketched in Figure I.2.32. There we have three successive rotations by $\pi/2$.

$$U = R_y\left(\frac{\pi}{2}\right)R_z\left(\frac{\pi}{2}\right)R_x\left(\frac{\pi}{2}\right) = \frac{1}{\sqrt{2}}(1 + iZ),$$

where we used that

$$R_k\left(\frac{\pi}{2}\right) = \frac{1}{\sqrt{2}}(1 + i\sigma_k).$$

This generates interference in more situations than the previous case, and applying it to $|\psi_1\rangle = |1\rangle$ we get:

$$U|1\rangle = \frac{1}{\sqrt{2}}(1 + iZ)|1\rangle = \frac{1}{\sqrt{2}}(1 + i)|1\rangle = e^{i\pi/4},$$

again this is consistent with $1/8$ of the total flux. ■ ■

Quantum tunnelling: magic moves

In this chapter we have considered the consequences of the quantessential particle-wave duality in typical wave type

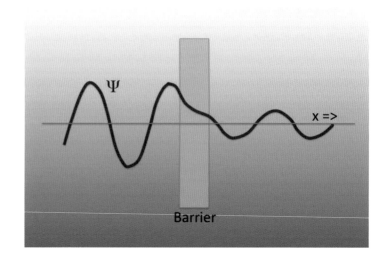

Figure II.3.45: *Quantum tunnelling.* The lowest energy state of a particle in the presence of a potential wall shows that the quantum particle is most probably found on the left-hand side, but still has a small probability to be on the right-hand side. The wavefunction decays exponentially in the wall but still has a non-vanishing value when it arrives at the other side.

phenomena like reflection, refraction, diffraction and interference. In this section we turn to the aspect of transmission, notably the effect of quantum tunnelling, which is another stunning instance where quantum theory overrides a classical veto. In the tunnelling process we should think of particles that can move through, or jump over a potential wall. This happens for example in the spontaneous decay of bound systems, and has a great application in scanning tunnelling microscopy (STM). Such processes are strictly forbidden by classical physics but have finite although small (meaning exponentially small) probabilities to occur in the quantum situation. It can be looked upon as a consequence of the quantum fluctuations in the system that 'follow' from the uncertainty relations.

Let us put a quantum particle in a bowl corresponding to a potential energy landscape as given in Figure II.3.45. Imagine the particle sitting in the origin at the bottom of

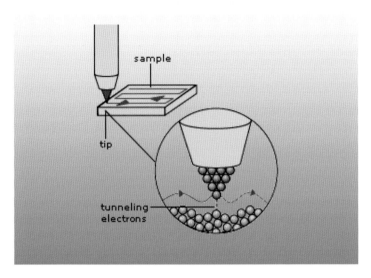

Figure II.3.46: *The scanning tunnelling microscope.* Fixing the tunnelling current, fixes the distance between the tip and the surface to be scanned. (Source: Flickr.)

Figure II.3.47: *STM surface imaging.* Image of scanning tunnelling microscope of a coral of atoms deposited on a surface. (Source: IBM.)

the bowl. Then clearly, if we do not add enough energy to overcome the height of the bowl, it will sit there forever, since from a classical point of view it is a stable situation. However, in the quantum world the problem is different; the lowest energy solution for the wavefunction is sketched in red and the important point to observe is that it is non-zero *outside* the bowl. In other words, if we square the wavefunction we get a large probability to find the particle where we expect it, but there is a non-vanishing probability of finding the particle outside. There is a small probability for the particle to 'jump' the wall to the outside world, where we might observe it. It jumps a wall of any height as long as it is thin enough.

In more physical terms you may think of a situation where a particle is bound (and thus sitting in some potential well), but if the well corresponds to a local minimum, then there is a (low) probability that the particle will tunnel out of the well, meaning that the system decays and emits the particle. This is for example what happens with nuclear α decay, certain nuclei will spontaneously emit an α particle

which is in fact just a ^{4}He nucleus consisting of two protons and two neutrons. It is this tunnelling phenomenon that explains the extremely – exponentially – small probabilities that are reflected in the extremely long half-life times of certain nuclei. Long means that the process takes place with a much lower frequency than the natural frequency f that occurs in the state corresponding with the energy E of the state, with $E = hf$.

A similar situation occurs if one sends a particle to a potential barrier (a wall) then classical physics may predict some energy and momentum transfer during the impact by which the particle is stopped or may be reflected, but what we never have is that the particle would have a finite chance to of moving through the wall (without destroying it). And this is exactly what happens in the quantum case, where one finds a definite probability of ending up on the other side as long as the wall has a finite size. The reflection and transition probabilities can be calculated and of course add up to one.

We discussed a realization of tunnelling currents in chapter II.1 for the Josephson junction. Another important application is the scanning tunnelling microscope (STM). The working is schematically depicted in Figure II.3.46. By driving a constant small current through the tip to the surface one wants to study, the tip will then precisely scan the surface, all the way down to atomic scales. The tip will never touch the surface and the 'wall' is provided by the thin insulating layer of air between the tip and the surface. The images taken by the microscope of the surface localizes the presence of isolated atoms or molecules on the surface. A nice example is given in Figure II.3.47. The STM scans the contour of the charge density density profile on the surface. People can be stopped by virtual walls, but walking through a real wall is quite something else, and that is what quantum particles apparently can do.

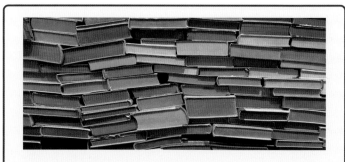

Further reading on interference:

— *QED:*
  The Strange Theory of Light and Matter
  Richard P Feynman Antony Zee
  (revised version)
  Princeton University Press (2014)

— *Quantum Interference and Coherence: Theory and Experiments*
  Zbigniew Ficek and Stuart Swain
  (Springer) (2005)

Chapter II.4

Teleportation and computation

Entanglement and teleportation

The Einstein–Podolsky–Rosen paradox

In 1935 Albert Einstein, Boris Podolsky and Nathan Rosen, confronted quantum physics with a profound objection concerning the quantessential property of entanglement. This led to a fierce debate between Bohr and Einstein closely followed by Schrödinger. In those days the problem was presented as a *gedanken* experiment involving a pair of spins or qubits which are entangled but widely separated in space. One may think of a spin-less particle at rest (a π_0 particle for example) decaying into two photons, because of momentum conservation both particles will fly off back to back and because of spin conservation the polarizations of the two photons have to be opposite. This means that without interactions the particles could separate and travel a long way, and we could imagine that one might arrive in New York and the other in Tokyo where Alice and Bob will make polarization measurements. The polarization state of the entangled pair is given by:

$$|\psi_{NT}\rangle = \frac{1}{\sqrt{2}}\left(|1,-1\rangle - |-1,1\rangle\right), \qquad (II.4.1)$$

where the first entry refers to the NY particle and the second to its Tokyo counterpart, and we for convenience have assumed the particles to be polarized in z-direction. Now

Figure II.4.1: *The Myth of Depth*, a 1984 painting by Mark Tensey. It makes you think of unusual, if not magical, ways information may propagate. It is the 'Spooky action at a distance,' Einstein was so worried about.(Source: ANP / Mark Garlick / Science Photo Library)

Alice in New York decides to make a polarization measurement. Let us suppose that she chooses to do this along the x-axis, and let us also suppose that she finds a value $+1$. Then we know that the first spin is projected on the $|+\rangle$ state. But as the spins are opposite it follows that instantaneously the spin of the particle in Tokyo must have changed to the $|-\rangle$ state. That this indeed has to be the case follows from the fact that we could have written the initial state also in the form

$$|\psi_{NT}\rangle = \frac{1}{\sqrt{2}}(|-,+\rangle - |+.-\rangle)\,,$$

and Alice's projects on the first term as we discussed in the previous section, so after Alice's measurement we have $\psi_{NT} \Rightarrow |+.-\rangle$. If Bob also decides to measure along the x-axis, then he will obtain the value -1. It is clear that the probalities for measurement outcomes can be precisely calculated for all possible independent choices that Alice and Bob could make.

There is a lot at stake in this proposed experiment and in the early days was it was too hard to perform. If the calculated and observed distributions would not match, then quantum theory would be in deep trouble, not to say falsified! As we will discuss later, starting in the 1980s, such experiments became feasible, and in fact unambiguously confirmed the quantum predictions.

Quantum key distribution. The above observations allow for a quite simple protocol to securely share a digital key, called the BB84 protocol, which was invented by Gilles Brassard and Charles Bennett in 1984, opened a research field in quantum informatics called quantum cryptography. Their protocol benefits from the fundamental principles of quantum mechanics and enables secure communication between parties. Nowadays, their protocol is commercially available and forms the core of many other protocols on quantum cryptography and quantum information in general. Brassard and Bennett shared the prestigious Breakthrough Prize in Fundamental Physics 2023 with David Deutsch and Peter Shor.[1] The Shor quantum algorithm for prime factorization will be discussed in the next section on quantum computation. The protocol is illustrated in Figure II.4.4. Alice and Bob take a large sequence of measurements on (in this case) parallel polarized entangled

---

[1]The Breakthrough Prize in Fundamental Physics is one of the largest prizes in science – both qua money and prestige – and was founded in 2012 by Yuri Milnor.

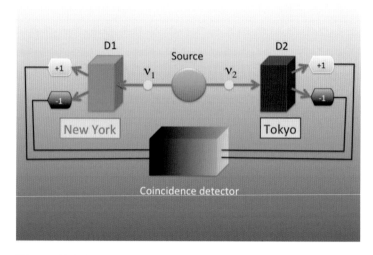

Figure II.4.2: *The Einstein–Podolsky–Rosen (EPR) paradox.* Two particles are created in a polarization entangled state, and a measurement outcome on the left particles completely determines the probabilities for the measurement outcomes on the right in any frame. The coincidence detector is there to make sure that measurements on members of the same pair are compared.

pairs and make a list of their sequence of polarizer settings and their outcomes. Afterward they may exchange the sequences of their polarization settings. If they now select the outcomes for the pairs where the setting was identical, then the outcomes must be the same, therefore this restricted sequence represents a shared digital code quantum computation as may be verified from the figure.

If one imagines an eavesdropper Eve somewhere measuring one of the photons, she cannot copy it and resend it. This means that the observed code that Alice and Bob observe will no longer coincide. So they can check whether their communication channel is secure. Clearly Eve cannot extract any key from her observations.

Is causality violated? Einstein's first worry was that this instantaneous non-local consequence of the act of mea-

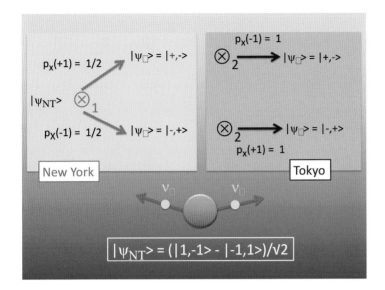

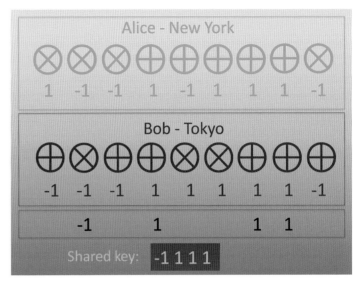

Figure II.4.3: *EPR schematic.* The measurement scheme for a particularly simple choice of measurements in the EPR experiment. The pair is created in the state $|\psi\rangle$ with opposite polarization in the z-frame. Alice in New York measures in the x-frame, so she finds outcome ± 1 with equal probability $p_x(\pm 1) = 1/2$. If Bob in Tokyo subsequently also measures in the x-frame, his outcome, according to quantum theory is completely fixed.

Figure II.4.4: *Quantum key sharing.* Using a sequence of parallel entangled photons for key distribution through the BB84 protocol. On top in green is the sequence of polarizer choices that Alice made and in the second line her measurement outcomes. In the red box we give the sequence of Bob and his outcomes. What we know for sure is that when the members of a pair are measured in the same polarization frame, the outcomes should be identical. And indeed, if we cross out the measurements where the frames are different, we are left with two identical sequences. If this happens not to be the case, Alice and Bob know that an eavesdropper is active somewhere.

surement of one of the particles of the entangled pair, would violate causality. Some information about Alice's measurement outcome appears to have been transmitted instantaneously to Tokyo, which means that it had to travel with a velocity exceeding the speed of light. And that is a no-go in Einstein's relativity!

So, the first task is to actually prove that the correlations between the measurement outcomes would necessarily require the transfer of information faster than light. If so, this would mean that such pairs could be used to transmit information faster than light, which in turn would imply the breakdown of special relativity in particular and of our cherished notion of causality in general.

The question should be: what can Bob learn from Alice making a measurement? As a matter of fact, the answer is:

nothing at all, at least as long as he doesn't know what the polarization axis is that she has chosen for her measurement, and what the outcome of her measurement was. But she can only inform him about that by conventional means using subluminal velocity media like email or Facebook. So this form of information sharing does not violate causality.

Hidden variables and local realism. The proposition of the EPR trio was that quantum theory, which clearly was in accordance with all available observations, was maybe not really wrong but at least incomplete. The paradox furthermore implied that once completed the theory would not need these 'spooky' instantaneous non-local kind of interactions. Any physically sound theory should obey the principle of *local realism*. Local realism maintains that each of the particles is always in a definite polarization state all along, but it just happens to be so that we don't know which state that is. The state is always completely determined but we don't know how it is fixed. Maintaining local realism would be possible if you say that the highly correlated nature of the outcomes could be a manifestation of ordinary statistics caused by the existence of certain *hidden variables*, which would cause such correlations. The need for that strange, non-local, instantaneous 'action at a distance' could be avoided if one knew these hidden variables and would measure them. In other words, Einstein was not arguing about the predictions of quantum theory *per se*, but the proposed probabilistic formalism would only be part of the story – a kind of effective description of nature, and not a fundamental ingredient of the resulting complete theory. His proposal would turn the fundamental indeterminacy of quantum theory merely into a lack of knowledge about the set of state variables. A fundamentally *undetermined* state would just become a fully determined, but *unknown* state.

This line of reasoning caused a rather deep controversy about the measurement problem and the interpretation of quantum theory. Because the tremendous successes of quantum theory continued to unfold, this Einstein–Bohr debate lingered on somewhat in the margins as a kind of pastime for philosophers of science, until in 1964 John Steward Bell, a British physicist working at the CERN accelerator center in Geneva, made the groundbreaking discovery that there are situations where quantum theory would directly contradict the local realist predictions. Bell turned Local Realism into a falsifiable hypothesis! The question was to set up a true EPR experiment and precisely measure the correlations between the measurement outcomes for the entangled pairs. Bell's proposal moved the question out of the realm of abstract epistemology into that of experimental physics. This deep question allowed for a definite answer. This is the subject of the next section.

The Bell inequalities

The discussion of Bell is about the EPR pairs and the measurements illustrated in Figure II.4.5. The question is indeed whether a hidden variable theory could ever account for the data as predicted by quantum theory. Is there a deterministic scheme which respects local realism that perfectly mimics the quantum theory and the measurements on entangled states? The difficulty is in some sense to produce the extremely strong instant correlations between measurement outcomes that quantum mechanics allows, even if the particles are far apart.

The correlator. John Bell devised an experimental test exactly based on these correlations. To stay in the language of the previous section, Bell proposed to consider the average of the product of measurement outcomes of Alice and Bob $P(a, b)$ where a and b are the (real) frames of Alice and Bob as depicted in Figure II.4.5(d). If we imagine that they both choose the same polarization, one finds for example that:

$$P(a, a) = -1 \text{ and } P(a, -a) = 1, \qquad \text{(II.4.2)}$$

because if they have the same frame the measurement outcomes will be opposite and the product becomes minus one. If the polarizers a and b are in the same direction but oriented oppositely, they both measure $+1$ and thus the correlator is plus one. Now it is clear that to calculate the correlator $P(a, b)$ in general for the quantum case, we just have to look at the figure, where we learn that if the angle between the frames of Alice and Bob is β and Alice measures $+1$ then Bob measures $+1$ with probability $p_b(+1) = \sin^2 \beta$. This is consistent with equation (II.4.2), because $P(a, a) = -\cos 0 = -1$ and $P(a, -a) = -\cos \pi = 1$, and similarly $p_b(-1) = \sin^2 \beta$. And if Alice measures -1 then also the probabilities $p_b(\pm 1)$ get interchanged. From these consideration one obtains the

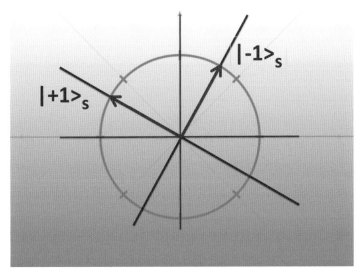

(a) The electron-positron pair is produced in some frame σ_s in the anti-symmetric entangled state $|\psi_{NT}\rangle = \frac{1}{\sqrt{2}}(|1,-1\rangle_s - |-1,1\rangle_s)$, which is represented by the double arrow.

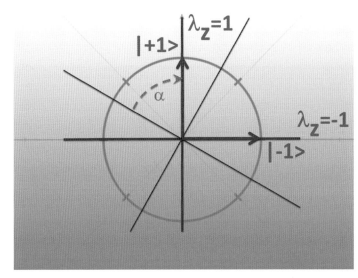

(b) The electron-positron pair state in the frame $\sigma_a = \sigma_z$ of Alice in New York. The antisymmetric form is preserved under rotations, and we just replace the subscript s with a.

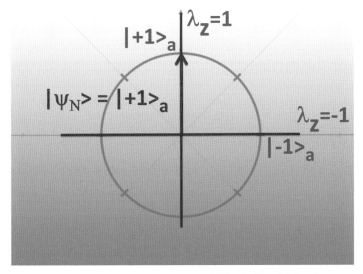

(c) The spin measurement in σ_a frame of Alice in New York. She measures the eigenvalue $\lambda_a = +1$, and projects the New York component on the $|+1\rangle$ state.

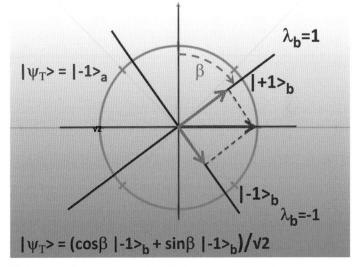

(d) After Alice's measurement the Tokyo component collapses to $|\psi_T\rangle = |-1\rangle_a$, from which the probabilities for the measurement outcomes in the σ_b of Bob follow.

Figure II.4.5: *The Einstein–Polodsky–Rosen paradox.* (a) A neutral particle decays into an entangled electron-positron pair; these travel in opposite directions to New York and Tokyo and have oppositely polarized spins in some frame. Alice and Bob make subsequently measurements in frames they may choose independently and each will measure an outcome ± 1. The sequence of subfigures explaines that the final probability for Bob is $\sin^2\beta$ to find $+1$, and $\cos^2\beta$ to find -1. These probabilities depend on Alice's choice and are instantly fixed after Alice has made her measurement.

following formula for $P(a, b)$:

$$
\begin{aligned}
P(a, b) &= \frac{1}{2}(1(\sin^2 \beta - \cos^2 \beta) - 1(\cos^2 \beta - \sin^2 \beta)) \\
&= \sin^2 \beta - \cos^2 \beta = -\cos 2\beta \,.
\end{aligned}
\tag{II.4.3}
$$

Introducing hidden variables. To describe the measurements in hidden variable theory we can introduce two functions $A(a, \lambda)$ and $B(b, \lambda)$ representing the measurement outcomes of Alice and Bob respectively, which are strictly local in the sense that they only depend on their own measurement frame, and now also on a hidden variable λ. A value for this variable is typically set at the moment when the particles are produced and that value stays fixed for both in the absence of interactions. Given λ and a choice of frame a, the outcome $A(a, \lambda)$ is fixed. The question is whether there exist such functions that reproduce the quantum results of equation (II.4.3). Here Bell brilliantly rephrased the question. Instead of just trying to directly prove or disprove the existence, he derived a condition (in fact a bound or inequality), which any hidden variable theory would have to satisfy under quite general assumptions, and subsequently showed that quantum theory allows for ample situations where this condition would be violated. Answering the question was now reduced to performing certain experiments and seeing whether the results would violate the inequality or not. If they do not, hidden variables would be a viable option, but if they do, that would be the demise of the theory of hidden variables and local realism!

The Bell inequality. Let us first agree that A and B can only equal ± 1, because they are measurement outcomes. The only thing we assume about λ is that it can take certain values with a probability $w(\lambda)$, where we have to require that $w(\lambda) \geq 0$ and $\Sigma_\lambda w(\lambda) = 1$. The classical 'local realist' correlator $P_{lr}(a, b)$ is then defined as the weighted sum:

$$
P_{lr}(a, b) = \Sigma_\lambda w(\lambda) A(a, \lambda) B(b, \lambda) \,.
\tag{II.4.4}
$$

For the case where the frames are equal we obtain the equality $A(a, \lambda) = -B(a, \lambda)$. To get the required inequality Bell introduced an arbitrary third frame c and considered the expression:

$$
\begin{aligned}
&P_{lr}(a, b) - P_{lr}(a, c) \\
&= -\Sigma_\lambda w(\lambda) [A(a, \lambda) A(b, \lambda) - A(a, \lambda) A(c, \lambda)] \\
&= -\Sigma_\lambda w(\lambda) [1 - A(b, \lambda) A(c, \lambda)] (A(a, \lambda) A(b, \lambda)) \,,
\end{aligned}
$$

where we have multiplied the second term in the first line with $A(b, \lambda)^2 = 1$ and taken out an overall factor equal to the first term. This yields the second line, where we have a factor in square brackets and one in parenthesis. The factor in square brackets is always larger or equal to zero, whereas the factor in parenthesis is either plus or minus one, and may depend on λ. The sum over λ may be over terms with alternating signs. Therefore, if we plainly set all these signs to minus one, then the right-hand side is a sum of only positive terms and the result is larger or equal than the right-hand side of the equation as it stands. And that is where the inequality comes in, we obtain a bound for the absolute value of the left-hand side:

$$
|P_{lr}(a, b) - P_{lr}(a, c)| \leq \Sigma_\lambda w(\lambda) [1 - A(b, \lambda) A(c, \lambda)] \,,
\tag{II.4.5}
$$

which yields the Bell inequality:

$$
|P_{lr}(a, b) - P_{lr}(a, c)| \leq 1 + P_{lr}(b, c) \,.
\tag{II.4.6}
$$

We see that the inequality involves three classical correlators and three frames that can be chosen independently.

Quantum violates the bound. The fundamental issue is now whether we can arrange a set of quantum measurements that yield correlators that may violate this inequality. If we succeed, those measurement outcomes could not have been obtained from a theory with hidden variables. It is not hard to find a simple example, let us return to Figure II.4.5(d) for which we already calculated that $P(a, b) = -\cos 2\beta$. Let us choose $a = Z, b = X$, and $c = (X + Z)/\sqrt{2}$ right in between a and b, then we obtain $P(a, b) = -\cos\frac{\pi}{2} = 0$ and $P(a, c) = P(b, c) = -\cos\frac{\pi}{4} = -0.71$. Substitution of these numerical values in equation (II.4.6) shows that the inequality is violated indeed: $0.71 \not\leq 0.29$!

In conclusion we may say that quantum theory is clear about what to expect, and the really big question was to 'just perform' such experiments. And that is what we turn to next.

Hidden no more

The history of EPR experiments performed since Bell published his inequalities is interesting on its own, because it was immensely hard to actually do the experiment in a way that would satisfy all critics. Indeed, as the stakes were so high all experiments were analysed with the highest conceivable level of scientific scrutiny.

There were always new loopholes that the experimenters had to try and eliminate, and probably there always will remain some far-fetched loopholes for example questioning whether the experimenters have a free will to really choose the settings randomly etc. Fortunately, over the last few decades impressive progress has been made, and experiments have so much improved that it appears that Einstein-Bohr debate is finally settled and that local realism seems no longer a tenable alternative for quantum theory.

And it is for that reason that only in 2022 the achievements were given the highest degree of recognition as the Nobel prize was awarded to three pioneers who successively developed the experimental set-ups that provided full proof evidence that the hidden variable theories implementing local realism were no longer feasible. The award went to Frenchman Alain Aspect, the American John F. Clauser

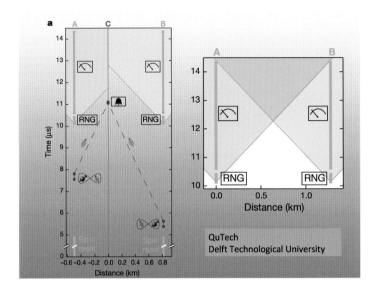

Figure II.4.6: *The Delft Experiment.* The setup of the 2015, loophole-free Bell inequality violation experiment, at Delft Technological University. The measurement stations A and B are 1.7 km apart, ensuring that the measurements are indeed spacelike separated and causally disconnected. (R. Hanson et al. *Nature*, Vol 526, 2015)

and the Austrian Anton Zeilinger, 'for experiments with entangled photons, establishing the violation of Bell inequalities and pioneering quantum information science.'

The Delft experiment. One of the more recent experiments is the 'loophole-free Bell inequality violation experiment' performed in 2015 by Ronald Hanson's group at the Delft Technological University in the Netherlands. It uses two electron spins in the maximally entangled antisymmetric state

$$|\psi\rangle = \frac{1}{\sqrt{2}}(|1, -1\rangle - |-1, 1\rangle).$$

We sketched the setup of the experiment in Figure II.4.6. It involves three stations A, B, and C. In A and B two electrons are prepared in the entangled state. First each of them emits a photon so that the photon and electron are entangled. The photons are then sent through an optical fiber to station C, where they are measured in a clever way so that that measurement can be used to verify that the electrons are indeed in the desired entangled state given above. This verification of the state to be measured is one of the loopholes that has weakened earlier attempts to corner the hidden variables option. The entangled electrons enter measurement devices in A and B, where independently a random choice between two distinct polarization directions is made for each of them. In A one chooses the observable a equal either Z or X, and in B the observable b being either $(-Z + X)/\sqrt{2}$ or $(-Z - X)/\sqrt{2}$. The stations A and B are 1.7 km apart, and therefore the choices and measurements are space-like separated, implying that there can't be any causal relation between them. This is indicated in the figure where the future light cones of the random choice events and measurement events at A and B are drawn, and one sees that they are outside each other's future light cones indeed. And this was another loophole that hampered earlier experiments. So this experiment really closes both the preparation and locality loopholes simultaneously and that leaves little room for the hidden variables scenario to survive. Again, one can calculate a bound on a weighted average S of the product of measurement outcomes x in A and y in B where,

$$S = |\sum_{ab} \langle\psi|a \otimes b|\psi\rangle|.$$

The classical bound respecting local realism can be shown to yield $S \leq 2$, whereas the quantum value can be calculated giving $S = 2\sqrt{2} \simeq 2.83$. The highly sophisticated 2015 Delft experiment of Ronald Hanson et al. measured a total of 245 trials over a period of 18 days; this yielded an average value 2.42 with a standard deviation of 0.2.

Conclusion. We conclude that spooky action at a distance is just there and we have to live with it. Quantum weirdness is not fake; it is rock solid! It turns out to be a blessing in disguise, because it implies the spectacular possibility of quantum teleportation, to which we will turn after we have described a second experiment that also refutes the idea of local realism.

A decisive three photon experiment

There is one more experiment on entangled states that I like to describe in some more detail. It is a wonderfully conceived and designed experiment, which in a sense is so clean and therefore easy to understand, that I think it really gave a final blow to the idea of local realism and hidden variables. It is called the Greenberger–Horne–Zeilinger or GHZ experiment[2] and involves *three* (in fact even four) photons in a maximally entangled state. At first makes it may look dauntingly complicated, but the prediction is so radically unambiguous, and the reasoning so straightforward that it really is a litmus test on the matter of local realism. The answer is a clean yes or no, and does not involve a bound that has to be violated. In this experiment the outcomes predicted by the quantum hypothesis on the one hand and local realism on the other are mutually exclusive and that makes this experiment so powerful and attractive. It brings the inner workings of quantum theory to the surface. The results unambiguously prove the existence of entanglement and therefore of quantum nonlocality.

To give you an idea of the experimental setup, we have reproduced the schematic in Figure II.4.7. From a photon source maximally entangled pairs are generated, each member goes through a beamsplitter and we end up with basically four entangled photons. One of the photons is used as a trigger, and if the four detectors fire simultaneously, one knows that the three entering in the three main detectors are in a maximally entangled GHZ-state. These three photons can be analyzed in detectors *det 1, det 2* and *det 3*. The detectors are space-like separated, meaning that the measurements cannot influence each other in a causal way, and they are designed such that you can

---

[2] The setup of the experiment was introduced in a paper in 1989 by Greenberger, Horne, and Zeilinger and the experiments were carried out by a European collaboration of Pan, Bouwmeester, Danielli, Weinfurter and Zeilinger in 2000 (Nature, Vol 403, 2000).

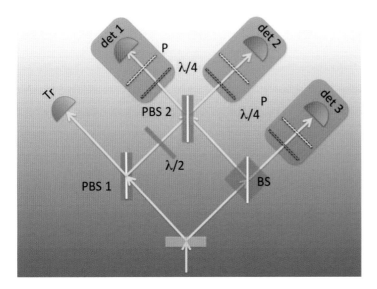

Figure II.4.7: *The GHZ experiment.* This exploits three entangled particles to unambiguously demonstrate that quantum theory violates local realism, thereby closing the door on the famous Bohr–Einstein debate. (Source: Nature, Vol 403, 2000)

switch between three different polarization bases, in particular the X-basis with eigenstates $|\pm\rangle$ and the Y-basis with eigenstates $|L/R\rangle$, and the Z-basis with eigenstates $|\pm 1\rangle$, the measurement outcomes can be either $+1$ or -1. If the detectors just are in the Z-basis, you can see how the entangled state is actually prepared by the array of beam splitters and the $\lambda/2$ wave plate. The criteria for data selection is (i) that the trigger (detector) selects the events with $\lambda_z = -1$ and (ii) that indeed all four detectors pick up a simultaneous signal. These criteria can only be met in two distinct cases which we have depicted in the two figures II.4.8.[3]

Let us now analyze the quantum predictions for the experiment which starts with the three-photon GHZ state:

$$|\psi\rangle = \frac{1}{\sqrt{2}}(|+1,+1,+1\rangle + |-1,-1,-1\rangle). \qquad \text{(II.4.7)}$$

[3]To be precise detector *det 3* is turned 60 degrees to invert the readout $(= 1 \leftrightarrow -1)$.

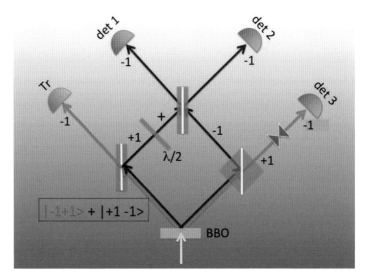

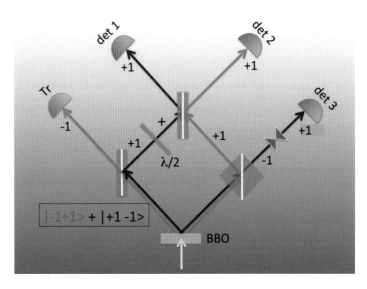

Figure II.4.8: *Contributions to GHZ.* The diagrams show the only two possible contributions to the three (or four) photon entangled state with trigger on -1, to a *ZZZ* measurement. (Source: Nature, Vol 403, 2000)

We can now express this state in various different bases, and GHZ proposed to study a sequence of four measurements with the detectors *det 1*, *det 2* and *det 3* in the following order first the cyclic variations *YYX, YXY, XYY* and finally an *XXX* measurement. Knowing the result of the first three measurements both the quantum-adepts and the local realist followers can take that data, turn their respective cranks and come out with a unique prediction for the possible outcomes of the fourth experiment and their probabilities. The beauty of this experiment is that opposing schools of thought come out with mutually exclusive predictions! So it is a real 'yes or no' for quantum versus local realism.

So let us see how the quantum analysis goes, and it is basically what we have been doing before only a little more of it. To determine the various possible measurement outcomes and the probabilities we have to rewrite the GHZ-state in the other bases, and because we know the linear combinations this is a matter of making the appropriate substitutions in the expression (II.4.7).

$$|+1\rangle = \frac{1}{\sqrt{2}}(|+\rangle + |-\rangle),$$

$$|-1\rangle = \frac{1}{\sqrt{2}}(|+\rangle - |-\rangle),$$

$$|+1\rangle = \frac{1}{\sqrt{2}}(|L\rangle + |R\rangle),$$

$$|-1\rangle = \frac{i}{\sqrt{2}}(|L\rangle - |R\rangle).$$

So for example in the YYX experiment we would encounter the state:

$$|\psi\rangle = \frac{1}{2}(|R, L.+\rangle + |L, R, +\rangle + |L, L, -\rangle + |R, R, -\rangle). \quad (II.4.8)$$

let us make some observations on this state. The probability of finding a $+1$ or -1 result for any of the three photons is 50% meaning that it is maximally random: it is like throwing with a fair coin. Next note that the outcomes of each possible pair out of the three photons also has equal probabilities: so say for the first two detectors one has the that the possible outcomes $(+1,+1), (+1,-1), (-1,+1)$, and $(-1,-1)$, each occur with 25% probability. Finally it is also clear that given the outcome of two of the measurements the third is completely fixed. If the first two give LR

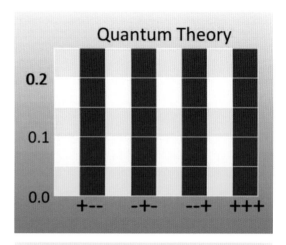

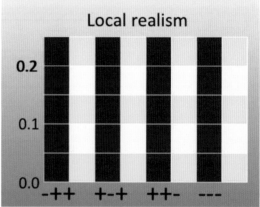

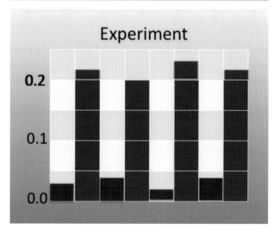

Figure II.4.9: *The decisive result.* The predictions of quantum theory (top) and local realism (middle) for the outcome of the XXX experiment are mutually exclusive. The experiment (bottom) strongly favors quantum theory. (Source: Nature, Vol 403, 2000)

or $(-1, +1)$, the third detector would have a $+$, meaning an outcome -1 for the product of the outcomes of *det 1, det 2* and *det 3*. It is clear that exactly half of the possible $2^3 = 8$ possible outcomes will occur in this experiment, and this selection is an expression of the correlations that quantum theory produces. And of course the same holds for the other three experiments in the sequence of four. Indeed for the fourth XXX experiment, we should express the state in the XXX-basis, which yields:

$$|\psi\rangle = \frac{1}{2}(|+,+,+\rangle + |+,-,-\rangle + |-,+,-\rangle + |-,-,+\rangle).$$
(II.4.9)

The thing to note here is that the product of the measurement outcomes of the three detectors will always be $+1$, whatever the component of equation (II.4.9) is that happens to occur.

Let us now do the analysis following the local realism line of reasoning. The idea is that the setup is such that there is no causal relation between them. This means that each of the photons should carry an element of reality for both the X and Y measurements, telling us what the outcome of such a measurement would be. Let us call these elements which are just numbers, x_i and y_i where $i = 1, 2, 3$ labels the detector, where these can only equal ± 1. If we now look at the possible outcome of the XYY measurement and its permutations, each of the photons can carry only one particular x_i and y_i, which should fit all three possibilities in (II.4.8). This leads for the first three measurements to the three equations:

$$y_1 y_2 x_3 = -1 \; ; \; y_1 x_2 y_3 = -1 \; ; \; x_1 y_2 y_3 = -1. \quad (II.4.10)$$

The neat thing is that the solution of these three equations completely fixes the product $x_1 x_2 x_3$, which then of course is the local realism prediction for the outcome of the fourth (XXX) measurement. If we take the product of the three equations (II.4.10), we get that:

$$(y_1 y_2 x_3)(y_1 x_2 y_3)(x_1 y_2 y_3) = (x_1 x_2 x_3)y_1^2 y_2^2 y_3^2 = -1.$$

With the squares of the y_i being $+1$, we get the prediction $x_1 x_2 x_3 = -1$. This answer is exactly opposite to the quantum prediction following from equation (II.4.9), which as we already mentioned, gives for the product $x_1 x_2 x_3 = +1$! If we go back to the 8 possible measurement outcomes for the XXX experiment, this would lead to what is depicted in Figure II.4.9, for the predictions, and the actual measurement outcome of the experiment showing extremely strong support for quantum theory.

Quantum teleportation

Quantum teleportation provides a method for privately sending messages in a way that ensures that the receiver will know if anyone eavesdrops. This is possible because a quantum state is literally teleported, in the sense of 'beam me up Scotty': A quantum state is destroyed in one place and recreated in another. Because of the no-cloning theorem that we discussed on page 64 of Chapter II.2, it is impossible to make more than one copy of this quantum state, and as a result when the new teleported state appears, the original state must be destroyed. Furthermore, it is impossible for both the intended receiver and an eavesdropper to have the state at the same time, which helps make the communication secure.

Quantum teleportation takes advantage of the correlation between entangled states as discussed in the previous sections. Suppose Alice wants to send a secure message to Charlie at a (possibly distant) location. The process of teleportation depends on Alice and Charlie sharing different qubits of an entangled state. Alice makes a measurement of her part of the entangled state, which is coupled to the state she wants to teleport to Charlie, and sends him some classical information about the entangled state. With the classical information plus his half of the entangled state, Charlie can reconstruct the teleported state. We have indicated the process in Figure II.4.10. We fol-

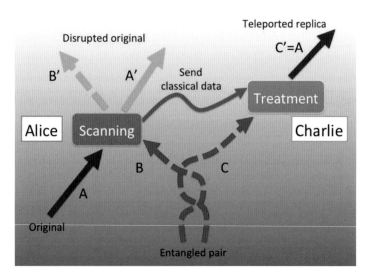

Figure II.4.10: *Quantum teleportation.* Teleportation of a quantum state using an entangled pair, as proposed by Bennett et al. in 1997. An explanation is given in the text.

low the method proposed by Bennett et al. in 1993, and first realized in an experimental setup by Zeilinger's group in 1997. In realistic cases the needed qubit states are typically implemented as left- and right-handed polarized light quanta (i.e. photons).

The simplest example of quantum teleportation can be implemented with three qubits. The (A) qubit is the unknown state to be teleported,

$$|\psi_A\rangle = \alpha|1\rangle + \beta|-1\rangle. \qquad (II.4.11)$$

This state is literally teleported from one place to another. If Charlie likes, once he has the teleported state he can make a quantum measurement and extract the same information about α and β that he would have been able to extract had he made the measurement on the original state.

The teleportation of this state is enabled by an auxiliary two-qubit entangled state. We label these two qubits B and C. For technical reasons it is convenient to represent

this in a special basis consisting of four states, called Bell states, which are written as:

$$|\Psi_{BC}^{(\pm)}\rangle = \sqrt{\frac{1}{2}}(|1_B\rangle|-1_C\rangle \pm |-1_B\rangle|1_C\rangle),$$

$$|\Phi_{BC}^{(\pm)}\rangle = \sqrt{\frac{1}{2}}(|1_B\rangle|1_C\rangle \pm |-1_B\rangle|-1_C\rangle).$$

$$(II.4.12)$$

The process of teleportation can be outlined as follows (please refer to Figure II.4.10).

1. Someone prepares an entangled two-qubit state BC (the *Entangled pair* in the diagram).

2. Qubit B is sent to Alice and qubit C is sent to Charlie.

3. In the *Scanning* step, Alice measures in the Bell states' basis the combined wavefunction of qubits A (the *original* in the diagram) and the entangled state B, leaving behind the *Disrupted original*.

4. Alice sends two bits of classical data to Charlie telling him the outcome of her measurements (*Send classical data*).

5. Based on the classical information received from Alice, Charlie applies one of four possible operators to qubit C (*Apply treatment*), and thereby reconstructs A, getting a *teleported replica of the original*. If he likes, he can now make a measurement on A to recover the message Alice has sent him.

We now explain this process in more detail. In step (1) an entangled two-qubit state ψ_{BC} such as that of equation (II.4.12) is prepared. In step (2) qubit B is transmitted to Alice and qubit C is transmitted to Charlie. This can be done, for example, by sending two entangled photons, one to each of them. In step (3) Alice measures the joint state of qubit A and B in the Bell states' basis, getting two classical bits of information, and projecting the joint wavefunction ψ_{AB} onto one of the Bell states. The basis of Bell states has the nice property that the four possible outcomes of the measurement have equal probability. To see how this works, for convenience suppose the entangled state BC was prepared in state $|\Psi_{BC}^{(-)}\rangle$. In this case the combined wavefunction of the three-qubit state is

$$|\psi_{ABC}\rangle = |\psi_A\rangle|\Psi_{BC}^{(-)}\rangle =$$
$$\frac{\alpha}{\sqrt{2}}\big(|1_A\rangle|1_B\rangle|-1_C\rangle - |1_A\rangle|-1_B\rangle|1_C\rangle\big)+$$
$$\frac{\beta}{\sqrt{2}}\big(|-1_A\rangle|1_B\rangle|-1_C\rangle - |-1_A\rangle|-1_B\rangle|1_C\rangle\big). \quad \text{(II.4.13)}$$

If this is expanded in the Bell states' basis for the pair AB, it can be written in the form:

$$|\psi_{ABC}\rangle =$$
$$\frac{1}{2}\Big[|\Psi_{AB}^{(-)}\rangle(-\alpha|1_C\rangle - \beta|-1_C\rangle)$$
$$+ |\Psi_{AB}^{(+)}\rangle(-\alpha|1_C\rangle + \beta|-1_C\rangle)$$
$$|\Phi_{AB}^{(-)}\rangle(\beta|1_C\rangle + \alpha|-1_C\rangle)$$
$$+ |\Phi_{AB}^{(+)}\rangle(-\beta|1_C\rangle + \alpha|-1_C\rangle)\Big].$$

$$\text{(II.4.14)}$$

We see that the qubit pair AB has equal probability to be in the four possible states $|\Psi_{AB}^{(-)}\rangle$, $|\Psi_{AB}^{(+)}\rangle$, $|\Phi_{AB}^{(-)}\rangle$ and $|\Phi_{AB}^{(+)}\rangle$.

In step (4), Alice transmits two classical bits to Charlie, telling him which of the four basis functions she observed. Charlie now makes use of the fact that in the Bell basis there are four possible states for the entangled qubit that he has, and his qubit C was entangled with Alice's qubit B before she made the measurement. In particular, let $|\phi_C\rangle$ be the state of the C qubit, which from equation II.4.14) is one of the four states:

$$|\phi_C\rangle = \begin{pmatrix} -\alpha \\ -\beta \end{pmatrix}; \begin{pmatrix} -\alpha \\ \beta \end{pmatrix}; \begin{pmatrix} \beta \\ \alpha \end{pmatrix}; \text{ and } \begin{pmatrix} -\beta \\ \alpha \end{pmatrix}.$$

In step (5), based on the information that he receives from Alice, Charlie selects one of four possible operators F_i and

uses it to measure the C qubit. There is one operator F_i for each of the four possible Bell states, which are respectively:

$$F = -\begin{pmatrix} 1 & 0 \\ 0 & 1 \end{pmatrix}; \begin{pmatrix} -1 & 0 \\ 0 & 1 \end{pmatrix}; \begin{pmatrix} 0 & 1 \\ 1 & 0 \end{pmatrix}; \text{ and } \begin{pmatrix} 0 & 1 \\ -1 & 0 \end{pmatrix}.$$
$$\text{(II.4.15)}$$

Provided Charlie has the correct classical information and an intact entangled state he can reconstruct the original A qubit by measuring $|\phi_C\rangle$ with the appropriate operator F_i.

$$|\psi_A\rangle = \alpha|1\rangle + \beta|-1\rangle = F_i|\phi_C\rangle. \quad \text{(II.4.16)}$$

By simply multiplying each of the four possibilities it is easy to verify that as long as his information is correct, he will correctly reconstruct the A qubit $\alpha|1_A\rangle + \beta|-1_A\rangle$.

We stress that Charlie needs the classical measurement information from Alice. If he could do without it the teleportation process would violate causality, since information could be transferred instantaneously from Alice to Charlie. That is, when Alice measures the B qubit, naively it might seem that because the B and C qubits are entangled, this instantaneously collapses the C qubit, sending Charlie the information about Alice's measurement, no matter how far away he is. To understand why such instantaneous communication is not possible, suppose Charlie just randomly guesses the outcome and randomly selects one of the four operators F_i. Then the original state will be reconstructed as a random mixture of the four possible incoming states $|\phi_C\rangle$. This mixture does not give any information about the original state $|\psi_A\rangle$. The same reasoning also applies to a possible eavesdropper, conveniently named Eve. If she manages to intercept qubit (C) and wants 'to measure it' before Charlie does, without the two bits of classical information, she will not be able to recover the original state. Furthermore she would affect that state. If Charlie somehow gets the mutilated state, he will not be able to reconstruct the original state A. Security can be achieved if Alice first sends a sequence of known states which can be checked by Charlie after reconstruction.

Superposition The strange thing about a qubit in comparison with its digital precursor is the fact that it can be in a state that is a 'superposition' of the '1' and the '0' state. This is possible because of the all-important *linear superposition principle* which is a basic ingredient of quantum theory. As a consequence of quantum information processing, the manipulation of qubits, i.e. changing their states by having them interact, is like doing parallel processing on a large scale. The exceptional power of the quantum computers of the future is a reflection of the ability to directly work with these linear superpositions. Here is an analogy that may help you understand why this is so. Imagine you would like to make a street map of a city to find the shortest route from point P on one side of town to point Q on the opposite side. As a single being you go and walk in the right direction, and to find the shortest route you should walk in principle all the possible routes that bring you from P to Q and compare their lengths. Parallel processing would mean that you hire a bunch of students to independently and simultaneously take different paths from P to Q. This certainly will save time. But now imagine that some *Dr Ghetto Blaster* comes along with a device which produces lots of sound at point P and his business partner *Dr Ghetto Digest* sits down at point Q with an impressive highly sophisticated listening device. He turns the machine on and in no time has reconstructed the street map. Imagine! The remarkable thing is that this is in principle possible because sound as an agent always takes all possible paths through town simultaneously, and interferes with itself on every corner, and all that information is encoded in the changes of the signal that we would receive in Q. It probes the street plan not sequentially but in parallel. A fashionable

version of this story is to say that you can hear the shape of a remote drum if somebody is playing it, or that you can hear the shape of a tin roof by listening to the rain pouring on it. This is so because there are many ticks and every tick in a sense 'contains' all frequencies and therefore these examples are classical analogues and show the potential power of the linear superposition principle. □

If the original and reconstructed sequence are perfectly correlated, then that guarantees that Eve is not interfering. Note that the no-cloning theorem is satisfied, since when Alice makes her measurement she alters the state ψ_A as well as her qubit B. Once she has done that, the only hope to reconstruct the original ψ_A is for her to send her measurement to Charlie, who can apply the appropriate operator to his entangled qubit C.

The quantum security mechanism of teleportation is based on strongly correlated, highly non-local entangled states. While a strength, the non-locality of the correlations is also a weakness. Quantum correlations are extremely fragile and can be corrupted by random interactions with the environment, i.e. by decoherence. As we discussed before, this is a process in which the quantum correlations are destroyed and information gets lost. The problem of decoherence is the main stumbling block in making progress towards large-scale development and application of quantum technologies. Nevertheless, the research group of Gisin et al. at the University of Geneva demonstrated teleportation over a distance of 550 meters using the optical fiber network of *Swisscom* in 2006.

A n important next step would be the construction of a network of quantum devices with links along which entangled states can be created and quantum information teleported securely. In 2022 the first successful steps were reported by the *QuTech* group of Hanson in Delft.

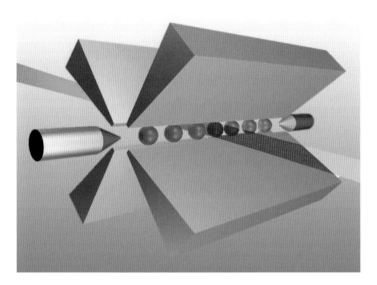

Figure II.4.11: *Trapped ions.* Ions trapped in a linear optical lattice. *(IQO Insbruck)*

Quantum computation

Quantum computation is performed by setting up controlled interactions that cause non-trivial dynamics and successively couple individual qubits together and generate a time evolution of the quantum state in a predetermined manner. And moreover ensuring that no other interactions take place that could corrupt the computation. A multi-qubit system is first prepared in a known initial state, representing the input to the program. Then interactions are switched on by applying forces, such as magnetic fields, that determine the direction in which the wavefunction rotates in its state space. Thus a quantum program is just a sequence of unitary operations that are externally applied to the initial state. This is achieved in practice by a corresponding sequence of quantum gates. When the computation is done measurements are made to read out the final state. Measurements are non-unitary operations that can also be part of the process.

Quantum computation is essentially a form of analog com-

putation. A physical system is used to simulate a mathematical problem, taking advantage of the fact that they both obey the same equations. The mathematical problem is mapped onto the physical system by finding an appropriate arrangement of magnets or other fields that will generate the proper equation of motion. One then prepares the initial state, lets the system evolve, and reads out the answer. Analog computers are nothing new. For example, Leibnitz built a mechanical calculator for performing multiplication in 1694, and in the middle of the twentieth century, because of their vastly superior speed in comparison with digital computers, electronic analog computers were often used to solve differential equations.

Then why is quantum computation special? The key to its exceptional power is the massive parallelism at intermediate stages of the computation. Any operation on a given state works simultaneously on all basis vectors and thus also on entangled states. The physical process that defines the quantum computation for an n qubit system thus acts in parallel on a set of 2^n complex numbers, and the phases of these numbers (which would not exist in a classical computation) are important for determining the time evolution of the state. When the measurement is made to read out the answer at the end of the computation we are left with the n-bit output and the phase information is lost.

Because quantum measurements are generically probabilistic, it is possible for the 'same' computation to yield different 'answers', e.g. because the measurement process projects the system onto different eigenstates. This can require the need for error correction mechanisms, though for some problems, such as factoring large numbers, it is possible to test for correctness by simply checking the answer to be sure it works. It is also possible for quantum computers to make mistakes due to decoherence, i.e. because of essentially random interactions between the quantum state used to perform the computation and the environment. This also necessitates error correction mechanisms.

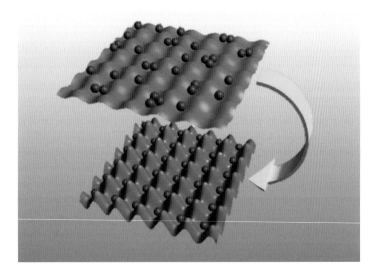

Figure II.4.12: *Optical lattice.* Atoms can be manipulated in a linear optical lattice. *(IQO Innsbruck)*

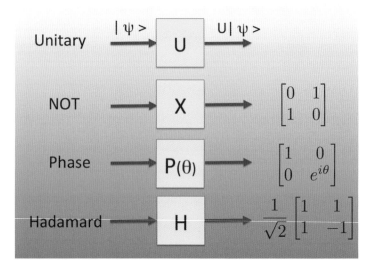

Figure II.4.13: *Gates.* Some standard one-bit quantum gates.

The problems caused by decoherence are perhaps *the* central difficulty in creating realistic physical implementations of quantum computation. These can potentially be overcome by constructing quantum systems where states are not encoded locally, but rather globally, in terms of topological properties of the system that cannot be disrupted by external (local) noise. This is called *topological quantum computing*. This interesting possibility arises in certain two-dimensional physical media which exhibit *topological order*, referring to states of matter in which the essential quantum degrees of freedom and their interactions are topological (see also Chapter III.3).

Quantum gates and circuits

In the same way that classical gates are the building blocks of classical computers, quantum gates are the basic building blocks of quantum computers. A gate used for a classical computation implements binary operations on binary inputs, changing zeros into ones and vice versa. For ex-

ample, the only non-trivial single bit logic operation is NOT, which takes 0 to 1 and 1 to 0. In a quantum computation the situation is quite different, because the states of qubits live in a two-dimensional Hilbert space and they represent complex superpositions of 0 and 1. This was discussed in considerable detail in Chapter II.1.

Single qubit gates. The set of allowable single qubit operations consists of unitary transformations corresponding to 2×2 complex matrices U such that $\mathrm{U}^{\dagger}\mathrm{U} = 1$. The corresponding action on a single qubit is represented in a circuit as illustrated in Figure II.4.13.

Some quantum gates have classical analogues, but many do not. As we mentioned, the X operator is the quantum equivalent of the classical NOT gate, and serves the function of interchanging spin up and spin down. In contrast, the Z operator rotates the relative phase of the two-component wavefunction by 180 degrees and has no classical equivalent.

Let us briefly discuss the typical one-qubit logical gates of

Figure II.4.13. First the NOT gate,

$$X = \begin{pmatrix} 0 & 1 \\ 1 & 0 \end{pmatrix},$$

as we mentioned this is the quantum equivalent of the classical NOT gate and acts by interchanging $|1\rangle$ and $|-1\rangle$. The next one is

$$P(\theta) = \begin{pmatrix} 1 & 0 \\ 0 & e^{i\theta} \end{pmatrix}.$$

The $P(\theta)$ operation is called the phase gate, since it changes the relative phase by θ degrees.

The third gate is the so-called Hadamard gate H,

$$H = \sqrt{\frac{1}{2}} \begin{pmatrix} 1 & 1 \\ 1 & -1 \end{pmatrix},$$

which creates a superposition of the basis states: $|\pm 1\rangle \Rightarrow |\pm\rangle$. In other words it flips between the Z- and the X-frames.

The general purpose of a quantum computer is to transform an arbitrary n-qubit input into an n-qubit output corresponding to the result of the computation. In principle implementing such a computation might be extremely complicated, and might require constructing quantum gates of arbitrary order and complexity.

Universal gate sets. Fortunately, it has been shown that the transformations needed to implement a universal quantum computer can be generated by a simple – so-called universal – set of elementary quantum gates, for example involving a well-chosen set of one- and two-qubit gates. Single qubit gates are unitary matrices with three real degrees of freedom. If we allow ourselves to work with finite precision, the set of all gates can be arbitrary well approximated by a small, well-chosen set. There are many possibilities – the optimal choice depends on the physical implementation of the qubits.

From the perspective of experimental implementation, a convenient two-qubit gate to use is the CNOT gate we have discussed before, see Figure II.1.17. The combination of the CNOT, the $P(\pi/4)$ and the Hadamard gate forms for example a universal set.

Shor's algorithm

Prime factoring. An algorithm is not an equation; it is more like an operational set of steps – a procedure – that is *guaranteed* to lead to a desired result. So it usually does involve equations and a mathematical proof. For the Shor algorithm the problem is to factor a large number, say of about 800 or 1000 digits, into its prime factors, in most cases there are just two of them. So we have a number N that can being written in a unique way as a product of two prime numbers a and b. One way to do this is just by trial and error. In fact by checking one after the other whether $2, 3, 5, \dots$ is a divisor of the number N. And this you may do by a simple subtraction scheme à la Euler, where you keep subtracting the candidate divisor and look whether you indeed hit zero. As we have argued in Chapter I.3, such schemes end up being extravagantly costly in the time it takes to actually factor a really big number. That time is significantly longer than the age of the universe and that should not surprise you. The one thing it makes at least clear is that patience will not suffice. The time dependence on N if one uses conventional digital computers is typically exponential. The showcase example of why quantum computers are indeed fundamentally different, and for a task like this one far superior, is the *Shor factorization algorithm* which is a quantessential algorithm, because it exploits non-commutativity of operators in a clever way.

The MIT applied mathematics professor Peter Shor proposed the algorithm in 1994 and was co-recipient of the 2023 Breakthrough Prize in Fundamental Physics.

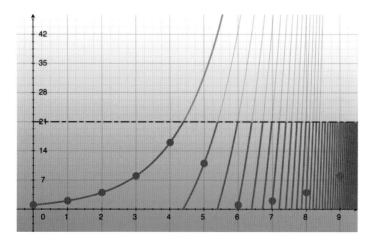

Figure II.4.14: *The periodic function.* We have displayed $f(x) = c^x \mod N$ (red curve). The blue points represent the (discrete) periodic function over the integers. We have chosen $c = 2$ and $N = 21$. The period equals 6.

The algorithm. The algorithm for factorization consists of three steps.
(i) construct a particular periodic function modulo N,
(ii) determine the period of that function,
(iii) given (i) and (ii) one can use an Euler method for finding largest common divisors to find the factors a and b such that $ab = N$.

(i) Construction of the periodic function. Choose an integer c and consider the function[4]

$$f(m) = c^m \mod N, \ m \ \text{integer}. \qquad (\text{II.4.17})$$

(ii) One can show that this function is periodic with a period we call r, so,

$$f(m + r) = f(m). \qquad (\text{II.4.18})$$

After substitution of f on both sides, it then follows that

$$c^r = 1 \mod N \ \rightarrow \ c^r - 1 = sN,$$

---
[4]The number $m = M \mod N$ is obtained by subtracting N from M until a number between 0 and N is obtained, which is the number m. In other words $M = m + kN$ for some k with $0 \leq m < N$.

where s is some integer. Now rewrite the left-hand side as:

$$(c^{r/2} + 1)(c^{r/2} - 1) = sN,$$

where we need r to be even for the factors to be integers. If r happens to be odd, one has to restart by choosing a different value for c and start all over.
(iii) The next step is to find the greatest common divisor of the individual factors on the left with N, after which one obtains the prime factors a and b of N. This last step can be done with an Euler subtraction scheme.

The hard part of this solution method is to find the period r of the function $f(m)$ because this r may be of order N itself. Determination can be done using a fast or integer Fourier transform of $f(m)$.

As we discussed wavefunctions, and non-commuting operators as hallmarks of quantum theory it is maybe nice to paraphrase this hard side of the problem and to see that quantum measurement is the clue. Firstly think of the function $f(m)$ as a wavefunction on a one-dimensional lattice corresponding to the natural numbers $0, 1, 2, 3, \ldots$. Now we also have discussed a momentum operator P which translates the position variable by one unit. And acting on the function it acts like $P \ f(m) = f(m + 1)$. Because of the periodicity of $f(m)$ we also have the relation $P^r f(m) = f(m + r) = f(m)$ from which we conclude that $P^r = 1$. From which it follows that the eigenvalues of the P operator are $p = e^{2\pi i s/r}$ with $s = 0, 1, \ldots, r$. In other words doing a measurement of the momentum of the state described by the wavefunction $f(m)$ tells us basically what r is![5] What we end up with is a periodic function with a support of r points on a circle and dual to that the momentum sample space also consisting of r points. This is of course due to the periodicity of the function. I recall the statement about the relation between the sample spaces of position versus momentum operators. A line is dual to a line. If the

---
[5]One may need more than one measurement, but one can check that rather easily.

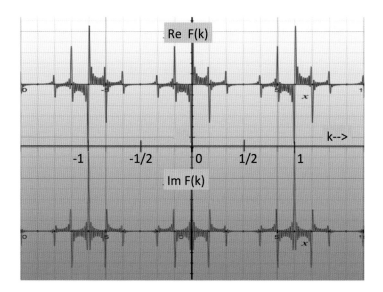

Figure II.4.15: *The Fourier transformed function* $F(k)$. We have displayed $\mathrm{Re}\ F(k)$ (blue curve) and $\mathrm{Im}\ F(k)$ (red curve). The peaks at multiples of $1/6$ stand out clearly, even in this crude 'iPhone' approximation causing some noise. This means that the periodicity of the original function $f(m)$ (the blue dots in the previous figure) would be 6.

x-space is infinite discrete then the sample space of the dual momentum is a angle or a circle, by bringing in the periodicity only a set of r points on the circle is left corresponding to the corners of a polygon. And in that case the P and X sample spaces are again the same. There are basically two identical polygons and there is a unitary transformation between the frames that correspond to the sets of eigenvectors corresponding to the eigenvalues. Stated differently the problem of factoring is to a large extent finding the right polygon hidden in the circle and indeed there are many (a countable infinity) to choose from.

The fast Fourier transform of a function $F(n)$ is defined as:

$$F(k) = \sum_m f(m)e^{2\pi i k m}, \qquad (\text{II}.4.19)$$

which combined with the fact that $f(n)$ has a period r leads to a powerful conclusion on the function $F(k)$. For the func-

tion (II.4.17) it leads to the strong condition:

$$e^{2\pi i k r} = 1 \ \rightarrow \ k = s/r\,; \ s = 1,\dots,r\,.$$

What this means is that we ask for the transformation of a (wave) function $f(x)$ on a one-dimensional infinite lattice, from the position state basis to a momentum state basis. We know that the momentum values for an infinite discrete space correspond to an angle $0 \le \theta \le 2\pi$ where in our case $\theta = 2\pi k = 2\pi s/r$. So what we learn is that the function f involves only r different momentum states. The fast Fourier transform just measures the momentum and determines the component of that momentum eigenstate. The magnitude of that component is not so relevant as what the actual allowed momenta are. So the momentum state is almost everywhere zero except in points that correspond to the corners of a polygon with r sides where they have the value $F(k)$.

Wouldn't it be fun to find an example where we would be left with a pentagon, what do I say, THE pentagon, in momentum space? Maybe that explains the Pentagon's interest in quantum computing and maybe they knew all along that the pentagon would play an important role somewhere....

So the data we need from the fast Fourier transform just corresponds to one or more measurements of the momentum in the state f. That will give us a value(s) $p = 2\pi s/r$ from which r can be determined. So it is now clear that quantum measurements implement an extremely efficient algorithm for fast Fourier transform on integer-valued functions. You just have to measure the non-commuting observable dual to the variable of the function, and that is the momentum. And that is the quantessence of super fast factorization.

Let us work out a simple example, and let us try to factor the number $N = 21$ with the algorithm. We first construct the function $f(x) = 2^x \bmod N$, it takes the values given in Table II.4.1. We see that the function has a period $r = 6$,

Table II.4.1: Tabulation of the function $f(x) = 2^x \bmod 21$.

x	0	1	2	3	4	5	6	7	8	9	10
f(x)	1	2	4	8	16	11	1	2	4	8	16

so we obtain the equation:

$$(2^3 + 1)(2^3 - 1) = 9 \times 7 = 21 \times s.$$

Now determine the largest common divisor from the factors on the left with 21:
$21 \bmod 7 = 0 \to 7$ is a factor of 21, and $21 \bmod 9 = 3 \to 3$ is a factor of 21. Thus we established the magical result that $21 = 3 \times 7$, One could say that we at least succeeded in cracking a nut by using a magnificient sledgehammer.

But to factor a 1000 digit number into two primes you will need this sledgehammer in the form of a sizable quantum computer to find the period, which after all might well be of the order of N itself!

Applications and perspectives

Quantum computation and security are challenging examples of the surprising interplay between the basic concepts of physics and information theory. If physicists and engineers succeed in mastering quantum technologies to allow for reliable and scalable qubits, it will mark an important turning point in information science with profound societal consequences. We had better get ready for an era of quantum supremacy!

Hardware developments. As we mentioned alrerady, at present there is a lot of work in progress trying to implement quantum computing in a wide variety of ways. I will refrain from going into any detail here firstly because that calls for many different types of expertise, and furthermore the developments go so fast and still make so many unexpected turns that I would run the risk that this book would already be out-of-date before it was published. It is absolutely clear however that basically all big tech companies are actively pursuing the quantum opportunities that suits them. In principle all that is needed to make a qubit is a simple two-level quantum system that can easily be manipulated and scaled up to a large number of qubits. The first requirement is not so restrictive, and many different physical implementations of systems with a single or a few qubits have been realized, including NMR, spin lattices, linear optics with single photons, quantum dots, Josephson junction networks, ion traps and atoms and polar molecules in optical lattices.

The much harder problem that has so far limited progress toward practical computation is to couple the individual qubits in a controllable way and to achieve a sufficiently low level of decoherence. Even small local perturbations due to the environment could destroy the delicate phase information in the linear superposition of states. With respect to this problem, a promising venue has surfaced with the advent of *Topological Quantum Computing* where quantum information is stored in topological degrees of freedom that are insensitive to local perturbations and interactions, making error correction procedures simpler to implement. This way of computing involves new states of matter, that exhibit what is called topological order. In Chapter III.3 we'll say more about this. On the software side impressive progress has been made, building on the fundamental quantum algorithms we have mentioned. There is of course also the possibility of developing hybrid classical/quantum devices. Nevertheless, with the great efforts now taking place, future developments could be surprisingly fast.

The challenge of quantum software. We are in a situation that looks like the early seventies where many institutions in what still was Silicon Valley to be started focussing on developing software for digital devices like PC's and laptops, that weren't really there yet. This major effort was to a large extent based on the strongly held belief that a digital era was on its way where every individual would own powerful devices, to play and work with. High level languages had to be developed to allow everybody to optimally process data, whether it concerned text, pictures, symbolic manipulation or music. It turned into an unprecedented show-case of public and private research and development efforts, which resulted in the present information era which in many ways has profoundly changed the human condition.

We are now in a comparable situation with respect to quantum computing. And again, even though the hardware is still quite remote, a strong case for quantum software should be made. If we were to have quantum computers at our disposal, the question of what miracles could they possibly perform strongly depends on the software that is available. We said in the introduction to this section that there are many problems where the intrinsic massive parallelism of quantum evolution might yield dramatic speedups in computation. The point is not that a classical computer would not be able to do the same computation – after all, one can always simulate a quantum computer on a classical one – but rather the time that is needed could drastically be reduced.

As we just discussed in some detail, a most spectacular speedup is achieved by the Shor algorithm (1994) for factoring large numbers into their prime factors. Because many security keys are based on the inability for digital computers to do this, the reduction from an exponentially hard to a polynomially hard problem has many practical applications for breaking security codes and current cryptography. This means that even today, one has already to worry about how one should save sensitive information, to make sure that it cannot be easily retrieved in the near quantum future. Quantum algorithms also allow one to provide new more secure crypto-codes that in principle allow users to run programs on untrusted systems and still keeping their data secret.

Another important application is the quadratic speedup by Grover's search algorithm (1996) over conventional search algorithms, addressing for example problems like the 'traveling salesman', in which large spaces of possibilities need to be searched and compared.

Machine learning is another hot topic where the discovery of an exponential speedup for solving certain systems of linear equations has led to flurry of new developments like algorithms for core problems like data fitting and supporting vector machines.

Finally, a vital application is the efficient simulation of quantum physical and chemical systems, which at present is an extremely costly business taking up much of our supercomputer capacity. This development is of importance to fields like chemistry, material science and high-energy physics. In this area a quantum computer naturally would offer an exponential speedup, which in turn would directly feed back into the successful development of new quantum technologies. Science is time and again an incredible innovation engine, we are standing at the dawn of a new era and wonder where quantum technologies will lead us.

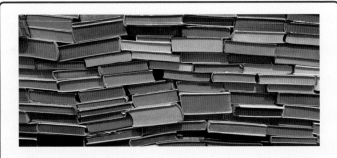

Further reading:

On the interpretation of quantum theory:

— *Quantum: Einstein, Bohr and the Great Debate About the Nature of Reality*
Manjit Kumar
Icon Press (2009)

— *The Interpretation of Quantum Mechanics*
Roland Omnes
Princeton University Press (1994)

On quantum computing:

— *Quantum Computing for the Quantum Curious*
Jessica Turner et al.
Springer Link (2021)

— *Quantum Information Theory*
Mark M. Wilde
Cambridge University Press (2013)

— *Quantum Computation and Quantum Information*
Isaac Chuang and Michael Nielsen
Cambridge University Press (2011)

Chapter II.5

Particles, fields and statistics

In fact the smallest units of matter are not physical objects in the ordinary sense; they are forms, ideas which can be expressed unambiguously only in mathematical language.

Werner Heisenberg

In Chapters II.1 and II.2, we mainly focussed on the qubit, because in its simplicity it was most suitable to demonstrate the quantessentials. In this chapter we turn to particles and fields. We start by discussing the one-particle Schrödinger and Heisenberg equations in more detail. Next we turn to fields and their quantization, and explain how the resulting Hilbert space describes multiparticle states. We close the chapter with a discussion of the topological origins of indistinguishability, Pauli's exclusion. principle and the spin-statistics connection.

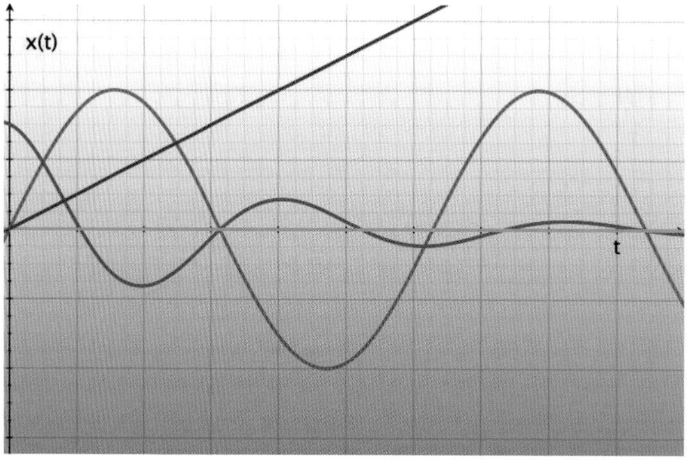

Figure II.5.1: *Moving particles.* Various particle motions as a function of time (t) in *configuration* (x) *space*. A particle successively: at rest (orange), moving with constant momentum (purple), in an oscillatory motion (red), and in a damped oscillation (blue).

Particle states and wavefunctions

Whereas the state of a single particle in classical physics is fixed by specifying its position and its velocity, i.e. by giving 6 numbers, the state of a quantum particle is specified by giving its wavefunction, a continuous function that extends over all of space. How different can the quantum world be?

Phase space. Let us consider a single particle with a given mass m and assume that it has no internal structure. In classical mechanics we specify its state by just saying what its position x and its velocity v or momentum $p = mv$ are. Once we fix its position and momentum at a given instant in time, Newton's laws would do the rest, given the force they completely determine the future states of the particle. The motion of the particle can be thought of as an orbit or trajectory parametrized by time in ordinary three-dimensional position or *configuration space* of the particle.

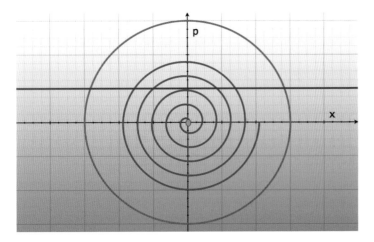

Figure II.5.2: *Particle motions.* The same particle motions as in Figure II.5.1 as a curve parametrized by t in *phase space* $(x(t), p(t))$.

In the one-dimensional case we would plot the position $x = x(t)$ with the value x on the vertical axis as a function of t along the horizontal axis. Alternatively we may think of the motion as a time parametrized curve through the combined momentum and position space which is also called the *phase space* of the particle. The phase space has twice the number of dimensions, because to the d components of the position vector one has to add the d components of the momentum vector.

We have given some examples of one-dimensional particle motions in the Figures II.5.1 and II.5.2, showing what they look like in configuration as well as phase space. So far the classical story of a particle.

wavefunctions. The story in quantum mechanics is very different. There the state of a particle at a given time t is described by its *wavefunction* $\psi(x, t)$ which is a function that even for a single particle is defined over all of position (configuration) space.[1] Note, however, that we do not

specify its velocity. If we just give the wavefunction over all of space at some initial time, then the Schrödinger equation would generate the future states given the expression for the kinetic energy and potential energy. The Schrödinger equation determines the time evolution of the wavefunction which in turn describes the particle state, and in that sense does for a quantum particle what Newton's equations did for the classical particle. We encountered this equation before in Chapter I.4 on page 158 but we will recall some of the results here for convenience. Our intuition about particles is deeply rooted in the Newtonian paradigm in that we think of a particle having a definite position a definite velocity, and that image is of course a long way from specifying some smooth function over all of space. Indeed this is nothing less then a conceptual leap that took the brightest minds a long time, first to bridge, and later to really swallow.

Particle-wave duality

In classical physics the particle and wave concepts are distinct and mutually exclusive. In quantum theory a particle may manifest itself in both guises. Here the concept of complementarity rears its head. The concept of a quantum particle transcends the classical distinction and appears to be both. Niels Bohr applied the wave picture to atomic orbits and obtained a discrete set of energy levels of which the lowest one is stable. A new door for fundamental physics opened up.

The vastly different framework of quantum mechanics we just outlined expresses the quantessential feature known as *particle-wave duality*. The wavefunction expresses the wave nature of a particle and the Schrödinger equation is a wave-type equation for the matter-wave that represents the particle in quantum theory. In the early days one referred therefore to quantum mechanics as 'wave mechanics.' That term sounded in the classical context rather like a

---

[1]For readers who are not already familiar with the notion of functions and what you can do with them I recommend looking at the *Math Excursion* on page 151 of Part III.

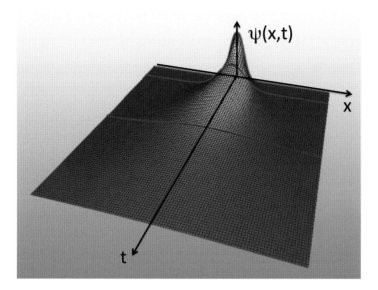

Figure II.5.3: *Particle probability density.* A quantum probability density of a particle $\Psi(x, t)$ as a function of x and t. It describes a particle at rest, well localized around the origin for $t = 0$ and then spreading out (disperse) over space as time progresses.

contradiction in terms, because in classical physics, particles and waves are fundamentally different concepts. Particles are supposed to be very much localized, while for waves the opposite holds, they typically are spatially extended. Particles can collide locally and exchange momentum and energy like billiard balls, while waves 'interact' typically by interference where the combined waves show a particular pattern of maxima and minima like water waves in a pond. We may ask what the special properties of a wave representing a particle are, or for that matter what the particle properties are of a wave, for example an electromagnetic wave.

Photons. To start with the latter, it was one of Einstein's seminal contributions to quantum theory to postulate the so-called *photon* as the quantum particle of light. Its defining properties are that this particle moves with the velocity of light, has zero mass, and an energy $E = h\nu$, where ν is the frequency of the light wave.[2] Thus a steady electro-

magnetic wave of a single frequency would correspond to a constant flux of particles with a fixed energy or momentum. The quantization of energy of radiation of a given frequency implied that the minimal amount of energy of a wave with frequency ν had to just be $h\nu$, and this quantization of energy was exactly what the radical postulate of Max Planck amounted to, the postulate which started off the whole quantum revolution. It was this assumption which rescued the classical black body radiation law of Rayleigh-Jeans from its demise in the high frequency domain as we pointed out in Chapter I.2.

Matter waves. It was the French physicist De Broglie who turned the relation around. He postulated the existence of matter waves: for any particle type with a mass m, the wavelength had to satisfy the relation $\lambda = h/p$, linking the wavelength to the momentum. This relation is consistent with Einstein's formula $E = h\nu$ once you realize that for a massless particle according to special relativity $E = cp$ as we pointed out in Chapter I.2, and that for a lightwave we have that $\lambda = c/\nu$.

The Bohr atom. Furthermore this picture of a matter wave was at the heart of the atomic model of Bohr, where a definite energy state of an electron would have a single wavelength but to make it periodic, it had to fit exactly on the classical circular orbit with that energy. Imposing this relation lead to the quantization of the wavelength, and thus of the momentum and therefore also to the quantization of the allowed energy for the atomic states. Bohr's picture of the atom predicted the discrete spectrum of energy

---

[2]This may at first sight seem problematic perhaps, because if a particle has mass equal to zero would then Einstein's own dictum – $E = mc^2$ – not decree that its energy would be zero as well? Not really, because we have to make the distinction between the *rest mass* m_0 of a particle and its *relativistic mass* m. These are related by $m^2 = m_0^2 + (p/c)^2$, showing that (i) if the momentum $p = 0$ indeed $m = m_0$, and (ii) that if $m_0 = 0$ then $m = |p|/c$. This tells us that in the latter case where the rest mass is zero, the relativistic mass is proportional to the momentum of the particle. Therefore, in relativity massless particles make complete sense and the photon is the omnipresent manifestation of that.

levels but most importantly also the existence of a lowest energy or *ground state* for the atom. The ground state corresponds to the largest wavelength that would fit on the orbit, i.e. being equal to that orbit. This point is all-important, exactly because the classical realization of an atom lacks a true ground state, the system would be unstable and the electron would fall into the nucleus in a short time, loosing energy by radiating. So the extremely stable atom as we know it in nature severely violated the laws of classical physics, and that was one of the reasons we had to give up, not just on the naive model of the atom but on the whole of classical physics! It was quantum theory that provided a fundamental understanding of the stability of matter.

Where is the particle? If a particle is represented by a wavefunction, the first question that comes mind is: 'but what about the position of the particle?' I have told you what the momentum of the particle is but where is it? Indeed, where is the particle if it is a kind of standing wave spread out around the nucleus? A perfect monochromatic wave has in principle an infinite extent. It is a periodic function like a sine or a cosine, but how can such a function ever single out any particular position for the particle? Well, you are right, it cannot.

The resolution of this tantalizing paradox has to do with the interpretation of the wavefunction and what it means to make a position measurement of a particle. We have touched on these matters already in Chapter II.2 where we learned that this comes about because of the incompatibility of different observable quantities and the frameworks that limit the degree to which questions may or may not have meaningful answers. For the moment we accept the euphemism that Niels Bohr invented for this inconvenient truth of particles being waves and *vice versa*: he called it *complementarity*. We return to these questions explicitly shortly.

The space of particle states

We extend the symbolic mathematical representation from qubit to particle states. It is profitable to also think of wavefunctions as state vectors. The square of the wavefunction defines a probability distribution of where to find the particle.

In previous chapters we looked at the space of quantum states of a system that classically corresponds to a system with a finite number of states, like an array of qubits. Now, we want to extend this discussion to a system of a particle with mass m that moves in Euclidean space. The essential difference is that the classical configuration space is now continuous.

Hilbert space heuristics. Essentially, making the step involves going from a discrete to to a continuous space and that is from a mathematical point of view a subtle matter. For that reason we will restrict ourselves here to rather heuristic arguments. If a particle could sit only in a discrete set of positions $x_i (i = 1, \ldots, N)$, then of course the analysis is reduced to the one we had in the previous chapters and we would introduce a set of corresponding basis vectors $|x_i\rangle$, which would be eigenvectors of the position operator X and hence satisfy the eigenvalue equation:

$$X|x_i\rangle = x_i|x_i\rangle, \qquad (\text{II.5.1})$$

and the state vector would be written as $|\psi\rangle = \sum_i \alpha_i |x_i\rangle$. The natural generalization for the continuous space case to write the following expression for the quantum state of a particle:

$$|\psi\rangle = \int \psi(x)|x\rangle \, dx. \qquad (\text{II.5.2})$$

All we know about the particle state $|\psi\rangle$ is that the state is encoded in the corresponding complex function ψ of the continuous position variable x. The *sum* over the discrete subscript i gets replaced by *integral* over the continuous variable x, which is symbolically written as $\int \cdots dx$.

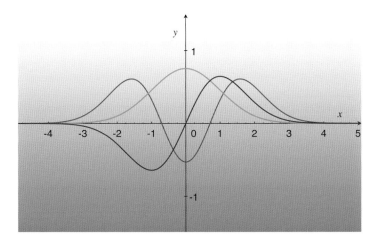

Figure II.5.4: *Harmonic oscillator wavefunctions.* wavefunctions of the three lowest energy states $\psi_n(x)$ with $n = 0, 1, 2$, of a quantum oscillator. The label n also gives the number of nodes: the even n functions are symmetric the odd ones are odd under $x \to -x$.

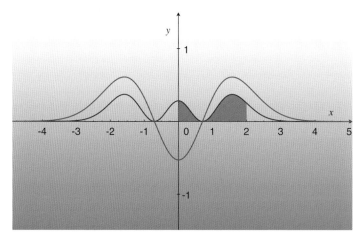

Figure II.5.5: *Harmonic oscillator probabilities.* The $n = 2$ wavefunction (red) and probability density (purple). The probability P_{02} is given by the shaded area. We talk about these states in detail in a later section on page 161.

And indeed, $\psi(x)$ is just the famous *wavefunction* that appears in the well-known Schrödinger equation we will get to later. To give you an idea we have depicted the three lowest energy states of a particle in a harmonic oscillator potential in Figure II.5.4. These will be discussed in more detail shortly. Talking heuristically one may say that the wavefunction represents nothing less than a vector in an infinite-dimensional vector space. In fact $\psi(x)$ is the '$|x\rangle$ component' of the state vector $|\psi\rangle$ which suggests that we should write it as such:

$$\psi(x) = \langle x|\psi\rangle, \qquad (\text{II.5.3})$$

leading to the expansion of the wavefunction in 'position eigen states',

$$|\psi\rangle = \int |x\rangle\langle x|\psi\rangle \; dx \, .$$

We have to make sure that we impose the *normalization condition* just as we did in the discrete case, in strict analogy it reads:

$$\langle\Psi|\Psi\rangle = \int \psi(x)^*\psi(x) \; dx = \int |\psi(x)|^2 \; dx = 1 \, . \quad (\text{II.5.4})$$

So what we learn is that quantum states of particles defined on a configuration space $\mathcal{X}$ correspond to elements of the space $\mathcal{H}$ of (complex) functions on $\mathcal{X}$ which are 'square integrable', meaning that they have to satisfy the condition (II.5.4). This space of square integrable functions is called the *Hilbert space*. One can also define a scalar product on the states that – not surprisingly – takes the form:

$$\langle\phi|\psi\rangle = \int \phi^*(x)\psi(x) \; dx \, ,$$

completely analogous to formula (II.1.4). This once more underscores the exceptional elegance of Dirac's *bra* and *ket* notation.

You could say that by going from classical to quantum description we transcend from some space of coordinates to the space of functions on that space of coordinates. The difference with the description of the classical state is rather dramatic indeed, and you may wonder how to make sense out of it. What is the link of the wavefunction which is defined over all of space and the ordinary point-like particles we observe?

Probability interpretation. The interpretation is also completely in line with what we expect from the discrete case: $\psi(x)$ is the (complex) *probability amplitude* for the probability $p(x)$ of finding the particle at point x. The absolute square of the amplitude $p(x) = |\psi(x)|^2$ defines a *probability density*, and hence the probability P_{ab} of finding the particle in the range $a \leqslant x \leqslant b$ can be expressed as:

$$P_{ab} = \int_a^b p(x)\,dx. \qquad (\text{II.5.5})$$

Formulas like the ones we have displayed in this section may at first look a bit daunting, and you may ask what the hell they mean. Well stay tuned in because it is not hard to visualize at all; the probability P_{ab} is just the area under $p(x)$ if you plot it as a function of x, between the points $x = a$ and $x = b$; This is depicted in Figure II.5.5 and for more details we refer to the *Mathematical Excursion on functions* in Appendix A of Part III.

As a matter of fact physicists love the bra and ket notation, it is compact and convenient to work with and it also keeps the conceptual structure of expressions remarkably transparent. And often progress originates in designing an optimal symbolic representation and notation.

This for the moment concludes our description of the space of quantum states that corresponds to a classical system with a continuous configuration space such as a particle moving in ordinary space. We saw that it is described by a complex wavefunction that may be considered as the components of a vector in an infinite-dimensional vector space of normalizable vectors which is called the Hilbert space. And we have mentioned that the square of the wavefunction corresponds to a probability density for where the particle can be found.

There are other pressing questions that immediately come to mind. You may ask: where did the velocity of the particle go, it appears nowhere in the specification of the quantum state? And what about its energy? Your point is well taken

indeed – thank you – and we will return to the question of how, and to what extent, a precise velocity or momentum or energy can be assigned to a particle in the next section. But before we do so, I want to discuss an explicit example of a set of wavefunctions for a particle that lives not only in one dimension, but on a circle, which is a finite one-dimensional space without boundary.

A particle on a circle

In this subsection we turn to a concrete example and look at a quantum particle that lives on a unit circle with an angular coordinate $0 \leq \varphi \leq 2\pi$. This may strike you as a particularly useless theoretical problem, but one should be careful with those judgements. A lot of applications of physics and in particular quantum physics have to do with settings that are effectively low dimensional. Quantum wires are one-dimensional. A particle that is confined to the edge of a planar disc lives on a circle. In fact the groundbreaking Bohr-model of the atom amounted exactly to quantizing a particle on a circle, as he basically quantized the particle on classical circular orbits. Another example are 'quantum dots', which are basically finite two-dimensional domains on which particles can live.

A particle on a circle will be described by some complex wavefunction $\psi(\varphi)$ that is normalized but also has to satisfy a continuity or periodicity condition such that[3] $\psi(\varphi) = \psi(\varphi + 2\pi)$.

---

[3]It is more precise to say that this is a condition one imposes *a priori* on physical grounds. If there is some defect on the boundary one could well imagine to impose a different, non-trivial boundary condition, for example $\psi(\varphi + 2\pi) = e^{i\gamma}\psi(\varphi)$. A more sophisticated treatment of the problem would be to say that we extend the set of observables to arbitrary translations x and decompose these into $x = 2n\pi + \varphi$. The discrete translations by $2n\pi$ form an invariant subgroup Z of the group of translations on the real line R; the different boundary conditions form representations of this Z group and these are labeled by the angle $0 \leq \gamma < 2\pi$.

Figure II.5.6: *La Danse.* Circle dance by the French painter Henri Matisse, painted in 1910. (©Succession Henri Matisse.)

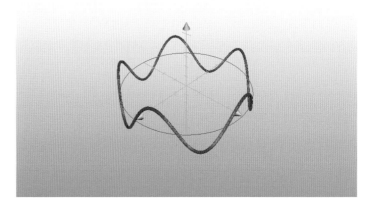

Figure II.5.7: *Going in circles.* We have depicted the $k = 5$ real wavefunction $\psi(\varphi) = \frac{1}{\sqrt{2\pi}}\cos(5\varphi)$ of a particle on a circle,

Momentum eigenstates. The periodic solutions are of the form

$$\langle\varphi|k\rangle = \psi_k(\varphi) = \sqrt{\frac{1}{2\pi\hbar}}e^{ik\varphi}. \qquad (II.5.6)$$

You would expect maybe periodic functions like cosines and sines, but as we allow complex functions it is much more natural to write then as simple exponential functions, and in a sense it amounts to the same thing because of that beautiful Euler identity $e^{ik\varphi} = \cos(k\varphi) + i\sin(k\varphi)$ as is explained in the *Math Excursion* about complex numbers on page 151 of Part III. The periodicity condition leads to the condition that $e^{2\pi ik} = 1$, which is satisfied only if k is restricted to integer values.

Observe that these periodic states $\psi_k(\varphi)$ have a wavelength $\lambda = 2\pi/k$ and using the relation of De Broglie $\lambda = h/p$ says that in these particular periodic states the particle carries a momentum $p_k = \hbar k$. What about the energy of the particle? If we think of a free particle with no force on it, the energy would just be the kinetic energy of the states $E_k = p_k^2/2m$ and therefore grows proportional to k^2. At this point, however, we could also assume that the particle is a relativistic particle, in which case the expression for the

energy of the k-th mode would be $E_k = \sqrt{p_k^2 c^2 + m^2 c^4}$ which for small momentum reduces to the previous expression but for large p_k we would get $E_k \simeq p_k c$ which is proportional to k. We can also immediately calculate the probability distribution for the states to equal:

$$p_k(\varphi) = \psi_k^*(\varphi)\psi_k(\varphi) = \psi_{-k}(\varphi)\psi_k(\varphi) = \frac{1}{2\pi}.$$

This probability density for where to find the particle is constant! This tells us that whereas the momentum of the particle is completely fixed with zero uncertainty, the position of the particle is maximally uncertain, because it corresponds to a uniform distribution over all of space. In these states there is no preference whatsoever for any position or region. The conclusion is that in this momentum framework the particle logically speaking has no position. A dramatic instance of the Heisenberg uncertainty principle. We return to this point later on, when we will show wavefunctions which to a certain extent look more like localized particles. These wavefunctions will be particular linear superpositions of this set of momentum eigenstates.

Just like in the discrete case for a general state we may

Position and momentum operators

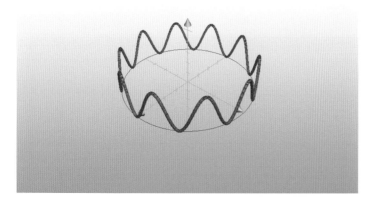

Figure II.5.8: *Going in circles*. The probability distribution $\rho(\varphi) = \frac{1}{2\pi}\cos^2(5\varphi)$ of a particle on a circle.

write a general expansion like:

$$|\psi\rangle = \sum_k \alpha_k |k>, \qquad (\text{II.5.7})$$

where the basis states $|k\rangle$ would equal

$$|k\rangle = \int \langle\varphi|k\rangle \, |\varphi\rangle \, \mathrm{d}\varphi = \sqrt{\frac{1}{2\pi}} \int e^{ik\varphi} \, |\varphi\rangle \, \mathrm{d}\varphi \, .$$

These states form an orthonormal basis, meaning that they satisfy the orthonormality condition[4]

$$\langle k|k'\rangle = \int \langle k|\varphi\rangle\langle\varphi|k'\rangle \mathrm{d}\varphi = \delta_{kk'} \, .$$

Now the sum in. the expression (II.5.7) extends over all integer values of k, indeed confirming our expectation that the quantum state of a particle on a circle is like a vector in an infinite-dimensional space. There is also a completeness relation for the basis in analogy with equation (II.2.10) which reads

$$\sum_k |k\rangle\langle k| = 1 \, .$$

---

[4]To prove it you need the functional relation that $\frac{1}{2\pi}\int\exp(i(k-k')\varphi)\,\mathrm{d}\varphi = \delta_{kk'}$.

In the earlier chapters we have been talking about quantum dynamical variables as operators or matrices. For example for the qubit we showed in Chapter II.1 that we could interpret the Pauli Z-matrix as the position operator, and the Pauli X-matrix as the momentum operator. So the first question that comes up if we think of particle states as wavefunctions, what the operator valued observables should look like. Something like infinite-dimensional matrices maybe? The answer is simpler than that and quite natural if you think of operators that have to act on functions. You can multiply functions by other functions, but more importantly we can differentiate functions. We should expect dynamical variables to be represented by differential operators. So let us first consider the momentum operator.

Momentum. In this section we look at the definition of momentum and position operators for a particle on a circle. The state vectors are the wavefunctions $\psi_k(\varphi)$ given in equation (II.5.6), we will show that the momentum corresponds to the differential operator,

$$P = -i\hbar\frac{\mathrm{d}}{\mathrm{d}\varphi} \, .$$

First observe that the functions $\psi_k(x)$ are eigenfunctions of P, because,

$$P\psi_k(\varphi) = \hbar k\psi_k(\varphi) \, ,$$

and recall that we argued in the previous chapter based on De Broglies heuristic argument that the momentum of a particle in the k-th state is indeed equal to $p_k = \hbar k$.

Generator of translations. At this point you might want to look at the *Math Excursion* on page 151 of Part III, where it is shown that the displacement of the state vector or wavefunction is also generated by the derivative or differential operator[5] $K = \frac{d}{d\varphi}$. We can formally put it in the exponent, just like the sigma matrices before, having the property:

$$e^{i\theta K}\psi_k(\varphi) = e^{i\theta k}\psi_k(\varphi) = \psi_k(\varphi + \theta). \qquad (II.5.8)$$

We see that this exponential operator just shifts the argument of the function by the factor in front of K in the exponent. This equation is the precise mathematical expression of the statement that the momentum operator (in fact $P/\hbar$ to be precise) acting on a function 'generates' spatial translations of its coordinate (position).

The position operator. What about the position operator Φ? It acts on the wavefunction as $\Phi \psi(\varphi) = \varphi\psi(\varphi)$, i.e. by just multiplying the wavefunction by the *variable* 'φ'. Note, however, that the $\psi_k(\varphi)$ are eigenfunctions of momentum P but *not* of position Φ (because k is a constant and φ is not, it is a coordinate, a variable). So the position operator 'multiplies' the wavefunction with the *function* 'φ'.

It may be useful to again point out the analogy with the qubit case in Chapter II.2, where the would-be position operator was Z and a would-be momentum operator could be X. We could then consider the states $|\pm\rangle$ defined in equation (II.2.4), which are eigenstates *not* of Z but of X, because $X|\pm\rangle = \pm |\pm\rangle$. And indeed, acting with Z on, for example the X eigenvector $|+\rangle$ would multiply each component with a different coordinate value, leading to $Z|+\rangle = |-\rangle$. So, acting with the coordinate operator on a momentum eigenstate changes it to another state.

Canonical commutation relations. Being eigenfunctions of momentum, the $\psi_k(\varphi)$ are also eigenfunctions of a Hamiltonian $H = P^2/2m$ describing a free particle of mass

m that moves on a circle. We also see that as we might expect the momentum and position operators do not commute, they satisfy the so-called *canonical commutation relations*:

$$[X, P] = i\hbar. \qquad (II.5.9)$$

To see that this is true it is most convenient to think of the commutator as an operator working on a (wave) function $f(x)$, then we obtain:

$$
\begin{aligned}
[X, P]\, f(x) &= -Xi\hbar\frac{df(x)}{dx} + i\hbar\frac{d}{dx} X\, f(x) \\
&= -i\hbar x\frac{df(x)}{dx} + i\hbar\frac{d}{dx}\,(x\, f(x)) \\
&= i\hbar(\frac{d}{dx} x)f(x) = i\hbar f(x).
\end{aligned}
$$

As the function appearing on both sides of the equation is *arbitrary* we may conclude that the statement (II.5.9) is true as a property of the operators.

Raising and lowering. Let us ask for the *raising* and *lowering* operators of this problem. Let us first try to find operators $Q_\pm$ that satisfy the commutation relations:

$$[P, Q_\pm(X)] = \pm a Q_\pm(X), \qquad (II.5.10)$$

and as

$$PQ_\pm - Q_\pm P = -i\hbar\frac{dQ_\pm}{dx},$$

we obtain an equation for the functions $Q_\pm(x)$:

$$-i\hbar\frac{dQ_\pm(x)}{dx} = \pm a Q_\pm(x).$$

The solutions to this equation are $Q_\pm(x) = c\exp(\pm iax/\hbar)$, and therefore one obtains for the operators:

$$Q_\pm(X) = c\, e^{\pm iaX/\hbar}. \qquad (II.5.11)$$

The interpretation is now as follows. The momentum of a particle on the circle has a discrete spectrum $\{\hbar k\}$ with integers $\infty < k < \infty$, for clockwise and counterclockwise moving particles. The smallest possible momentum state

---

[5]The difference between P and K is a matter of units or dimensions, the dimension of the differential operator is [1/length] to get the dimensions of momentum we have to multiply by a constant with dimension [lenght × momentum] = [joule × second] and yes – not surprising – that constant is nothing but Planck constant $\hbar$.

has $k = 0$ and the raising and lowering operators (II.5.11) sequentially generate all the eigenfunctions $\psi_k(x)$ if we choose $a = 1$. We clearly have to adjust the value of a to comply with the imposed boundary condition.

Heisenberg's uncertainty. It is amusing to check the Heisenberg uncertainty relation by verifying that indeed $\Delta x = L$ and $\Delta p = p_0 = \hbar\pi/L$ satisfy:

$$\Delta x \Delta p \;=\; \hbar\pi \geq |i\langle\psi_0|[X,P]|\psi_0\rangle|$$
$$=\; \hbar\langle\psi_0|\psi_0\rangle = \hbar.$$

We see that these states do not saturate the lower bound on the uncertainty relation. That lower bound is $\hbar/2$, as we showed in Chapter II.2 on page 83.

Energy generates time evolution

Time evolution. If we talk about time evolution of a classical system, we think in the first place of Newton, but in the realm of computation we also think of the physical implementation of a sequence of logical gates. A computation is in that sense a discrete dynamical process whose rate is set by the speed or clock time of the chip, today being of the order of nanoseconds. We process information by manipulating it through interacting with it in a controlled way by having logical gates acting. That is similar to applying a force to get ourselves moving as we saw in the previous chapters. Now even in the heyday of classical mechanics many different approaches were formulated in attempts to solve specific dynamical problems by people like Hamilton, Jacobi, Laplace, Lagrange, Legendre and others. We discussed some of them in Chapter I.1 on page 16.

In Figure II.5.9 we have indicated various paths that lead from the domain of classical mechanics to the corresponding quantum equations. I am going to discuss them sequentially, and start with the Schrödinger equation.

Wave mechanics: the Schrödinger equation

The wavefunction of a quantum system evolves in time according to the famous Schrödinger equation. Dynamical changes in a physical system are induced by the underlying forces acting on the system and between its constituent parts, and their effect can be represented in terms of what is called the energy or Hamiltonian operator H. For a single qubit system the operators can be represented as 2×2 matrices, for a two-qubit system they are 4×4 matrices, etc. The Schrödinger equation can be written

$$i\hbar\frac{d|\psi(t)\rangle}{dt} = H|\psi(t)\rangle. \qquad (II.5.12)$$

This is a linear differential equation expressing the property that the time evolution of a quantum system is generated by its energy operator. Assuming that H is constant, given an initial state $|\psi(0)\rangle$ the solution is simply

$$|\psi(t)\rangle = U(t)|\psi(0)\rangle \text{ with } U(t) = e^{-iHt/\hbar}. \qquad (II.5.13)$$

The time evolution is *unitary*, meaning that the operator $U(t)$ satisfies $UU^\dagger = 1$.

$$U^\dagger = \exp(-iHt/\hbar)^\dagger$$
$$= \exp(iH^\dagger t/\hbar) = \exp(iHt/\hbar) = U^{-1}. \qquad (II.5.14)$$

Unitary time evolution means that the length of the state vector remains invariant, which is necessary to preserve the total probability for the system to be in any of its possible states. The unitary nature of the time evolution operator U follows directly from the fact that H is hermitian: $H^\dagger = H$. Any hermitian 2×2 matrix can be written

$$A = \begin{pmatrix} a & b+ic \\ b-ic & -a \end{pmatrix},$$

where a, b and c are real numbers.[6]

---

[6] We omitted a component proportional to the unit matrix as it acts trivially on any state. We speak of the part that has no trace.

Stationary states. From equation (II.5.13) results it is also immediately clear what the importance is of the eigenstates of the Hamiltonian – the energy eigenstates. An energy eigenstate $|\psi_n\rangle$ satisfies by definition $H|\psi_n\rangle = E_n|\psi_n\rangle$, and thus for such states:

$$|\psi(t)\rangle = \exp(iE_n t/\hbar|)\,\psi(0)\rangle. \qquad (II.5.15)$$

The state is not quite time-independent, but it changes only by an overall phase factor, which means that the probability density $|\psi|^2$, or the expectation value of any operator will not change over time. The state is strictly speaking not *static* and therefore called *stationary*.

Time dependence. But if we act on a state that is not an eigenstate of the energy, we get a time dependent solution. For the simple example of a single qubit, suppose the initial state is

$$|\psi(0)\rangle = |+\rangle \simeq \sqrt{\frac{1}{2}}\begin{pmatrix} 1 \\ 1 \end{pmatrix}.$$

On the right, for the sake of convenience, we have written the state as a column vector. Consider the energy of a spin in an external magnetic field B directed along the positive z-axis.[7] In this case H is given by $H = b\,Z$. Now the initial state is a linear combination of two different energy eigenstates. From equation (II.5.13) it follows that,

$$U(t) = \exp(\frac{-ibt}{2\hbar}Z)$$
$$= \begin{pmatrix} \exp(-ibt/2\hbar) & 0 \\ 0 & \exp(ibt/2\hbar) \end{pmatrix}. \qquad (II.5.16)$$

We obtain an oscillatory time dependence for the state, not just a phase factor, i.e.

$$|\psi(t)\rangle = \sqrt{\frac{1}{2}}\begin{pmatrix} e^{-ibt/\hbar} \\ e^{ibt/\hbar} \end{pmatrix}$$
$$= \sqrt{\frac{1}{2}}\left[\cos\frac{bt}{\hbar}\begin{pmatrix} 1 \\ 1 \end{pmatrix} + i\sin\frac{bt}{\hbar}\begin{pmatrix} -1 \\ 1 \end{pmatrix}\right]. \qquad (II.5.17)$$

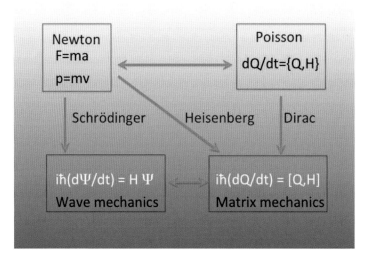

Figure II.5.9: *Ways to go quantum.* Various pathways from different but equivalent formulations of classical mechanics to the Schröodinger and Heisenberg – also equivalent – formulations of quantum theory.

The state oscillates between the $|+\rangle$ with probability $p_+ = |\langle+|\psi(t)\rangle|^2 = \cos^2 bt/\hbar$ and $|-\rangle$ with $p_- = |\langle-1|\psi(t)\rangle|^2 = \sin^2 bt/\hbar$. This simple example applies in some form or another to numerous physically relevant two-level systems.

We see that, in contrast to classical mechanics, the time evolution equation is first order in time and linear in the wavefunction. In general the Hamiltonian can be a complicated function of the basic dynamical variables and therefore it is only in rare situations that one can find an exact analytic solution. On the other hand it is also surprising to see how a relatively small number of exactly solved problems can serve to get a deep insight in, and feeling for, what kind of behavior quantum systems exhibit.

---

[7]Quantum spins necessarily have a magnetic moment, so in addition to carrying an intrinsic angular momentum they also interact with a magnetic field.

Matrix mechanics: the Heisenberg equation

In the previous section we have considered the time evolution of the state generated by some particular Hamiltonian which we assumed to be time independent. In that Schrödinger type description the operators one considers are mostly time independent and the time-dependent state $|\psi(t)\rangle$ is a solution to the Schrödinger equation with the given Hamiltonian which characterized the system and its interactions. There is a complementary view which was developed by Heisenberg, it is often called *'matrix mechanics'* which lead to the Heisenberg equation. In his view, which in a sense is closer to classical dynamics, the dynamical variables, meaning observables like matrices, are the objects that change in time whereas the state remains fixed. The simplest way to see how this comes about is to rewrite the definition of the expectation value of an operator A in a suggestive way as:

$$\langle\psi(t)|A|\psi(t)\rangle = \langle\psi(0)|e^{iHt/\hbar}Ae^{-iHt/\hbar}|\psi(0)\rangle$$
$$= \langle\psi(0)|A(t)|\psi(0)\rangle. \qquad (II.5.18)$$

In other words we have defined time-dependent observables for the system through the relation:

$$A(t) \equiv e^{+iHt/\hbar}Ae^{-iHt/\hbar}.$$

By calculating the time derivative of the above expression one arrives at Heisenberg's quantum equation of motion:

$$i\hbar\frac{dA(t)}{dt} = [H, A(t)], \qquad (II.5.19)$$

and we have an equation that tells us that the time evolution of operators acting on the state space is generated by the commutator with the Hamiltonian of the system. Note that the commutation relations of observables are unchanged by the transformation, so we still have the canonical commutator $[X, P] = i\hbar$. I would also like to remind the readers who happened to read my discussion on Poisson brackets on page 16 of Part I, that there is indeed a striking similarity between the classical Poisson brackets and

the Heisenberg commutator equations. The recipe is to make in equations (I.1.14) to (I.1.16) the following replacement

$$\{\ ,\ \}_{\mathrm{pb}} \quad \Rightarrow \quad -\frac{i}{\hbar}[\ ,\ ],$$

to obtain the canonical quantum equations! This was by the way the method Dirac used to 'quantize' systems.

It is illuminating to keep both formulations in mind. Certain questions can be answered more easily in the Schrödinger picture and others in the Heisenberg picture.

Symmetries and conservation laws. The Heisenberg equation yields a direct understanding of the existence of 'constants of the motion' or conservation laws. For physical variables described by operators Q that commute with the Hamiltonian i.e. $[H, Q] = 0$, the Heisenberg equation teaches us that $dQ/dt = 0$ and thus that Q is conserved in time. Such operators that commute with the Hamiltonian are by definition called *symmetry operators*. You see that energy is one of them, and that had better be so, because time independence of the Hamiltonian was after all our starting point. Depending on the system and its Hamiltonian we will find out about the conserved quantities this way, like momentum, angular momentum, the Lenz vector, charge, isospin etc. Indeed summing up these examples one realizes how important these basic conservation laws are, as they allow us to characterize the states by properties that are robust in time, and that allows us to label and assign names to things! After all, your name would be useless if it were to change every day.

Degeneracies. The other consequence of having conserved quantities is that if Q acts on an eigenstate of the Hamiltonian then it may well make another state, but that state will have the same energy as the first one. You can use the conserved quantities or symmetry operators to generate 'degenerate states' in the spectrum. The statement is stronger than that, because you can always find enough symmetry operators to resolve all degeneracies and label the different orthogonal states that are degenerate in energy by labels referring to conserved quantum numbers. We saw this principle already at work in Chapter I.4 where we discussed the discovery of the electron spin. This was achieved by lifting the degeneracy by introducing an external magnetic field, which broke the rotational symmetry of the system.

A framework of symmetry operators. So in choosing a framework, we often like to include the Hamiltonian as one of the operators. The next thing you may want to do is to add operators that commute with H, which in other words correspond to conserved quantities. These operators form a closed algebra in the sense that if Q_1 and Q_2 commute with H, then also their commutator $[Q_1, Q_2]$ will commute with H. This way we can construct a commutator or Lie-algebra of symmetry operators including the Hamiltonian. This algebra is then called the *symmetry algebra* for the system.

Next we follow the instructions for a consistent framework and select, out of all those conserved quantities, a maximal number which do *mutually* commute. That defines a sub-algebra of the full symmetry algebra, consisting of observables whose combined eigenvalues form the sample space, for that framework. In fact such a maximal set of mutually commuting independent symmetry operators is called the *Cartan subalgebra* of the symmetry algebra. This algebra is named after the famous French mathematician Élie Cartan, who succeeded in completely classifying all possible finite-dimensional (complex) Lie-algebra's. Many of those play a crucial role in quantum physics.

The next chapter is devoted to different kinds of symmetry and their breaking, and it will become clear that the notion of symmetry is one of the guiding principles that has played a leading role in the development of modern physics.

Generators of symmetries. So we have arrived at a rather quantessential picture linked to (continuous) symmetries. The operators Q that are conserved generate the symmetries, and they can therefore be used to label the states, and furthermore they are physical observables. If I say that the Heisenberg equation just tells you that the Hamiltonian generates a time translation, what I mean is that an infinitesimal change of an observable A in time, $-i\hbar \, dA/dt$ equals the commutator with the Hamiltonian. One can also write for example:

$$-i\hbar \frac{dA}{dx} = [P, A],$$
$$i\hbar \frac{dA}{dp} = [X, A],$$

which states that the operator dependence on position or momentum is generated by their 'duals,' the momentum and position operators respectively. Similarly the commutator with the angular momentum component L_z generates an infinitesimal rotation around the z-axis of the operators. We see that the Heisenberg equation is in fact one of many. It is the equation that expresses the time-translation-symmetry of the underlying space-time, from which energy conservation is derived.

Classical lookalikes

In our discussion of (free) particle states we have clearly found two extremes: (i) the momentum states $|k\rangle$, where the momentum and energy have no uncertainty, but the uncertainty in position is maximal and (ii) the position states $|\varphi\rangle$, where the converse would hold. Neither of these seems close to what we think about when we talk about a classical particle moving on a circle. We know that we are free to consider any state of the type given in (II.5.2) and therefore we can ask whether it is possible to find a particular linear combinations of basic quantum states that look more like the classical ones.

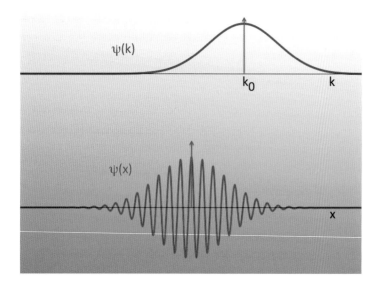

Figure II.5.10: *Wave packets.* We make a 'gaussian' superposition of plane waves with momentum k given by $\psi(k)$ (the blue curve). Then the wavefunction in x-space (the red curve) is as depicted at the bottom, and the enveloping curve of the wavy pattern is again a gaussian.

Wave packets. This is certainly possible, as actually Schrödinger already pointed out. He studied what are called 'wave packets.' These are smooth linear combinations of say momentum eigenstates, which are localized in both position and momentum space. These packets have an average momentum k_0 and an average position and look in many aspects as extended particle-like objects.

The starting point is simple, namely to look for states where the uncertainty in canonically conjugate (incompatible) variables is minimized and balanced, respecting the Heisenberg uncertainty relations. But because the Schrödinger equation is linear we may consider arbitrary linear combinations of the states, and are then time-dependent solutions because the different momentum components have different energies.

Such a wave packet can be defined by specifying a func-

tion $\psi(k)$ and looking at the state

$$|\psi\rangle = \int \psi(k)|k\rangle \, dk .$$

As the formula suggests the function is just the ' wavefunction in momentum space', as we may write:

$$\psi(k) = \langle k|\psi\rangle .$$

Now let us take a smooth gaussian (normal distribution) centered around some momentum k_0,[8]

$$\psi(k) = \left(\frac{2\alpha}{\pi}\right)^{1/4} e^{-\alpha(k-k_0)^2} .$$

The factor in front makes sure that the state is properly normalized, so that all probabilities add up to one. We have displayed this function in Figure II.5.10 and indeed it is nicely peaked with a certain width around k_0.

Now we want to see what this package deal means for people who live in ordinary x or φ space. Using equation (II.5.6) we calculate:

$$\psi(\varphi) = \langle \varphi|\psi\rangle = \int \langle \varphi|k\rangle\langle k|\psi\rangle \, dk =$$
$$= \left(\frac{1}{2\pi\alpha}\right)^{1/4} e^{ik_0\varphi} e^{-\hbar\varphi^2/4\alpha} .$$

What do we see? First of all we see that the wavefunction of the state is also gaussian in φ space! That is nice because it does indeed mean that the packet is also well localized in position space, just as we wanted it. What we also see is that the width of that distribution is like the inverse of the width in momentum space. To be precise we have $\Delta k = \sqrt{1/2\alpha}$, and $\Delta\varphi = \sqrt{\alpha/2}$, which shows that the packet is optimal in the sense that it saturates the lower bound on the uncertainties imposed by Heisenberg: $\Delta k \, \Delta\varphi = 1/2$. Finally we see that the wavefunction in position space also has a factor $e^{ik_0\varphi}$, which makes the

---
[8]We discussed the gaussian or normal distribution in the *Math Excursion* on probability and statistics at the end of Chapter I.1. There it was also explained why this distribution pops up everywhere.

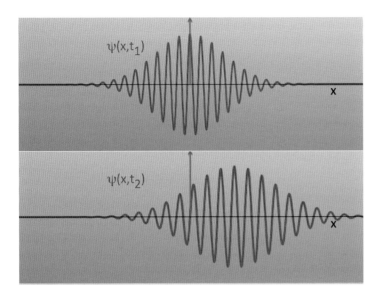

Figure II.5.11: *Wave packet dispersion*. The time evolution of the free wave packet according to the Schrödinger equation has two generic features:(i) it moves forward with the group velocity of the package which is the effective velocity of the 'particle', and (ii) the package will broaden (disperse) over time.

function periodic (and complex). The red curve depicted in the figure is (the real part of) the wave packet in coordinate space.

Propagation and dispersion. Let us assume that the configuration at $t = 0$ is the one we just described, then it is interesting to see what happens in time exactly because the packet is made up of momentum components that propagate with different speeds. The question is therefore what that means for the time evolution of the packet as a whole. We don't want to go through the calculation here, but the important message is sketched in Figure II.5.11. The first point to mention is that the center of the packet, or the *envelope* of the wavy pattern, moves with the so-called *group velocity*. This is a velocity which is different from the *phase velocity* of the individual momentum components. One typically sees the effect that the wavy pattern moves faster than the envelope and one sees the small wave appear on the left (increasing of amplitude) and

disappear at the right (decreasing of amplitude) of the envelope. The second point to mention is that the packet broadens in time, it *disperses*. If one calculates the probability distribution $p(\varphi)$ the periodicity drops out and we get a pure gaussian that is broadening, as we displayed already in Figure II.5.3 for a particle at rest. This dispersion worried among others Schrödinger himself quite a bit, because it basically blocked a direct interpretation of the wave packet as a particle, which basically seemed to disintegrate on quite short time scales. It was this aspect that was resolved by the probabilistic interpretation (the so-called *Copenhagener Deutung*) proposed by Born.

Raising and lowering operators.

Let us briefly talk about yet another way to represent the general particle state (II.5.7), which utilizes ladder or raising and lowering operators that are completely analogous to what we did for the qubit in (II.2.13) and (II.2.14). First we look for an operator that can step from a state $|k\rangle$ to $|(k+1)\rangle$. Consider the following so-called step operators:

$$t_\pm = e^{\pm i\Phi} \qquad (II.5.20)$$

where Φ is the coordinate operator given in (II.5.1) that satisfies $\Phi\ |\varphi_0\rangle = \varphi_0\ |\varphi_0\rangle$. Applying $t_\pm$ yields

$$t_\pm|k\rangle = e^{\pm i\Phi} \sqrt{\frac{1}{2\pi}} \int e^{ik\varphi}\ |\varphi\rangle\ d\varphi$$

$$= \sqrt{\frac{1}{2\pi}} \int e^{ik\varphi}\ e^{\pm i\varphi}\ |\varphi\rangle\ d\varphi = |k \pm 1\rangle \qquad (II.5.21)$$

where we let the operators act on the state $|\varphi\rangle$ in going from the first to the second line. So with $t_\pm$ one may step through the spectrum.

This is not yet what we want; what we really want is operators that start from some lowest energy states. The energy of the free particle state to be equal $E_k = p_k^2/2m = \hbar^2 k^2/2m$ then the lowest energy state is $|0\rangle$ with $E_0 = 0$. We like the right and left moving states to be generated from some lowest energy states. Consider then, instead of

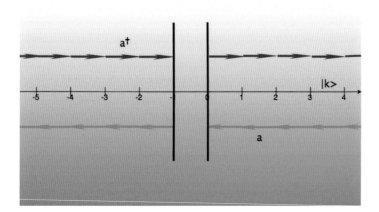

Figure II.5.12: *Step operators*. Action of the ladder or step operators $a^\dagger$ (raising-purple) and a (lowering-green) defined in equation (II.5.22) on the space of states labeled by $|k\rangle$. There are two sectors: the right movers with $k \geq 0$ and the left movers with $k \leq -1$.

the operators $t_\pm$, the two related ladder operators[9]:

$$a = e^{-i\Phi}P, \quad a^\dagger = Pe^{i\Phi}, \qquad (\text{II}.5.22)$$

these satisfy interesting commutation relations:

$$[a, a] = [a^\dagger, a^\dagger] = 0, \quad \text{and} \quad [a, a^\dagger] = 2P + 1. \quad (\text{II}.5.23)$$

Furthermore we see that for a free particle (with m=1) we can write the Hamiltonian as:

$$H = \frac{1}{2}a^\dagger a = \frac{1}{2}P^2. \qquad (\text{II}.5.24)$$

If we apply the operators to some state $|k\rangle$, we obtain:

$$a^\dagger |k\rangle = (k+1)|k+1\rangle, \quad a|k\rangle = k|k-1\rangle,$$

which illustrates the fact that these operators basically raise or lower the momentum of the state by one unit. These constructions demonstrate two surprising properties of the states and operators. With these operators you can indeed

walk through the sample space of states but you will run into certain 'no trespassing' signs, where the next step you make you would let you disappear into nothing! The first one tells you that if you act with a you may come down from positive k al the way down to $k = 0$, but not any further because $a|0\rangle = 0$. However if you start from $|k = -1\rangle$, then a will walk you down all the way to minus infinity. Something similar happens with $a^\dagger$: it walks you up from any negative value until you hit $|-1\rangle$ where it halts, but starting at $|0\rangle$ it will bring you all the way to plus infinity. What this means that the spectrum naturally breaks up into two pieces: one of which you could define as the right movers with $k \geq 0$ and the other as the left movers with $k < 0$.

State operators. We can now also construct operators that directly create any momentum state from the ground-state. For example the state $|k\rangle$ can be obtained by acting k times with $a^\dagger$ on the ground state $|0\rangle$, as the following calculation shows:

$$|k\rangle = \frac{a^\dagger}{k}|k-1\rangle = \dots = \frac{(a^\dagger)^k}{k!}|0\rangle.$$

The general state $|\Psi\rangle$ could also be symmetrically represented like an operator:

$$|\Psi\rangle = \Psi|0\rangle = (\alpha_0 + \Sigma_{k=1}\frac{1}{k!}(\alpha_k a^{\dagger k} + \alpha_{-k}b^k))|0\rangle,$$
$$(\text{II}.5.25)$$

where we have defined what you could call a 'particle-state' operator Ψ and b is a shifted operator $b = e^{-i\Phi}(P - 1)$. The correspondence between states and these type of step operators acting on a 'vacuum' or 'ground' state will be of great use if we move from quantum particles to quantum fields as we will do in the next section. ∎

[9]In the remainder of this section we set $\hbar = 1$, to keep the formulas simple.

The harmonic oscillator

Oscillators everywhere! The harmonic oscillator or the 'particle in a harmonic oscillator potential' is a system that is treated extensively in any book on quantum physics and classical physics alike. In spite of the fact that we do not see swinging pendulums all over the place, the simple truth is that the world around us is actually largely made up of oscillators! One way to understand that is to realize that most 'things' are in a state of equilibrium, in other words they are in a state of minimum energy. And yes, if you perturb a system in equilibrium, it will start to oscillate about its equilibrium state. You knock on the table, you drop a stone in the lake, the days, the seasons, economic cycles, the orientation of the Earth's axis, the strings of your guitar and of string theory, the rhythms of life: all are oscillatory motions in some suitable space.

So imagine the horizontal axis describing the displacement of some relevant variable from equilibrium, and let us call that variable, yes indeed, x, then along the vertical axis we plot the energy V (as a function of x). This function generically will have a particular shape. It will have a minimum at $x = 0$, and if we think that we study small perturbations we might look at V(x) close to the origin and describe it effectively as an expansion in (positive) powers of x. The first term would be linear, but that could not be because it would not correspond to a minimum anymore, the minimum would have shifted away. So the first relevant term would be the quadratic term which we write as $V(x) = \frac{1}{2}\omega^2 x^2$. You get the bowl-shaped potential depicted in Figure II.5.14. In Newtonian mechanics this would imply a force $F = -dV/dx = -\omega^2 x$, thus a linear force trying to move the system back to the equilibrium position. This is not surprisingly called a harmonic force. As you can think of a marble rolling forth and back in the bowl. We discussed this dynamical system at length in Chapter I.1. It is important to now look at quantum oscillators because the microscopic world is also beset with them. This is a model

Figure II.5.13: *The stepwell of Chand Baori. These remarkable stepwells in India were once used to store water. Chand Baori is made up of 3.500 steps over 13 stories. The steps look like states forming a discrete spectrum of some quantum system.*(Source: Wikimedia.)

system that at first looks like one of these totally boring academic, dry-nerd-drill-home-trainer kind of things. The deadliest didactic horse ever. No! Imagine, its applications on all rungs of the quantum ladder are quite stunning and we will come across a few of them. So, please stay with me for this one.

If we return to basics, our starting point is the simple Hamiltonian for a unit mass particle in a harmonic potential:

$$H = \frac{1}{2}(p^2 + \omega^2 x^2). \qquad (II.5.26)$$

The classical equations are,

$$\frac{dx}{dt} = p\,, \qquad \frac{dp}{dt} = -\omega^2 x\,.$$

We will treat these equations in the Heisenberg picture meaning that we have time dependent operators $X(t)$ and $P(t)$ with the canonical commutation relations:[10] $[X, P] =$

---

[10] if we postulate them at $t = 0$, the unitary time evolution ensures

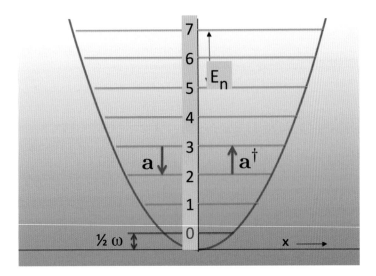

Figure II.5.14: *Harmonic oscillator.* Action of the ladder or step operators $a^\dagger$ (raising) and a (lowering) defined in equation (II.5.29) on the space of energy eigenstates $|n\rangle$. The ground state $|0\rangle$ has energy $E_0 = 1/2\omega$.

$[X(t), P(t)] = i\hbar$. Interestingly the equations can then be solved by using (commutator) algebra only. These are coupled equations, and you can decouple them by using the complex linear combinations which are as we will see *raising and lowering operators*:

$$a(t) = \sqrt{\frac{1}{2\omega}}(\omega X + iP) \equiv \tilde{X} + i\tilde{P} \qquad (\text{II.5.27})$$

$$a^\dagger(t) = \sqrt{\frac{1}{2\omega}}(\omega X - iP) \equiv \tilde{X} - i\tilde{P}. \qquad (\text{II.5.28})$$

The solutions have simple phases:

$$a(t) = a e^{-i\omega t} \qquad a^\dagger(t) = a^\dagger e^{+i\omega t}, \qquad (\text{II.5.29})$$

these satisfy simple commutation relations:

$$[a, a] = [a^\dagger, a^\dagger] = 0, \text{ and } [a, a^\dagger] = 1. \qquad (\text{II.5.30})$$

Furthermore we see that for the particle in a harmonic potential we can write the Hamiltonian as:

$$H = \omega(a^\dagger a + \frac{1}{2}). \qquad (\text{II.5.31})$$

that they remain valid over time.

These operators raise or lower the energy of energy eigenstate with one step. This follows from the commutation relations:

$$[H, a] = -\omega a, \qquad (\text{II.5.32})$$

$$[H, a^\dagger] = +\omega a^\dagger. \qquad (\text{II.5.33})$$

Let us define the eigenstates $|n\rangle$ of the Hamiltonian as

$$H |n\rangle = E_n |n\rangle, \qquad (\text{II.5.34})$$

then with (II.5.32), we obtain that applying $a^\dagger$ to a state $|n\rangle$, creates the state $|n + 1\rangle$, because

$$H \{a^\dagger|n\rangle\} = (E_n + \omega)\{a^\dagger|n\rangle\},$$

and similarly for $|a\rangle$ with a minus sign on the right-hand side of the equations. Now we can see what we have gained with these manipulations. First we better assume that there is a lowest energy state $|0\rangle$ and as the energy cannot be lower we have to assume that the lowering operator gives zero when acting on this state:

$$a|0\rangle = 0, \qquad (\text{II.5.35})$$

and thus:

$$H |0\rangle = \frac{1}{2}\omega |0\rangle.$$

From this one can show other quantessential properties:

$$E_n = (n + \frac{1}{2})\omega,$$

and,

$$|n\rangle = \frac{(a^\dagger)^n}{\sqrt{n!}} |0\rangle.$$

The results are summarized in Figure II.5.14. There are a few points worth mentioning. Firstly, the spectrum is equally spaced, and we have degenerate left and right movers. So it easy to construct raising and lowering operators. It is worth mentioning here already that later on in this chapter we will see an application of the oscillator algebra in field theory, where the operators $a^\dagger$ and a do not move you through the spectrum of states of a single particle, but rather they act as creation and annihilation operators of particles in a given state, acting on a multi-particle Hilbert space. The second point is that the ground state has a non-vanishing 'zero point energy' equal $\frac{1}{2}\omega$, which basically follows from the uncertainty relations which do not allow the quantum particle be at rest at the bottom of the potential. The momentum (energy) cannot be zero. And indeed if you think of a table which is made up of zillions (or better 10^{25} or so) of oscillating particles you may wonder about the energy that appears to be just sitting there. In the cellar as it were, an incredible amount of vacuum, energy. What if....? May be we should just be cavalier about it and put in the same category as our friend the 'filled Dirac sea', where the physics basically only starts once you are on top, at the surface.

Constructing the wavefunctions. The explicit expressions for the wavefunctions $\psi_n(x) = \langle x|n \rangle$ are most easily obtained recursively starting from the ground state. The ground state wavefunction can be constructed by solving the equation (II.5.35) as follows:

$$a|0\rangle = 0$$

$$\Rightarrow \quad (\omega X + \frac{d}{dx})\psi_0(x) = 0.$$

This is a differential equation with the (normalized) gaussian solution:

$$\psi_0(x) = (\frac{\omega}{\pi})^{1/4} e^{-\frac{\omega}{2}x^2}.$$

The higher states are obtained by repeatedly applying the raising operator $a^\dagger = \sqrt{\frac{1}{2\omega}}(\omega X - d/dx)$ on this ground state. So one just has to differentiate the ground state which is relatively easy to do. The resulting wavefunctions $\psi_n(x) = \langle x|n \rangle$ for the lowest n values were already displayed in Figure II.5.4 on page 149.

Coherent states

Let us return to the question of constructing quantum states that do look like a classical particle . These correspond to a *wave packet*, where we start combining waves in such a way that they have a reasonable width both in momentum and position space. We look for states that have a minimal spread about the average values of the variables, thereby making the uncertainty around a corresponding point in classical phase space in all directions as small as possible. Such states were already considered by Schrödinger and are nowadays called *coherent states*. They represent a wide class of states that just like the oscillator system have found many applications. These vary from quantum mechanics, optics, quantum chemistry, atomic physics, statistical physics, nuclear physics, particle physics, quantum information theory, group theory, and cosmology, to mention a few.

Let us now apply this idea to the states of a particle in the harmonic oscillator potential. We introduced the classical version of the harmonic oscillator already in the first chapter of Volume I on page 14. The periodic motion in configuration space that corresponds to a circular motion in phase space is characteristic. We now want to construct quantum states that show similar behavior. These cannot be the stationary energy eigenstates we have just been constructing in this subsection.

Minimal uncertainty states. From the commutator,

$$[\tilde{X}, \tilde{P}] = i\hbar,$$

directly follows the standard form of the uncertainty relation:

$$\Delta(\tilde{X})\,\Delta(\tilde{P}) \geq \frac{\hbar}{2}. \tag{II.5.36}$$

What we would like to find is a state where we have that

$$\Delta(\tilde{X}) = \Delta(\tilde{P}) = \Delta,$$

$$\Delta^2 = \frac{\hbar}{2}.$$

The states that achieve this are eigenstates of the lowering operator a, so we have:

$$a\,|\lambda\rangle = \lambda\,|\lambda\rangle,\qquad(\text{II.5.37})$$

these eigenstates have the basic property that $\lambda = \langle\lambda|a|\lambda\rangle$, but also that:

$$\langle E\rangle = \langle\lambda|E|\lambda\rangle = \frac{\omega}{2}\langle\lambda|(a^\dagger a + \frac{1}{2})|\lambda\rangle = \frac{1}{2}\omega(|\lambda|^2 + 1).$$

Let us pause here for an instant. The question here is not to construct a ground state or an eigenstate of a given Hamiltonian, it rather is to construct eigenstates of the annihilation operator, with some eigenvalue λ. This problem is analogous to the construction of the translation operator that we discussed in equation (II.6.6). If we have an eigenfunction of position, where the expectation value of x is given by zero, we may apply the translation operator $T(a)$ to it, and shift the argument of the wavefunction so that $\psi(x) \to \psi(x+a)$. Then the vacuum expectation value will shift to $\langle x\rangle = -a$. And indeed the procedure is closely related, the desired state can be made out of the vacuum by a 'translation' operator built from the conjugate variable, in this case not the translation generated by the momentum P, but by $a^\dagger$:

$$|\lambda\rangle = e^{\lambda a^\dagger}|0\rangle.\qquad(\text{II.5.38})$$

So, if we write $a = (\tilde X + i\tilde P)$, then such states have the property that:

$$(\tilde X + i\tilde P)|\lambda\rangle = ((\langle\tilde X\rangle + i\langle\tilde P\rangle))|\lambda\rangle = \lambda\,|\lambda\rangle.\qquad(\text{II.5.39})$$

Because for an eigenstate, the expectation value of the operator is equal to the eigenvalue. Bringing terms to the other side we obtain that:

$$|\tilde X - \langle\tilde X\rangle| = |\tilde P - \langle\tilde P\rangle|,$$

which establishes that the variances are equal: $\Delta(\tilde X) =$

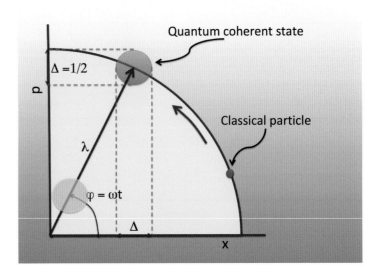

Figure II.5.15: *A fuzzy particle.* Phase space picture of the coherent state wavepacket with its fixed uncertainties for large values of λ. The coherent state x and p expectation values follow the classical trajectories but they carry a disk of uncertainties with diameter $\hbar/2$ along.

$\Delta(\tilde P) = \Delta$. From the equation (II.5.39)

$$\langle a^\dagger a\rangle = \lambda^2 = \langle(\tilde X - i\tilde P)(\tilde X + i\tilde P)\rangle =$$
$$= \langle(\tilde X^2 + \tilde P^2 + i[\tilde X,\tilde P]\rangle =$$
$$= \langle\tilde X^2\rangle + \langle\tilde P^2\rangle - \hbar.$$

Taking the absolute square of equation (II.5.39), which contains the expectation values. This gives the result:

$$\lambda^2 = \langle\tilde X\rangle^2 + \langle\tilde P\rangle^2.$$

Combining the two previous results we obtain the equation for the sum of the variances:

$$\Delta(\tilde X)^2 + \Delta(\tilde P)^2 = 2\Delta^2 = \hbar,$$

giving $\Delta^2 = \hbar/2$ which is the minimum value allowed.

A fuzzy particle. What have we learned? Firstly that it is indeed possible to construct wave packets or coherent states in which the uncertainties in position ϕ and momentum n match. In fact we found a continuum of different states $|\lambda\rangle$ that satisfy those conditions, and these states are labeled by the real parameter λ. Secondly we saw that average momentum is of order lambda, while the width of the momentum distribution in such a state is fixed and equal $\frac{1}{2}\hbar$. This means that if we increase λ the probability cloud of the particle becomes relatively narrow. The resulting overall picture is displayed in Figure II.5.15. The radial direction is the 'a' or therefore λ axis with real component x and imaginary component p. The time dependence of $a(t)$ is $a(t) = a\exp(i\omega t)$ as given in equation (II.5.29), so ωt is the angular variable in the figure. The resulting expectation values $\langle x(t)\rangle$ and $\langle p(t)\rangle$ describe the same trajectory in phase space as the classical particle would do. The classical periodic motion was depicted in Figure II.5.1 and the corresponding circular motion in phase space in Figure II.5.2 on page 146. We have emphasized that the uncertainties in postion and momentum are fixed and independent of λ, which means that the approximation of the classical picture improves if we increase λ. This basically corresponds to the limit of high momentum or energy levels, where you would indeed expect classical behavior because the energies are large compared to the ground state level. However, note that as a function of time, the packet will broaden because the various momentum components move at different velocities. We depicted this type of broadening as a function of time in Figure II.5.3. ■ ■

The energy spectrum of coherent states.
In this final paragraph of this section we show what the states $|\lambda\rangle$ look like if we decompose them in energy eigenstates. To do so we use a cute little trick. Note that the a operator, because of the commutation relation with $a^\dagger$, can be thought of as differentiation with respect to $a^\dagger$. This means that we can write:

$$a|n\rangle = a\left(\frac{(a^\dagger)^n}{\sqrt{n!}}|0\rangle\right) = n\left(\frac{(a^\dagger)^{n-1}}{\sqrt{n!}}|0\rangle\right) = \sqrt{n}\,|n-1\rangle.$$

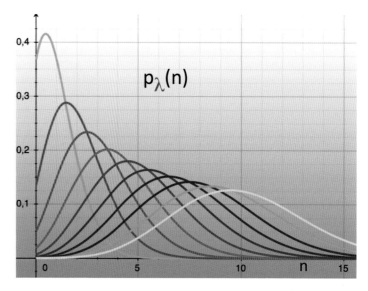

Figure II.5.16: *Coherent states.* The probability distributions $p_\lambda(n)$ given in equation (II.5.40) for finding energy $n \sim \lambda^2$ in a coherent state $|\lambda\rangle$ for $\lambda^2 = 1, \ldots, 10$.

The states $|\lambda\rangle$ can be obtained by finding a recursion relation for the coefficients α_n in (II.5.25) by imposing the defining equation (II.5.37):

$$a\left(\sum_{n=0}^{\infty}\alpha_n|n\rangle\right) = \sum \alpha_n\sqrt{n}|n-1\rangle = \lambda\left(\sum_{n=0}^{\infty}\alpha_n|n\rangle\right).$$

Matching corresponding components we obtain the recursion relation:

$$\alpha_n = \frac{\lambda}{\sqrt{n}}\alpha_{n-1}.$$

This means that the states are given by:

$$|\lambda\rangle = N\sum_{n=0}^{\infty}\frac{\lambda^n}{\sqrt{n!}}|n\rangle,$$

with the normalization constant[11] $N = \exp(-|\lambda|^2/2)$. So what we have constructed here are coherent states parametrized by a parameter λ which have minimal and equal uncertainties for both conjugate phase space variables.

_____
[11]Normalization of the state gives:
$\langle\lambda|\lambda\rangle = N^2 \sum_{n=0}^{\infty}|\lambda|^{2n}/n! = N^2\exp(|\lambda|^2) = 1$.

These states have many momentum components; in fact we can calculate the energy distribution, for large λ it becomes:

$$p_\lambda(n) = |\langle n|\lambda\rangle|^2 = \left(\frac{|\lambda|^{2n}}{n!}\right) e^{-|\lambda|^2}. \qquad (\text{II}.5.40)$$

These are so-called Poisson distributions and we have plotted them in Figure II.5.16 for values $\lambda^2 = 1,\ldots,10$. We easily calculate the average :

$$\langle n\rangle = \langle\lambda|n|\lambda\rangle = \langle a^\dagger a\rangle = \lambda^2. \qquad (\text{II}.5.41)$$

whereas for the average of n^2 we obtain:

$$\langle n^2\rangle = \langle a^\dagger a a^\dagger a\rangle = \langle(a^\dagger)^2 a^2 + a^\dagger a\rangle\lambda^2 = \lambda^4 + \lambda^2.$$

Combining the two we find for the variance:

$$(\Delta n)^2 = \langle n^2\rangle - \langle n\rangle^2 = \lambda^2. \qquad (\text{II}.5.42)$$

We see that the the the average of n is proportional to λ^2 while the width of the distribution goes like λ. This means that for increasing λ, the distribution relatively narrows . This is of course consistent with our calculation from the uncertainty relation (II.5.36) where we found the same variance. The resulting situation is summarized in Figure II.5.15. ■ ■ ■

Figure II.5.17: A 1962 conversation between Dirac (left) and Feynman (right) at a conference in Warsaw. (Source: Courtesy of Caltec Photo Archives.)

Fields: particle species

In this section on quantum fields we bring together a number of insights that we have touched upon in previous chapters. When saying field theory, we start by thinking about *free fields*, these are described for example by the Maxwell equations, the Klein–Gordon or the Dirac equation. All of them are relativistic wave equations and the question is what it means to *quantize* them.

Let us make some observations first.
(i) Fields are defined over all of space and they typically have an infinite number of degrees of freedom, and in that sense you can think of them as equivalent to an infinite number of particles.
(ii) You can think of the fields as being the generalized coordinates, meaning to say that the configuration space which for a single particle is just 'x'-space is now the space of field configurations.
(iii) In Chapter I.1 we have shown that for a field like the electromagnetic field we can define an energy and a momentum density and the logic of field quantization is to run the same program as before, and impose canonical quantization conditions for fields (as coordinates) and their associated momenta.

Thie procedure is quite involved and it took about thirty years before the first consistent field theory named Quantum electrodynamics (QED) was completed.

Field quantization. Without going through any calculations, which are generally quite messy and extensive, let me nevertheless give you some feeling for the results which are strikingly simple and beautiful.[12] And to transcend the swamp of words let me take the example of the simple scalar particle described by the Klein–Gordon field $\phi(x, t)$, which has to satisfy the relativistic equation

$$(\Box + m^2)\phi(x^\mu) = 0.$$

This has solutions which can be expanded as a sum of plane wave solutions with coefficients a and a^* look like:

$$\phi(x^\mu) = N \sum_k \frac{1}{\sqrt{\omega_k}} [a_k e^{ik^\mu} + a_k^* e^{-ik^\mu}],$$

with the definitions $x^\mu = (ct, \mathbf{x})$ and $k^\mu = (\omega_k, \mathbf{k})$ and moreover the K-G equation imposes $\omega_k = \sqrt{\mathbf{k}^2 + m^2}$. The coefficients have to be each other's complex conjugates to make the field real. In this case the momentum field would just be $\pi(x^\mu) = d\phi/dt$ which is indeed the time derivative of the 'coordinate' field.

Oscillators once more. In the present context the fields are the observables! So the quantum fields are operators, and as they are time-dependent, they are Heisenberg type operators. What that means is that in the above expression which is called mode expansion, the field ϕ on left-hand side becomes an operator, and on the right-hand side the operator property is carried by the coefficients. The modes are just the classical plain waves multiplied by operator coefficients a_k and their conjugates $a_k^\dagger$. These act now like creation and annihilation operators. Performing the calculational gymnastics of imposing the commutation relations for the fields ϕ and π in the end boils down to commutation

---

[12]In this section we have set $\hbar = c = 1$ for convenience.

relations between the operator coefficients. The upshot is surprisingly simple:

$$[a_k, a_{k'}] = [a_k^\dagger, a_{k'}^\dagger] = 0, \qquad \text{(II.5.43)}$$

$$[a_k, a_{k'}^\dagger] = \delta_{k,k'}^{(3)}. \qquad \text{(II.5.44)}$$

But now the air clears up! Compare this result with the commutation relations in (II.5.30). What have we got? We have obtained an infinite number of harmonic oscillators, each labeled by a momentum vector $\mathbf{k}$, and having a frequency ω_k. So, one (free) quantum field is equivalent to an infinity of oscillators and that rings an infinity of bells. The energy or Hamiltonian H of the field is *not* so surprising:

$$H = \sum_k \omega_k \left(N_k + \frac{1}{2}\right),$$

with $N_k \equiv a_k^\dagger a_k$, the so-called *number* operator. There is also a total momentum vector $\mathbf{P} = \{H, \mathbf{P}\}$ for the field:

$$\mathbf{P} = \sum_k \mathbf{k}_\mu \left(N_k + \frac{1}{2}\right).$$

The above equations naturally combine in an energy-momentum four vector P_μ for the field.

Multi-particle Hilbert space. And what does the Hilbert space for such a free field look like? Well, first we define a vacuum state $|0\rangle$ with the defining property that is annihilated by all a_k operators. Now we act with a creation operator on the vacuum:

$$a_k^\dagger |0\rangle = |n_k\rangle \text{ with } n_k = 1.$$

This means that we have made a step in energy of $E = \hbar\omega = \sqrt{(mc^2)^2 + (\hbar\mathbf{k}c)^2}$, where I have put the constants back in. That energy corresponds exactly to the relativistic energy of a single particle of mass m with energy $E = \hbar\omega_k$ and momentum $\mathbf{p} = \hbar\mathbf{k}$. So, we are not raising the energy of a single particle. No, every time we work with an $a^\dagger$ operator we *create* an additional particle of the type described by the field in the corresponding momentum state.

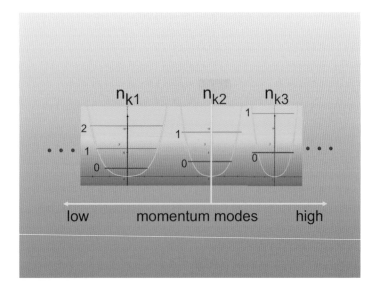

Figure II.5.18: *Quantum field modes.* A quantum state of a quantum field is labeled by the energy-momentum ($\vec{k}$) modes of the single particle, and the number of particles n_k that are in that mode.

And the annihilation operator does exactly the opposite. How charming and quantessential: the same algebra in another context creates another reality! The upshot is that we have a multi-particle Hilbert space, often called Fock space, with states,

$$|\{n_\mathbf{k}\}\rangle, \text{ with } N \, |\{n_\mathbf{k}\}\rangle = n_k \, |\{n_\mathbf{k}\}\rangle .$$

We have ended up with a clip and clear framework indeed.

The Klein–Gordon field is the simplest one to think of because it is just a field with one real component, but what about the other fields, like the Maxwell and Dirac field? Yes and no, their quantization is both similar but at the same time very different, also because their classical content is very different. In the Dirac case we have to understand what it means to have the Dirac sea and how to implement the anti-particles. Now the basic relations for the operators

are *anti-commutation relations*,

$$\{b_{s,\mathbf{p}}, b_{s',\mathbf{p}'}\} = \{b_{s,\mathbf{p}}^\dagger, b_{s',\mathbf{p}'}^\dagger\} = 0 \qquad (\text{II.5.45})$$

$$\{b_{s,\mathbf{p}}, b_{s',\mathbf{p}'}^\dagger\} = \delta_{ss'}\delta_{\mathbf{p},\mathbf{p}'}^{(3)}, \qquad (\text{II.5.46})$$

and an identical set for the anti-particle creation and annihilation operators $d_{s,\mathbf{p}}^\dagger$ and $d_{s,\mathbf{p}}$. The index s denotes the spin state of the (anti-)particle. The anti-commutator is defined as the symmetric product, for example:

$$\{b_{s,\mathbf{p}}^\dagger, b_{s',\mathbf{p}'}^\dagger\} \equiv b_{s,\mathbf{p}}^\dagger, b_{s',\mathbf{p}'}^\dagger + b_{s',\mathbf{p}'}^\dagger, b_{s,\mathbf{p}}^\dagger .$$

This definition has a profound implication that becomes manifest if you look let the equation for a vanishing commutator work on the vacuum. It yields the result,

$$b_{s,\mathbf{p}}^\dagger, b_{s',\mathbf{p}'}^\dagger|0\rangle = -b_{s',\mathbf{p}'}^\dagger, b_{s,\mathbf{p}}^\dagger|0\rangle .$$

The two-particle states on the right and left have two particles in the same individual states but they are interchanged. We have interchanged two identical particles and that gives a crucial minus sign because of the anti-commutators. The relation with the Pauli principle becomes even more direct if you put $p' = p$ and $s' = s$, because then you get that that particular state equals minus itself, which means that that state is equal to zero! It says that such a state is just not there. It is not the ground state but a true no-state: a clearer statement of exclusion is hardly imaginable! With the Dirac equation everything fell into place: the spin appeared as necessary ingredient, along with the exclusion principle after the correct quantization. And then anti-matter as a bonus. How delightful! For the Maxwell field, it is the gauge invariance which has caused some profound headaches. But today all these difficulties have been overcome, and these type of (gauge) fields and their quantization form the basis of a consistent description of all particles carrying forces or interactions in the Standard Model.

Interactions. Of course if we discuss quantum field theory there is more than the quantization of free fields, it is a multi-particle framework but the all-important interactions are left out. Isn't this about throwing out babies with the bathing water? No! This is a basic framework that is an absolutely vital starting point for any further going discussion.

Perturbative approaches. We have in Chapter II.1 already described some of the interactions that are present in the standard model. The basic interactions are characterized by certain interaction vertices, diagrams where different particles interact at a given space-time point. That point is where particles are annihilated and created in particular states that ensure that all the conservation laws like energy, momentum or charge, are respected. Each complete diagram then contributes to the overall probability amplitude for the process to take place.

This approach is called a *perturbative approach*, which is an iterative procedure to get ever better results, because in the calculations you include more and more complicated, higher-order diagrams. And as long as the coupling constant is small – and for QED for example the coupling strength is $\alpha = e^2/4\pi\hbar c \simeq 1/137$ – the higher order terms become tiny.

This way relatively low-order calculations already give incredibly accurate answers. And this scheme has led to the spectacular demonstrations of the power of quantum field theory, as for example in the calculation of the anomalous magnetic moments of the electron and the muon. The calculations are up to fourth order in α, and coincide with the best observed values up to 10 significant digits. This makes it the most accurately verified prediction in the history of physics!

Beyond perturbation theory. But in many situations it is necessary to go beyond perturbation theory. If either the particle density is large, or if the temperature gets very low, or the interactions become strong, one needs other approaches. And in the past century a lot of progress

The other currency

G: Hey Orange, I really like the stuff you told me about Dirac.
O: I am happy you liked it, Green. But you are right, he's a kind of a genius!
G: Yeah. That's what I thought, but more an anti-genius may be, chr chrr chrr!
O: He must have been very happy, with making discoveries of such profound importance for mankind.
G: Yeah. Hey Orange, I presume he must have become very, very rich.
O: You mean like Bill Gates or Warren Buffett.
G: or Prince or Picasso?
O: or Irving Stone or...
G: or Oprah!
O: Yes, you would think so Green. But no, I have to disappoint you.
G: But Orange, if you do such great works...
O: It didn't happen.
G: You mean that others have stolen his ideas?
O: No Green, it is not that. You have to understand Green, for scientific achievements like Einstein's of Dirac's or Heisenberg's there are no rights.
G: Are you telling me that they forgot to manage their copyrights or patents? These brilliant men didn't do their homework, is that it, chr chrr chrr.
O: Quiet down Green. Respect! Let me tell you this: a formula isn't like a novel, or a song, or baseball game, or a paperclip, or a diesel engine, or a talk show.
G: Are you saying that in the big scheme of things it is just marginal.

O: Yes indeed, Green, thank you. Now you understand what I mean.

G: Thank you Orange, I think I am going to have a peanut butter jelly sandwich! A Schrödinger-Dirac--Heisenberg sandwich! chr chrr chrrr.

O: Green! Listen, the scientist have another type of currency.

G: Like bitcoins?

O: Yes Green, but they call them *citations*.

G: What do those buy you?

O: Well, you know, Green, you know this game called monopoly? You can make a lot of money ...

G: I am getting really hungry. Thanks Orange. □

has been made in developing alternative non-perturbative ways of using field theory. We will discuss some important examples in the context of condensed matter physics in Chapter III.3.

Often situations where perturbation theory breaks down have to do with identifying some highly non-trivial ground state and start from there. For example it may be that a certain particle-type will condense in the ground state, so that it is no longer an eigenstate of the number operators $N_{s,\mathbf{k}}$. In fact one finds that some number density operator has a non-vanishing expectation value in the new ground state. The ground state of the super conductor is a canonical and beautiful example.

The phenomenon of superconductivity was discovered by Kamerlingh Onnes, but It took more than half a century to arrive at a really deep understanding of the underlying mechanism. Among other things the message to science seemed to be: 'Never give up!'

Let us briefly indicate what it means that the ground state of a physical system is characterized by some condensate.

Think of the electrons in a conductor: they interact over relatively long distances via the lattice vibrations, which after quantization go under the name *phonons*. This phonon induced interaction between the electrons turns out to be attractive, and leads to a pairwise binding of the electrons of opposite spin and momentum. The electrons form so-called Cooper pairs. These pairs having spin equal zero, are of course bosons and therefore they can all condense in the same state. Indeed the ground state is a coherent state of Cooper pairs, which can be thought of as a linear combination of states with all possible different numbers of pairs in it. The system gains an enormous energy by dropping in this ground state, because the exclusion principle had pushed the individual electrons up to quite high energies. And starting from this ground state one has been able to prove all relevant properties of superconductors, using the successful BCS theory developed by the American physicists, John Bardeen, Neil Cooper and Robert Schrieffer, who received the Physics Nobel prize in 1964.

Ground states as coherent states. This situation is similar to the one we encountered in the previous section about the harmonic oscillator, looking at the phenomena of coherent states. In view of the almost uncomfortably close analogies between field theory and simple oscillators, it is imperative to ask about coherent states in field theory. What do they look like and what would the physics be like? Multi-particle coherence! What kind of bulk properties would that correspond to? And what low energy excitations would be there? Do we recognize them? What are interactions those 'trivial' agents could have engaged in, to give rise to such weird states? Here we enter a domain of what P.W. Anderson so beautifully characterized as 'more is different.' Many identical particles can, because of the interactions they have, give rise to highly non-trivial, highly diverse – but also highly non-recognizable – forms of collective behavior. Just like people, I am tempted to say. We have already encountered some of them, like quark confinement and the Higgs mechanism, but in the final part of the book on structural hierarchies we will discuss many complex collective manifestations that emerge from the astonishing simplicity which we have exhibited here. The rich diversity of the condensed states of matter is the smashing consequence of having simple basic agents with simple basic interactions.

Particle spin and statistics

A quantessential principle with tremendous explanatory power is Wolfgang Pauli's exclusion principle, decreeing that two or more Dirac-type particles (like electrons, neutrino's, or quarks) cannot occupy the same quantum state. Not all particles obey the principle, but if the particle does, it is called a fermion, *and it also needs to have half-integral spin, just like the usual fermions described by a Dirac like equation. In this section we discuss a more direct and therefore more accessible approach to quantum statistical properties, based on the topology of the two-particle configuration space. The discourse is systematically built up, starting from the notions of indistinguishability and exclusion to describing particle interchange and the spin-statistics connection.*

Indistinguishability

In quantum field theory, the loss of particle identity
is inevitable

In quantum field theory the states correspond in general to many-particle states. These states are described by one field, or wavefunction, and this implies that individual particles are no longer distinguishable entities. A severe loss of identity in the quantum world. It is a world where only family names exist; first names are just not there.

Figure II.5.19: *The Encounter.* This magical etching of Maurits Escher's was made in 1944. (© 2023 The M.C. Escher Company.)

The fact that multi-particle states are related to a single field implies an additional property, namely, that the corresponding particles loose their individuality. Individual particles of a given type, described by one type of field become indistinguishable. It may be that some state of an electron field describes two electrons, one electron in state A and one in state B, but you cannot say that particle 1 sits in A and particle 2 sits in B. They are like identical twins carrying a family name only but no first name. There is no 'John is at home' and 'Peter is at school', even though you *can* say that one is at home and the other at school. There is no 'who is who' in electron land (what a relief!), just strict anonymity and for that matter perfect democracy. Particles have a family name only. It may remind you of extremely strict school outfit rules: identical uniforms, identical shoes, and identical haircuts, in an attempt to wash away individual differences. Not my cup of tea. Anyway, this severe quantum loss of identity affects the counting of the available number of 'different states', and therefore the statistics properties of ensembles of such quantum particles. The statistical properties of the particles in turn are quantessential for understanding their collective behavior.

We will later return to the basic reason for that loss of individuality, being that all multi-particle/antiparticle states of a given species correspond to states of a single field describing that species, say the electron field or the photon field.

Exclusion

We have seen that quantization basically implies the study of wavefunctions of the classical configuration space. So we want to just focus on the special case that is of particular interest. Imagine that we have two particles that are 'identical', meaning that they are indistinguishable. These two-particles states are described by a single wavefunction defined on the two-particle configuration space, depending on the two position coordinates x_1 and x_2. But the indistinguishability of the particles implies that certain configurations which look different at first have to be identified. If somebody asks us to count the number of different (distinguishable) states, then we have to identify all configurations where the positions of identical particles are interchanged. Again, it's like a class where we have an identical twin, and we ask on how many different class configurations there are. Assuming that the twins are indeed indistinguishable by all means, we would have to count the state where twin A is in the front row and twin B in the back row and the configuration where they have switched places, as one and the same configuration. You see that the condition of indistinguishability affects the way we count the number of possible states, and therefore what the statistical weights are that we have to assign for certain configurations to occur.

There is however another important distinction we want to make right from the start. We may want to implement an exclusion rule saying that twins are not allowed to sit on the same chair. They may like each other but their sympathy is limited and sitting on the same chair is just out of the question. A rare occasion where the teacher and the twins seem to fully agree! Back to identical and indistinguishable particles, imagine the first particle has coordinate x_1 and the second x_2. The quantum state is then described by a two-particle wavefunction $\psi(x_1, x_2)$ depending on both coordinates. The question is now what we can say about the wavefunction if the two particles get interchanged, i.e. $\psi(x_1, x_2) \to \psi(x_2, x_1)$. Yes, their configuration is identical in that there is no experiment that can distinguish the two situations from each other – the usual nightmare for all twins. But does that imply that the wavefunctions have to be strictly equal? That's the question.

Unobservable phases? Taking into account all lessons we have been exposed to so far, we can say that the two wavefunctions can only differ by a subtle attribute that is not observable, namely the overall phase. It is subtle and seems completely innocuous but as we will see it is of crucial importance. This sounds indeed paradoxical, a supposedly unobservable phase that manifests itself. Let us first give the argument the naive and sloppy way, and say that the wavefunctions differ by a phase factor:

$$\psi(x_2, x_1) = e^{i\alpha}\psi(x_1, x_2).$$

We expect that if we interchange them once more we will get back to the original state, from which it follows that we have to demand that:

$$e^{2i\alpha} = 1,$$

and this constraint has two solutions (modulo 2π) $\alpha = 0$ and $\alpha = \pi$. This in turn implies that there are two different solutions for the wavefunction under interchange of two identical particles:

$$\psi(x_2, x_1) = \pm\psi(x_1, x_2),$$

implying that the wavefunctions are either symmetric or antisymmetric under the interchange. And indeed the particles that obey the symmetric rule are called *bosons*, the antisymmetric guys are called *fermions*. We see that the antisymmetric solution implies that the particles cannot sit in the same spot, because if so that wavefunction would have to satisfy $\psi(x,x) = -\psi(x,x)$ implying that $\psi(x,x) = 0$! This 'unobservable' phase has huge quite observable consequences! This is so because the origin of *this* type of phase is topological.

Because of the indistinguishability requirement, the Hilbert space of two-particle states breaks up in two disconnected pieces being the even and odd functions. The phase is not the overall phase but the phase acquired under the interchange operation, and indeed the interchange should not change the observable probability distribution, which it doesn't.

Apparently fermionic particles obey an *exclusion principle* and such particles behave physically totally different from their bosonic counterparts, who are not subject to this exclusion principle and may like to hang out in the same spot. Indeed, they do like to sit on top of each other if it gets really cold!

The topology of particle exchange

Two-particle configuration space. It will turn out that the possibility of non-trivial quantum statistics is directly linked to the connectivity properties of the configuration space of two identical particles and the topology of particle exchange. It is therefore worth considering in more detail what this 'two-particle configuration space' really looks like.

We start by taking two coordinates x_1 and x_2 which take values in some ordinary space $\mathcal{M} \sim \mathbb{R}^3$ for example. Instead of choosing x_1 and x_2 we may also choose as coordinates the 'center of mass' coordinate $X = (x_1 + x_2)/2$ and the 'relative coordinate' $x = (x_1 - x_2)/2$. During inter-

Figure II.5.20: *Shinkichi Tajiri: Meandering paths (1997)* 'Meandering paths, unavoidably returning to an empty shell.' Looking at this work from a quantum perspective it depicts the entangled world-lines of particle pairs, first created and later annihilated. Indeed, the net effect is a transformation of the vacuum state. (Source: info@tajiri.nl.)

change we may keep X fixed (the origin, say), for example by moving the two particles around the center of mass that is located exactly half way between them. The interchange $x_1 \leftrightarrow x_2$ corresponds to a move from $x \leftrightarrow -x$ while keeping X fixed. So, we are left with studying the 'x' space. This space is again a copy of $\mathcal{M}$, but not quite, because in this space points, that are mirror images through the origin of each other, meaning the points x and $-x$ have to be identified if the particles are indistinguishable. Furthermore, the physical interchange in ordinary space corresponds to a closed loop in this reduced x space.

Three or more dimensions. We can take care of this doubling by cutting the space in half,[13] so we take away the bottom half of the space, say, all points with z negative $(z < 0)$, as we have indicated in Figure II.5.21. This solves the problem almost but not quite, because the space we are left with has acquired a bottom where strange things still happen. Indeed, in the bottom $z = 0$ plane we still have to identify the mirror points. But now this is at least something we can do 'by hand'.

Connectivity. The connectivity of the space is determined by studying the classes of possible loops in the space. Let us first discuss that and then return to the question of interchanges. In Figure II.5.21 I have drawn two paths. The first one is the green loop denoted σ, which is a loop that can smoothly be contracted to the red base point, hence it is the 'trivial' loop. This trivial loop means that there is basically no exchange and therefore the phase of the two particle state cannot change, so we conclude that $\sigma = +1$. The second red curve is again a closed loop because the beginning and endpoint are the same point, but now we can not contract the loop. The smooth deformations can only involve motions of the pair of red points into other mirror pairs in the bottom plane, if you were to lift them out of the plane they would no longer be the same point, and you would cut the loop – not so much a smooth deformation rather a killer move. And you cannot bring them together through the origin, because that point is taken out. So, the red loop is truly non-contractable and clearly belongs to a different topological class. We conclude that the reduced space clearly has some 'nontrivial' topology. The question is to find out what values the phase τ could take.

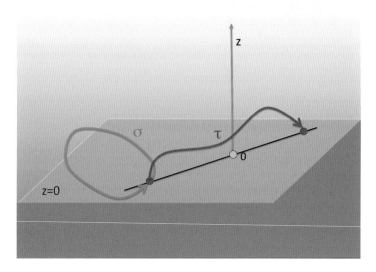

Figure II.5.21: *Topology of two-particle configuration space.* The two-particle configuration space, is $\mathbb{R}^3$ but with the bottom half and the origin removed. And on the $z = 0$ plane a point and its mirror image through the origin are identified. So there are two inequivalent types of closed paths possible. The green loop, which is contractable to a point, belongs to the trivial class; $\sigma = 1$. The red path, which is also closed but not contractable, belongs to the other, non-trivial class.

Interchanges As we said already an interchange $x_1 \leftrightarrow x_2$ corresponds to a move from $x \leftrightarrow -x$. Furthermore the path connecting the two points in x-space is not allowed to pass through the origin, because then they would meet at the same point and we would like to allow for an exclusion principle. An admissible move is depicted in the top graph of Figure II.5.22. In the reduced x-space this interchange is schematically depicted in the lower graph of the figure. We do allow the wavefunction to acquire some *constant* phase factor τ and that factor cannot change under a continuous deformation of the path from x to $-x$ through x-space. This means that the admissible phases τ label the different topological classes of closed paths that are possible in x-space. We have discussed these classes before, on page 83 of Chapter I.2, and learned that these are called *homotopy classes*.

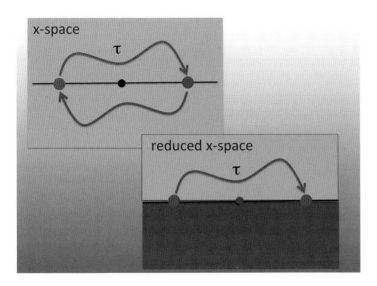

Figure II.5.22: *Interchange.* Particle interchange denoted by τ, in the space of the relative coordinate $x = (x_1 - x_2)/2$ amounts to moving from some point representing the pair, from x to -x along some path. In this particular case we have in fact that $x = x_1$ (red curve) $= -x_2$ (blue curve). The system has then moved to an indistinguishable two-particle state which means that the wavefunction can at most acquire a phase and we write $\tau\psi(x) = e^{i\gamma}\psi(x)$.

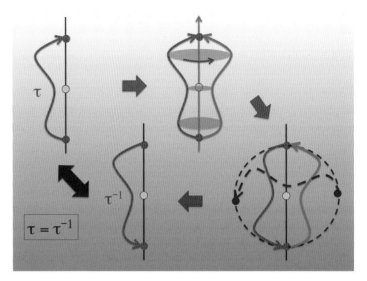

Figure II.5.23: *Topological equivalence.* The phase factor τ is the same for all interchanges along (closed) paths that can be smoothly deformed into each other. So τ labels a class of paths. In this figure we show that the class of τ and τ^{-1} are actually the same by a sequence of smooth deformations (rotations). Note however that the first move from red to blue is only possible if the dimension of the space is $D \geq 3$. In that case $\tau^2 = 1$ or $\tau = \pm 1$.

Let us now turn to Figure II.5.23 where we establish a relation between the interchange process τ and the reverse process represented by τ^{-1}. The top-left diagram is again τ and the bottom-left diagram represents by definition τ^{-1}.

Now we can do two subsequent smooth deformations of the path: in the top-right diagram we go from red to blue by just rotating around the blue axis, and in bottom-right diagram we go from blue to red again by rotating along the dark red trajectory indicated. Note that this deformation only involves mirror points (as is evident from the intermediate dark red dashed loop), so the loop remains closed and the origin is circumvented as required.

What we now learn from comparing the red path in the bottom-right diagram and the path corresponding to τ^{-1} is that these two paths can be smoothly deformed into each

other, and therefore belong to the same class. The conclusion is that we have shown the surprising fact that $\tau = \tau^{-1}$, in other words that $\tau^2 = 1$, which implies that τ can only take the values $\tau = \pm 1$.

And therefore we confirmed that the quantum theory allows for only two fundamental types of particles: bosons with wavefunctions that are symmetric under particle interchange and fermions with wavefunctions that are antisymmetric.

But we also have the added restriction that the fermionic $\tau = -1$ solution requires the exclusion principle, corresponding to removing the origin of $x-$ space.

Finally, let us make a crucial observation that has been

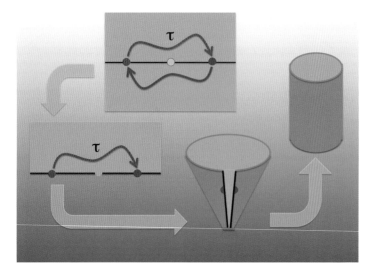

Figure II.5.24: *The two-dimensional case.* We start with the plane in which we do the interchange, the origin is excluded and we have to identify x and $-x$. This lets us remove the lower half of the plane. Then on the bottom boundary of the remaining top half space we still have to identify mirror points through the origin. This means the space becomes topologically a cone but without a tip. And that is topologically equivalent to a cylinder.

for a long time overlooked. The first 'red to blue' deformation can only be performed if the dimensionality of space is at least three; it requires $D \geq 3$! The question that remains is: what is so special about the two-dimensional case?

The two-dimensional surprise! In two dimensions the relative 'x' space is a plane with the origin taken out, and with opposite points identified. The paths of the particles are each other's mirror image just as we see in the top picture of Figure II.5.24. So again we go one step further and cut away the lower half-plane. Then we don't have to make any additional identifications except for points on the boundary. It is easy to visualize what that means. You can fold the half lines making up the boundary, together, literally by identifying the mirror points as indicated in the figure, and what you obtain is a cone! But: a cone without a tip. It is more like a *tipi* or an Indian tent with a hole in

the top serving as a chimney to let the smoke out. Topologically speaking a cone without a tip is not a cone but a cylinder. And so, after all these topological moves we have shown that the space M_2 becomes an R^2 related with X, times a cylinder, $R \otimes S^1$, for x. The important conclusion is that interchanges in the original two-particle space $\mathcal{M}_2$, correspond to closed loops on this cylinder. And therefore the question of a topological characterization of 'identical' particle types is then reduced to the question of equivalence or homotopy classes of closed loops on a cylinder.

What we see is that the situation in two dimensions is special indeed, because we can imagine closed paths that wind around one time, two times, or n times around the cylinder and these are all inequivalent. So there is an infinity of classes which can be labeled by the set of (positive and negative) integers also referred to as winding numbers and denoted by $\mathbb{Z}$. And there is even a further property, you can compose loops, by joining end of the first loop (γ_1) to the beginning of the second (γ_2), then you get a combined loop ($\gamma_3 = \gamma_1 \cdot \gamma_2$). The corresponding classes of the loops will then add: $n_3 = n_1 + n_2$.

So in two dimensions it is in principle possible to have particles which satisfy $\tau^n = 1$ for any n, meaning that the phase factor of the two-particle state under interchange would be $\tau = \exp 2\pi i/n$. And that is why Frank Wilczek coined the generic name *anyons* for such particles because they evidently can have *any* phase.

And indeed, this observation would have the bold implication that in two dimensions the statistics factor could be any rational fraction of 2π, $\alpha = 2\pi/N$. By the ribbon argument which we explain in the next subsection, this would also imply that the spin value should be $s = 1/N$. How exotic: a correspondence between fractional spin and statistics!

Life in lower dimension is not always less interesting ap-

Figure II.5.25: *Feynman in discussion at the Les Houches Summerschool in 1979.* Feynman urged students including myself (who took the picture) to try and think of a simpler explanation of the exclusion principle.

parently! That can't be right! As a matter of fact, it is true, and there are states of matter on interfaces or with planar geometries where such particles exist. For example as collective excitations in (quasi) two-dimensional media like the 'fractional quantum Hall phases,' that are exhibited by certain conductors at extremely low temperatures, as we will discuss in Chapter III.3.

A historical aside. The topological nature of the particle exchange statistics goes back to work of the Norwegian Physicists Jon Magne Leinaas and Jan Myrheim from 1977. They applied the very same argument we employed in Figure II.5.22 and discovered the exceptional situation in two-dimensions. In 1980 I published a paper where I constructed explicit soliton solutions that exhibited fractional spin as well as (non-)abelian statistics properties. It was in the eighties that the extensions of these ideas took off within my own group, also guided by important developments in condensed matter theory such as the work of Laughlin and Wilczek on the fractional quan-

tum Hall effect, and string theory and topological field theories by Witten. This has lead to a quite rich research field, nowadays called *topological order* or *topological matter*, in which these exotic features are realized and I myself was deeply involved. This research field is expected to have important applications in scalable and controllable quantum information processing and storage. And that is a good reason to explore these topological arguments a little further. It is an attractive type of physics, because it involves global analysis, which appeals to conceptual imagination rather than calculus type of skills. It's fun when basic (or fancy) physics meets basic (or fancy) mathematics; it really looks like these two fields of science are 'convicted' to each other. A marriage forced by nature on the one hand and a *marriage de raison* as the French say on the other, that should be a happy one.

The spin-statistics connection

We have in previous sections mentioned the remarkable connection between the fact that particles having half-integer spin happen to be fermions while the integer spin particles are always bosons. This spin-statistics connection between interchange properties and spin was not at all obvious from the start, and it only became clear once Dirac wrote down his famous equation for the electron and its anti-particle the positron that both properties were a necessary consequence of the brilliant interpretation of that equation given by Dirac.

But now we understand the topological argument for the interchange factor from carefully looking at the two- (or multi-) particle configuration space as we did in the previous section, one wonders whether there is not a more direct argument for the connection of this factor to the spin. There is, as we will show next, and it again turns out to illuminate the possibility of fractional spin for those aforementioned anyonic excitations.

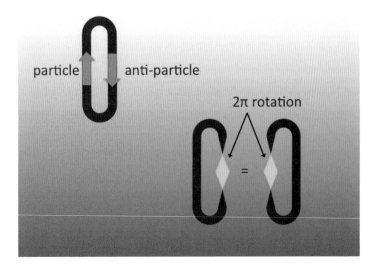

Figure II.5.26: *Ribbon diagrams.* The ribbon diagram of the creation and subsequent annihilation of a particle anti-particle pair, where the arrow indicates the direction of the charge current (left). The effect of rotation of a particle on the state is equivalent to the effect of a rotation of an antiparticle (right); the net effect is a change of of the vacuum state by a phase factor $R(2\pi)$.

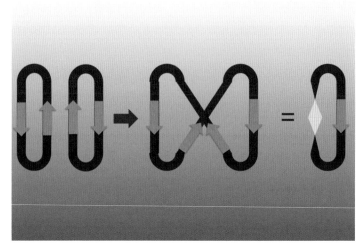

Figure II.5.27: *Spin – statistics connection.* Two pairs are created and annihilated, corresponding to a trivial effect on the vacuum state. The pictures on the right demonstrate the topological equivalence of the interchange of two identical particles with a rotation on one of them. This implies that $\tau\psi = R(2\pi)|\psi\rangle = \pm|\psi\rangle$, where the plus sign holds for *bosons* and the minus sign for *fermions*.

Ribbons. The trick is basically to realize that a particle with spin should be represented by a ribbon instead of a line. Let us imagine creating a particle anti-particle pair and subsequently annihilating it, then we get a diagram like in Figure II.5.26. We can of course also rotate the particle say over an angle of 2π before annihilating the pair, this corresponds to a full twist of the ribbon. What is demonstrated in the diagram on the right, is that we can move the twist smoothly from the particle line to the antiparticle line, which shows that their spin should equal. The rotation will change the phase of the two-particle wavefunction by an angle $\alpha = 2\pi s$ where s is the spin of the (anti-)particle.

To demonstrate the equivalence of a rotation by 2π to an interchange we go to the next Figure II.5.27. There we first create two pairs, then we cut the two identical particle rib-

bons and reconnect them to arrive at the diagram in the middle where the ribbons show that we interchanged the particles. In other words we have applied the interchange operator τ to the wavefunction describing the middle two particles. As indicated in the diagram on the right, the complete exchange diagram can be smoothly deformed into the diagram where one of the particles is rotated over 2π. This you can actually verify by taking a ribbon and literally repeat the described actions. What this says is the wavefunction of the state is acted on by the interchange operator τ shifting the phase of the state by an angle α, but this phase should be equal to $2\pi s$ according to the topological equivalence of the two diagrams.

So this simple argument nicely shows the topological nature of the statistics factor and of the spin-statistics connection. And who would have expected that you could give

#	A	B	C
1	1	2	
2	1		2
3		1	2
4	12		
5		12	
6			12
7	2	1	
8	2		1
9		2	1

Marbles
distinguishable
$\Rightarrow$ 9 states

#	A	B	C
1	x	x	
2	x		x
3		x	x
4	xx		
5		xx	
6			xx

Bosons
indistinguishable
$\Rightarrow$ 6 states

#	A	B	C
1	x	x	
2	x		x
3		x	x

Fermions
indistinguishable
exclusion
$\Rightarrow$ 3 states

Table II.5.1: *State counting.* Counting states for 2 identical particles that can occupy one of three states. The tables list the possible 2 particle configurations for classical particles, bosons and fermions.

a 'ham handed' experimental 'proof' of the spin-statistics connection just using two identical belts!

Statistics: state counting

We return to the standard setting of more conventional quantum theory and illustrate how indistinguishability, exclusion, and interchange properties do affect the statistical properties of ensembles of particles. This becomes clear if one starts counting the available 'distinct' states.

Let us illustrate this state counting by considering a simple example of two identical particles labeled 1 and 2 that can be in either one of three states A, B and C. In the tables on the next page we have listed the distinct configurations for classical particles ('marbles') which are supposed to be distinguishable, for quantum particles that are indistinguishable but do not obey the exclusion principle (bosons), and for quantum particles that do obey the exclusion principle (fermions). Because the counting of available states

is different allowing for 9, 6 and 3 states respectively, the probabilities are directly affected. For example assuming equal probabilities for each allowed state, one may ask a question like: 'What is the probability p that the two particles sit in the same state?' Clearly for the marbles the answer is $p = 1/3$, for the bosons $p = 1/2$ while for the fermions we have $p = 0$.

For the case at hand we can define the two-particle state $\Psi_{ij}(1, 2) = \psi_i(1)\psi_j(2)$ as a product of the states of the individual particles where i and j could be A, B or C. We can thus think of Ψ_{ij} as a 3×3 matrix , for the classical states there indeed are $3 \times 3 = 9$ entries, for the bosons we have to require that the state would be symmetric $\Psi(1, 2) = \Psi(2, 1)$ corresponding to a symmetric matrix which indeed has 6 independent entries, while for fermions we have to require the state to be antisymmetric $\Psi(1, 2) = -\Psi(2, 1)$ corresponding to an antisymmetric matrix having only 3 independent entries because the diagonal ones have to be zero. Indeed the state vector Ψ where the fermions would be in the same state would

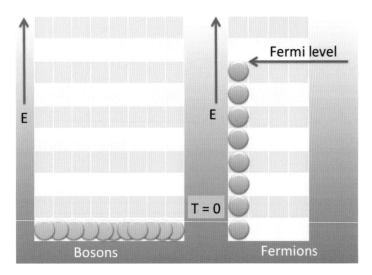

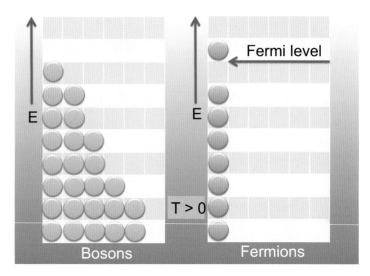

Figure II.5.28: *Bosons and fermions at* T = 0. The distribu-tions for the two particle types at T = 0. The energy levels are along the vertical axis, and the occupation number is indicated by the number of balls.

Figure II.5.29: *Bosons and fermions at* T ≥ 0. Axes are the same as in previous figure.

mean $\Psi_{ii} = -\Psi_{ii}$ implying that it has to vanish, saying nothing less than that that there is no such state.

These basic statistical properties of particles have pro-found physical consequences if we study many particle systems and their collective behavior. For a system in ther-mal equilibrium with its environment, there will be a cer-tain probability of a certain energy level to be occupied or not, which means that in a large system of many particles you get a distribution which tells you how many particles there will be on average at a certain energy level. Now dependent on the type of particle, these distributions are different, especially if one goes to low temperatures and low energies where the quantum behavior becomes mani-fest.

What do we roughly expect to happen? Let us start with taking the zero temperature case, this is shown in Figure II.5.28. Indeed for the bosons we expect that they all con-gregate or better condensate in the ground state. This is

in contrast with the fermions where we expect that for N fermions, the lowest N states would be filled, while the higher states would be empty. The highest filled level is called the Fermi level, corresponding to the Fermi energy. Now if we heat the system up, particles may get excited to higher levels, and fall back again until a certain temper-ature dependent distribution over states is reached. So, in Figure II.5.29 we have indicated what that looks like. Clearly for the fermions where all lower levels are filled already the thermal excitations can only take place near the Fermi level. Fermionic excitations create in fact also a hole, near the Fermi level one necessarily creates particle-hole pairs.

The functional form of the three distributions can be deter-mined exactly, and are are depicted in Figure II.5.30 for two different temperatures. They have the following functional form:

$$n_T(E) \sim \frac{1}{e^{(E-\mu)/kT} + m},$$

where for m=0 we have the classical Maxwell–Boltzmann distribution corresponding to the blue curves, while for m =

+1 we have the Bose–Einstein distribution corresponding to the red curves, and finally for $m = -1$ the Fermi–Dirac distribution corresponding to the dark red curves. You may think of these distributions as function of particle state energy, parametrized by the temperature and the chemical potential (Fermi energy) denoted by μ. Let us make some observations concerning these distributions.

i. Note that the axes in Figure II.5.30 are labeled orthogonally to those in Figures II.5.28 and II.5.29.

ii. Observe that for high enough energy all the distributions look the same for all temperatures, which is the statement that all particles approximately show the classical behavior. The quantum distinctions get washed away by the violent thermal fluctuations.

iii. Drastic differences however show up for low values of relevant energy scale $E - \mu$. Whereas the fermion occupation number necessarily is smaller than or equal one, the boson occupation number increases rapidly if the energy goes to zero. In fact, if we lower the temperature to absolute zero the fermion distribution function becomes a step function indicating that up to the Fermi-level, all states are occupied (here μ is the fermi-level, or the surface of the Dirac sea). For bosons we see that all particles will pile up in the same lowest energy state.

iv. There is actually a real phase transition where a so-called Bose-condensation takes place where all particles sit in the quantum same state. This is in fact an example of a special *macroscopic quantum state* that stands out because of its so-called quantum coherence. Such states exhibit truly spectacular properties, such as superfluidity, meaning that the system forms a quantum fluid with zero viscosity. In certain metals this can lead to the phenomenon of superconductivity, where the electric resistance vanishes at very low temperatures. We will return to these subjects in later chapters.

You may wonder how such peculiar rules like exclusions and indistinguishability can be implemented in a mathematically consistent way. It turns out that to do multi-particle (often called many body) quantum physics, you basically

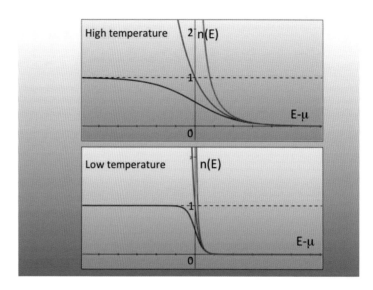

Figure II.5.30: *Particle distributions.* The distributions for three particle types, giving the occupation number $n(E)$ of a state at energy $E - \mu$ for two temperatures. The red curves are for bosons, the blue ones for 'marbles' and the dark red ones for fermions. This figure is rotated 90^0 clockwise with respect two the previous figures.

have to use the formalism of quantum fields. In this formalism we have operators that can create or annihilate (anti)particles in any admissible energy-momentum state. And one finds that the different types of statistics are direct consequence of the basic relations between these particle creation and annihilation operators. For bosons we that the creation and annihilation operators satisfy *commutation relations* meaning that

$$[a_k^\dagger, a_{k'}^\dagger] = 0 \; ; \; [a_k, a_{k'}] = 0 \text{ and } [a_k, a_{k'}^\dagger] = \delta_{k\,k'},$$

where the commutator of two operators A and B is defined as $[A, B] = AB - BA$. For fermions these are replaced by *anticommutators* where the anti-commutator is defined as $\{A, B\} = AB + BA$. If two creation operators anti-commute one has in particular that

$$\{c_k^\dagger, c_k^\dagger\} = 0,$$

meaning that putting two particles in the same state gives

zero, it just can't be done. This necessary choice of commutation or anti-commutation relations for the basic operators is forced upon you by the requirement of a physically consistent interpretation of the theory. That choice
accounts for all characteristic differences between bosons
and fermions in particular the appearance of completely
symmetric or antisymmetric wavefunctions.

More for less: two-dimensional exotics

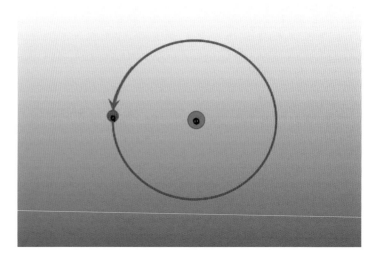

It is like the telephone game in kindergarten. The
children are sitting in a circle and you whisper the
first kid a sentence in her ear, then she has to pass
it on till it went all the way around. The last person speaks out loud what the sentence was he
received. Then they compare the sentences, and
share their unbelief that such distortions are possible. That is presumably how lies emerge. This
metamorphosis, amounts to a non contractable loop
in language space, a nontrivial linguistic holonomy.

The Aharonov–Bohm phase. We recall the discussion
we had in Chapter II.3 on the Ahoronov–Bohm phase shift.
If you carry a charge q along a loop γ, around localized
flux then the loop integral of A along γ yields the magnetic
flux through (any) two-dimensional surface hat is bounded
by the loop. This implies that the loop operator W_γ basically measures the magnetic flux:

We considered a well-defined narrow magnetic flux tube
piercing through the surface as in Figure II.5.31. If we adiabatically move a charge around the flux Φ, the state will
change according to,

$$|q, \Phi\rangle \rightarrow W_\gamma(q, \Phi)|q, \Phi\rangle,$$

where the phase factor W equals

$$W_\gamma(q, \Phi) = e^{iq\Phi}.$$

Figure II.5.31: *The Aharonov–Bohm phase factor.* If we carry
a charge q along a loop γ around a localized magnetic flux Φ,
then the state will acquire a phase factor $W_\gamma = \exp iq\Phi$.

An important property of this phase is that it is not only
gauge invariant but also topologically invariant, meaning
that you can deform the loop any way you want as long as
you don't cross the flux.

Anyons as flux-charge composites. Let us return to our
discussion about two-dimensional particles and their spin
and statistics properties. Let us look once more at Figure II.3.33 but in a different way. I now think of the charge
and flux as one composite object. The situation is like
in Figure II.5.32, where we look from far away and do not
worry about the (internal) structure of the pair. The interpretation of the figure is then that we rotate the composite over an angle of 2π, and we see that the state of this
funny particle has changed by $W(q, \Phi)$. This means that
our conclusion has to be that the composite must carry
some spin s, which causes the non-trivial phase factor of
the state under rotation by 2π. By definition for a particle
carrying spin s, the corresponding factor is given by,

$$e^{2i\pi s} = e^{iq\Phi} \quad \Rightarrow \quad s = q\Phi.$$

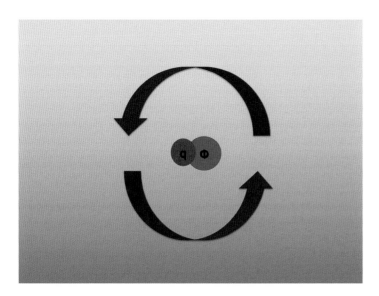

Figure II.5.32: *Flux-charge composite.* We think of the charge flux pair as a composite particle. Then the electromagnetic phase factor can be interpreted as due to a '(fractional) spin' s of the composite.

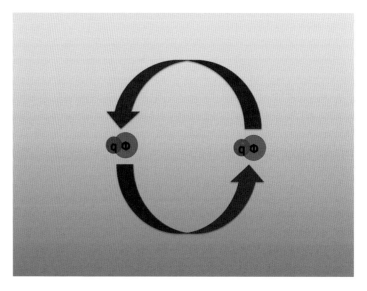

Figure II.5.33: *Interchange statistics of composites.* For the composite particle it follows that the spin- statistics connection holds.

For example, if in the superconducting layer, a single electron would bind with a minimal flux ($\phi_0 = \pi/e$) we would have $s = e\phi_0/2\pi = 1/2$, this would be a spin-half composite particle!

The spin-statistics connection for composites. We argued that the composites can have fractional spins depending on which fluxes and charges are allowed. But is it also true that they would exhibit the corresponding exchange properties? Can we establish a spin-statistics connection using the ribbon diagrams of Figure II.5.27 ? Let us start with the phase factor of two composites as in Figure II.5.33. The combined state after a full rotation would obtain a phase factor of twice $W(q, \Phi)$, because the charge q_1 would encircle the flux Φ_2 and at the same time q_2 the flux Φ_1, giving us $2q\phi$ as the fluxes and charges are equal. So we have to take the square root, as we only want to do the interchange, so we do get indeed the same result as the spin factor.[14] This way we have established

the exotic spin and statistics properties that are possible in two dimensions.

A historical aside. These particles are called *anyons*, a name coined by Frank Wilczek, because they can acquire any phase upon rotation or interchange. These so-called quantum-Hall systems were discovered by the German physicist von Klaus von Klitzing, and the fractional version of it by Störmer and Tsui. The theory of this phenomenon involving the fractionally charged anyons with fractional spin along the lines we just pointed out was developed by the Americans Robert Laughlin who shared the Nobel prize with Störmer and Tsui in 1988, and Frank Wilczek who already had received a Nobel prize for the theory of the strong interactions.

There are now many proposals for phases of condensed matter that feature these local anyonic excitations. Such phases share a property called *topological order*. It was

---

[14]The possible extra minus sign from taking the square root cannot

be resolved at this level of the analysis. Note however that it allows for implementing that the constituents would be a fermion to start with.

the Russian theoretical physicist Alexei Kitaev who pointed out that such anyons would be ideally suited to build quantum information devices with, because anyonic qubits are intrinsically fault tolerant. This highly desirable property derives from the topological nature of the quantum phases, which makes that these cannot be destroyed by local interactions and such error generating effects would be exponentially suppressed. One may manipulate the phases on multi-anyonic, multi-qubit states by just moving them around each other, or as it is called by 'braiding' them. Because of their topological nature computations with anyons would correspond to particular braids or knots of their world lines. And computation would boil down to some kind of quantum knitting! ■

Textbooks on particles and fields

— *Particles, Fields and Forces: A Conceptual Guide to Quantum Field Theory and the Standard Model*
Wouter Schmitz
Springer (2019)

— *The Quantum Theory of Fields*
Steven Weinberg
Cambridge University Press (2013)

— *An Introduction To Quantum Field Theory*
Michael E. Peskin and Daniel V. Schroeder
CRC Press (1995)

— *PCT, Spin & Statistics, and All That*
Ray F. Streater and Arthur S. Wightman
Princeton University Press (2000)

Chapter II.6

Symmetries and their breaking

Symmetry, as wide or as narrow as you may define it, is one idea by which man through the ages has tried to comprehend and create order, beauty and perfection.

Hermann Weyl

Symmetries play and have played a crucial role in the development of the modern physical sciences. It is a rich subject and its manifestations are quite diverse and display remarkable analytical and esthetical aspects. Central to this topic are the mathematical notions of a Lie group *and a* Lie algebra. *In the quantum context these symmetries are implemented by certain sets of operators (observables) that act on the Hilbert space of the system. We have encountered them already as they arise naturally at many levels in the framework of quantum theory. The connections between formal mathematical and physical concepts are summarized in the table on page 213, and I recommend that you regularly consult the table while reading this chapter.*

In this chapter we have split the applications between the well-known 'ordinary', rigid, *or* global symmetries *and the so-called* gauge *or* hidden *or* local symmetries. *The former are like the familiar translations or rotations, or isospin transformations, while the latter refer to the internal symmetries that are tied in with the fundamental interactions. Electrodynamics is a simple example of a gauge theory,*

and we have already discussed itsgauge symmetry already in Chapter I.1. Gauge symmetries are especially powerful because they are restrictive in the sense that they impose the way particles can interact in a consistent way. The dynamical equations underlying the Standard model are pretty much an expression of this principle of local gauge invariance. The mathematical concepts are those of differential geometry and the theory of fiber bundles, as we pointed out in the section on the 'Physics of geometry' of Chapter I.2

After the discussion of symmetries themselves, we move on to talk about breaking the symmetries. Symmetry breaking is another powerful concept that has found a rich variety of applications in fundamental physics on all scales, from say the cosmos all the way down to the phenomena of ferromagnetism in condensed matter or the Higgs mechanism in particle physics.

Symmetry breaking encompasses a hierarchical perspective on the increasing diversity and complexity we observe in nature as a hierarchical pattern resulting from a sequence of symmetry breaking transitions. We will discuss examples of the breaking of global as well as local symmetries.

Symmetry and its breaking are deep and delightful subjects that teach us about the mathematical intricacies of fundamental interactions and their structural beauty.

Let me start this chapter by stepping back and revisiting some statements I have made along the winding road we have taken so far, and looking at them again from the point of view of symmetry. Symmetry pops up everywhere and that indicates that there are many entries into this quantessential subject. Whereas symmetry leads to unity, similarity, and degeneracy, breaking symmetries does the opposite, it is a mechanism explaining how symmetry can get lost. The mechanism is quite generic and it is therefore important to understand its systemic signatures.

Nature started from a highly degenerate situation at a very high temperature (energy) and then created (evolved) diversity by going through a series of symmetry breaking transitions that took place when the ambient energy or temperature lowered. In an expanding universe like ours the loss of symmetry is as natural as it is inescapable.

By changing a circle into an ellipse and then to an arbitrary closed curve, one goes from a symmetry of continuous rotations in the plane, to two mirror symmetries, to no symmetry at all. It is a sequence of ever more symmetries being broken. Note however that from an information point of view, the information content increases with decreasing (or the breaking of) symmetry. Indeed you move from a curvature along the closed curve that is constant, to a curvature that is a periodic to a random function, and the amount of data you need to describe them increases.

Too much symmetry is boring because it is extremely redundant and predictable, but the same holds for too much randomness because of an extreme lack of structure. Excitement and beauty apparently reside halfway in between, and that is maybe why nature has chosen a path of breaking more and more symmetries. At present we encounter remnants of lost symmetries like subtle and hidden memories. But that is what makes nature so interesting. Life as an 'avenue of broken symmetries' so to speak. It allows science to gain a deeper and more unified understanding of the hidden patterns underlying reality.

Symmetries of what?

> The symmetries that are important in physics, are not the symmetries of things but the symmetries of equations.
>
> *Steven Weinberg*

We think of a group of symmetries as a set of operations or transformations that leave something invariant. This can be an object like a triangle or a sphere, and we speak of the '*symmetries of objects*', and this is certainly its most familiar manifestation. We may also think of the *symmetries of spaces*, these are transformations on the space, meaning transformations of the coordinates in such a way that the properties of that space do not change. For example flat space $\mathbb{R}^3$ has a huge group of symmetries: we can translate it over an arbitrary distance in any direction, we can rotate it around any axis through any point over any angle, and we can scale it by any amount around any point. With an infinite flat space you wouldn't see the difference, it is invariant under all those transformations and combinations of them. And besides that it has also discrete mirror symmetries, a transformation called *parity*. It makes you wonder whether it is this incredible overkill of symmetry that makes flat space so boring.

Yet another, and in physics crucial, application is to study not so much the symmetries of things, but rather the *symmetries of equations*, which means again that we make a transformation on the dynamical variables that leave the (system of) equations invariant.

Realizations of symmetry in nature. People I trust have told me that the Inuits have 32 words for snow, and that presumably is because they know a lot more about it than I do. By living in the snow for centuries they have learned to differentiate and appreciate an immense diversity in something that I just call 'snow.' Something similar has happened with the notion of symmetry in physics and its mirror images in mathematics.

With all these different approaches comes a correspondingly rich terminology referring to what we are precisely talking about. One speaks of *discrete* versus *continuous*, *finite* versus *infinite*, *space-time* versus *internal*, *local* versus *global*, *broken* versus *unbroken*, *approximate* versus *exact*, *normal* versus *super*, *classical* versus *quantum* symmetries. This summary suffices to justify a chapter on this topic, a chapter in which I will guide you through some of this extensive jargon in a way that emphasizes the basic concepts.

Groups, algebras and their representations. The framework for the following discussions on symmetry is summarized in the table on page 213, and it shows that in the class of continuous symmetries the mathematics is mostly that of Lie groups and algebras. These are quite abstract, mathematically precisely defined objects themselves, but the beauty is that it comes with an important part denoted as representation theory. Physicists perceive the notion of symmetry mostly through the particular representations that are manifest in nature. Let me recall the observables $\{X, Y, Z\}$, the Pauli matrices, and the fact that their commutation relations form the non-commutative Lie algebra denoted as $\mathfrak{su}(2)$.[1] It is called the 'defining' representation of this algebra because it is in the form of 2×2 hermitian matrices, working on a two-dimensional complex vector space – the state space of a single qubit. But exactly the same algebra, meaning an identical set of commutation relations, is obeyed by the angular momentum operators $\{L_x, L_y, L_z\}$. That is a different representation of the same algebra in terms of differential operators working on a space of functions – the Hilbert space, quite different from 2×2 matrices but satisfying the same algebra. If we furthermore restrict to states of a given angular momentum l, (think of the hydrogen atom) then these form

a $(2l + 1)$-dimensional vector space and the rotations are then generated by a specific set of three $(2l+1) \times (2l+1)$ hermitian matrices. And all these sets form inequivalent representations of the same algebra, labeled by the quantum number l. We will be somewhat cavalier about making distinctions between the abstract notions of an algebra or group and their representations. In physics we mostly work within the context of particular, often unitary, representations. You may think of representation theory as the physical contextualization of abstract group theory.

Symmetries and conserved quantities

Heisenberg equations. I choose a route that starts with symmetries of a Hamiltonian (operator), leading from there to the notion of conserved quantities, and from there to frameworks for labeling the energy eigenstates of that Hamiltonian. Let me start from the basic Heisenberg equations which apply to quantum systems on all levels:

$$i\hbar\frac{\mathrm{d}A}{\mathrm{d}t} = [A, H].\qquad(\text{II}.6.1)$$

Remember that in this formulation the dynamical variables or observables are time dependent, and in that sense the Heisenberg approach is closer to the classical one, because it is formulated in terms of the observable quantities only.[2] This in contrast with the Schrödinger equation which describes the time evolution of quantum states, and those are not directly observable.

Symmetries and conservation laws. The equation says that the time evolution of the system is generated by the Hamiltonian H. In particular, an infinitesimal change in time, corresponding to acting with $i\hbar\mathrm{d}/\mathrm{d}t$ on the variable, is equal to taking the commutator of that variable with the

---

[1]To be precise, it is one-half times the Pauli matrices that satisfy the $\mathfrak{su}(2)$ algebra. Commutation relations are nonlinear so the scale is exactly fixed. This factor one-half turns out to be important.

[2]Note the similarity between the Heisenberg equations and the Poisson equations discussed in the section on classical mechanics of Chapter I.1.

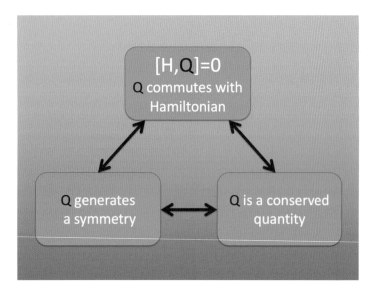

Figure II.6.1: *The quantessence of symmetry.* If an observable Q commutes with the Hamiltonian, then it is conserved in time, and generates a symmetry of the system.

Hamiltonian. Consider now an observable Q_i which commutes with the Hamiltonian or energy operator, so:

$$[Q_i, H] = 0 \quad \Rightarrow \quad \frac{dQ_i}{dt} = 0.$$

The equation teaches us that observables that have a vanishing commutator with the Hamiltonian do not change in time. They are constants of the motion and are conserved in time. It means that if the dynamics of the system follows the Heisenberg evolution equations, and we start with a state corresponding to a certain (eigen)value q_i for the observable Q_i, that the evolution will take place in a subspace of the Hilbert space labeled by that eigenvalue, and by some eigenvalue E of the Hamiltonian as well, because the energy operator H is (by definition) a conserved quantity. Everybody commutes with themselves after all.

This reasoning leads to an interesting picture: we have a system characterized by a set of basic variables (think of position and momentum) and a huge set of derived observables (like energy or angular momentum), and these

observables form a closed operator algebra under commutation. In the *Math Excursion* on vectors and matrices on page 176 of Volume III we explain that these algebras of observables that close under commutation are in mathematics referred to as *Lie algebras*. We present an overview of the relation between mathematical and physical aspects of symmetry in the table on page 213.

Lie algebra of observables. What we say is that such a Lie algebra is a rather abstract thing, but it has representations in the form of matrices or differential operators. This we saw for example with the algebra of the canonical variables X and P, which reads:

$$[X, P] = i\hbar \quad \Rightarrow \quad X \to x \text{ and } P \to -i\hbar \frac{d}{dx},$$

and therefore has a representation where X is represented by the ordinary number variable x (like it appears as argument of the wave function). Acting with X on a wavefunction $\psi(x)$ means multiplying that wavefunction with x. P is represented by the differential operator as indicated in the equation above. It is the infinitesimal displacement operator. This was worked out in the section on position and momentum operators on page 153.

Translation invariance and momentum conservation. Let us explore this a little further along the lines of energy conservation for the simple mechanical system that we discussed in the section on Newtonian mechanics in Chapter I.1. If we consider the energy of a particle then that usually consists of a kinetic part $P^2/2m$ and a potential part $U(X)$. Suppose that we make the additional assumption that the potential energy is constant and does not depend on X, then the canonical commutation relations above imply that $[P, H] = 0$ and hence the momentum is conserved. In the classical argument one would normally say that the force $F(x) = -dU/dx = 0$ and Newton's second law then tells us that $dp/dt = F = 0$, leading to the same conclusion.

We encountered this situation for example in the section

about the 'free particle on a circle' of Chapter II.5 where we found that states were labeled by the quantized momentum $p = \hbar k$ (k-integer), being a conserved quantum number. So we chose a framework consisting of the energy and the momentum operator, with as *sampling space* just the momentum eigenvalues $-\infty \leq p \leq +\infty$. Here we see that if an underlying space-time symmetry, like translation invariance, is also present in the Hamiltonian, then indeed, the spectrum reflects that. But there is always a dual aspect. On the one hand the momentum P which is the conserved quantity, but on the other that very same P is the generator of the symmetry transformations being the translations. We have illustrated this general relationship in Figure II.6.1.

Rotations and angular momentum conservation. Let us now consider a more complicated example where symmetry tells us a lot about the spectrum, the case of the Hydrogen atom. The spectrum exhibited a large degeneracy which explained and depicted already in Chapter I.4 in Figure I.4.9. The states are labeled by three integer-valued quantum numbers: the energy related quantum number $n = 1, 2, \ldots$, the angular momentum quantum number $l = 0, 1, \ldots, n - 1$ and the magnetic quantum number $-l \leq m \leq l$. In this problem we have a spherically symmetric electric force field centered at the nucleus in the origin. The energy consists of two parts, a kinetic part $\mathbf{p}^2/2m$ and a potential part $-k/|\mathbf{x}|$ and each part depends only on the length of the vectors and therefore is invariant under rotations. So we expect that the generators of rotations commute with the Hamiltonian and that they are therefore conserved, and somehow their sample spaces should be reflected in the labeling of the degenerate states with equal energy. Indeed, the generators of those rotations around the x, y, and z axes are the corresponding angular momentum observables/operators defined as a vector $\mathbf{L}$:

$$\mathbf{L} = \mathbf{X} \times \mathbf{P}.$$

Furthermore, the three components are conserved, as one

can indeed show:

$$[H, L_i] = 0 \quad i = 1, 2, 3.$$

But now a further complication pops up: the conserved components of $\mathbf{L}$ do not commute among each other. We have:

$$[L_1, L_2] = i\hbar L_3, \quad \text{and cyclic permutations.} \qquad \text{(II.6.2)}$$

This algebra of real three-dimensional rotations, denoted as $so(3)$ happens to be identical to the by now familiar $su(2)$ Lie algebra. To describe the system we need to choose a framework $\mathcal{F}$, which means that we have to choose a subset of mutually commuting operators. Conventionally one chooses the following set: H, $\mathbf{L}^2 = L_1^2 + L_2^2 + L_3^2$ and L_3 with the eigenvalues:

$$\begin{aligned} H \, |\psi_{nlm}\rangle &= \frac{E_0}{n^2} \, |\psi_{nlm}\rangle; \\ \mathbf{L}^2 \, |\psi_{nlm}\rangle &= \hbar^2 l(l+1) \, |\psi_{nlm}\rangle; \\ L_3 \, |\psi_{nlm}\rangle &= \hbar m \, |\psi_{nlm}\rangle. \end{aligned} \qquad \text{(II.6.3)}$$

And as we mentioned before, for a fixed value of the principal quantum number n, there are in fact $2n^2$ degenerate states as a consequence of the symmetries that are present in the problem. The set of those states form a basis for all allowed states with an energy corresponding to that value of n. If we take $n = 3$, we should have $l = 0$, $l = 1$ and $l = 2$, but the symmetry algebra $so(3)$ given in (II.6.2) does not change the value of l, only the values of m from $-l$ to $+l$, which means that the rotational symmetry only accounts for the $(2l + 1)$-fold degeneracy for each value of l. The conclusion therefore is that for $n = 3$, the spectrum consists of the three distinct *irreducible representations* of the rotation group (labeled by $l = 0, 1, 2$), see also Figure II.6.2. That suggests that there is may be more symmetry present in this problem, a topic we will return to shortly.

Let us make another observation here. In the choice of the framework we at once introduced the operator $\mathbf{L}^2$, which is

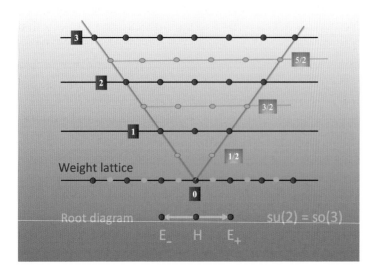

Figure II.6.2: *The representations of* $su(2) \simeq so(3)$. The group SU(2) has three generators that form the algebra $su(2)$. The root diagram has the diagonal L_3 which forms the Cartan sub-algebra $\mathcal{H}$, while the arrows represent the raising and lowering operators $E_{\pm} \simeq L_{\pm}$. The weights of all (unitary) representations are on the weight lattice. We furthermore depicted the weight diagrams of various irreducible representations labeled by successively $l = 0, 1/2, 1, 3/2, \ldots$.

strictly speaking not part of the Lie algebra. It is a quadratic combination of generators that has the nice property that it commutes with all of the $su(2) \simeq so(3)$ generators: $[\mathbf{L}^2, \mathcal{A}] = 0$. Such invariant polynomials (also called Casimir operators or Racah invariants) play an important role in Lie algebra theory because you can use them to label or identify the inequivalent representations. And indeed the eigenvalue $l(l+1)$ (or for that matter l) labels and distinguishes the infinitely many different (irreducible) representations of the algebra by $(2l+1) \times (2l+1)$ matrices.

Vectors and spinors. Let us return to the abstract algebra (II.6.2) of $so(3)$. We have mentioned that this algebra is identical to the algebra $su(2)$ generated by (a half times) the Pauli matrices X, Y, and Z. And this implies that the algebra not only has integer l representations, but also

half-integral, so-called spinor, representations. And as you see these do not show up in the orbital angular momentum part, but in the part associated with the spin of a particle, which is a degree of freedom that is not present at the classical level. Actually saying that there is no classical equivalent is of course not correct. We have shown that the classical system underlying the spin-half, quantum degree of freedom, is just the classical two-state system of a bit or Ising spin. Not much 'rotational' about it and that is what is implied by saying that it has no classical analogue. But if you 'believe' the mathematics, the half-integral representations had to be there somewhere, and yes they showed up in the anomalous Zeeman-effect that brought Uhlenbeck and Goudsmit in 1925 to their bold conjecture of the 'intrinsic spin' of the electron, and 5 years later became a compulsory ingredient of any particle obeying the Dirac equation. This we discussed already in Chapter II.1.

So what we learned from these examples is that the Lie algebra $so(3)$ which happens to be the same as $su(2)$ has an infinity of inequivalent (unitary) representations labeled by an integer or half-integer quantum number $j = 0, \frac{1}{2}, 1, \ldots$ and that that representation can be realized by $(2j + 1) \times (2j + 1)$ hermitian matrices. There is a basic distinction between the integer and half-integer eigenvalue representations: physicists refer to the integer ones as *vector representations* and to the half-integer ones as *spinor representations*. In the hydrogen atom we saw all the representations showing up, in the discussions we had on the qubit we start off with a single spin one-half (doublet) representation, but as we mentioned before in the n-qubit space we have a much bigger symmetry group acting corresponding to $SU(2^n)$, which contains the product group of n individual $SU(2)$ as a subgroup.

An additional dynamical symmetry. Let us return to the spectrum of hydrogen and note that there is still something we haven't explained. The degeneracy observed at energy level n equals $2n^2$. It involves a degeneracy of *different* l representations, which cannot be accounted for by the

We have constructed **A** at various points of a classical Newtonian elliptic orbit in Figure II.6.3, and we see that it is indeed a constant of the motion. Note that it takes some use of the 'like-rule' to get the orientation right and then you see that the vector is parallel to the long axis of the ellipse and points in the direction of the 'perihelion.' It is surprising that such a conserved vector-like quantity exists, but you expect on the quantum level to be responsible for the extra degeneracy with respect to the quantum number $l = 0, 1, \ldots, n - 1$.

That explains by the way that in the Newtonian theory the elliptic orbit is completely fixed in space, and moreover it also explains that this feature disappears if we add a correction term coming from Einstein's general theory of relativity. That term concerns a small $1/r^3$ contribution, that breaks the symmetry and therefore the ellipse is no longer fixed in space and starts rotating in the plane of the orbit. This is the well-known 'perihelion precession' that was observed for the planet nearest to the sun *Mercury* already in the nineteenth century, and could indeed be accounted for by Einstein's theory. It illustrates the notion of an approximate symmetry it is not an exact symmetry but nevertheless teaches us about essential features of the system.

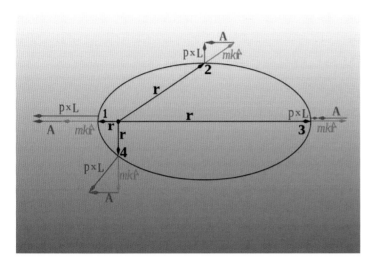

Figure II.6.3: *The Runge–Lenz vector,* $\mathbf{A} = \mathbf{P} \times \mathbf{L} - mk\hat{\mathbf{r}}$ *is an additional conserved quantity in the problem with a central* $-k/r$ *potential, where the origin of the coordinate* **r** *is in one of the focal points.* **A** *points always parallel to the long axis of the ellipse in the direction of the 'perihelion.'*

rotational symmetry. It could be 'accidental,' but that would be hard to believe if you have stayed with me so far. You would probably bet that it *must be* the consequence of yet another symmetry that we still have to disclose and that would make the whole picture even more striking.

Indeed, that symmetry is there, as there are in fact three more (independent) observables that commute with the Hamiltonian if it has a central 1/r potential. The presence of this symmetry is directly linked to the particular form of the interaction potential and is therefore called a *dynamical symmetry*. The generators form a vector just like the angular momentum and that vector is called the Runge–Lenz vector after its (re)discoverers.[3] This vector usually denoted by **A** is defined as:

$$\mathbf{A} = \mathbf{P} \times \mathbf{L} - mk\hat{\mathbf{x}}. \qquad (\text{II.6.4})$$

The full symmetry of the hydrogen atom

After all this struggling with vector products you may like to know what the total symmetry algebra of the hydrogen atom really is. This algebra is six-dimensional, and is indeed generated by the three **L** and the three **A** components. They form a closed algebra and it is in fact the algebra $so(4)$ of the rotations in four dimensions. So here we are, we set up a problem in three dimensions and now we get a spectrum exhibiting a manifest $so(4)$ symmetry. It underscores that the algebra has many representations and these may show up in all kinds of contexts

---

[3]It has an interesting history with many rediscoveries going back to the early 18th century. Pauli was the first to use it to solve the hydrogen atom in an article from 1926.

which have nothing whatsoever to do with a physical four-dimensional space. Here it surfaced because besides the rather evident spatial rotational symmetry of the problem, there turned out to be the additional, somewhat hidden *dynamical* symmetry (dynamical because it depends on the particular $1/r$ behavior of the potential and not on the underlying space). Including that symmetry allowed us to fully resolve the degeneracies in the hydrogen spectrum.

Raising and lowering operators. We see that we have chosen a consistent framework $\mathcal{F} = \{H, L^2, L_z\}$ to label the states. They are mutually commuting, but now you may ask what happened to the other symmetry operators – L_x and L_y for example – that commute with the Hamiltonian but *not* with L_z. We basically know what their meaning is as we showed before that they can be regrouped into raising and lowering operators that step up and down the different m values (within a single l representation). And similarly the components of the Runge–Lenz vector can be used to step up or down the value l of the total orbital angular momentum. So in this case these are operators that make steps not in energy but rather in other quantum numbers that label the degenerate states.

So if we go to the table on page 213, we see that a framework $\mathcal{F}$ typically involves a set of $\mathrm{rank}\ \mathcal{A}$ operators forming a so-called Cartan subalgebra $\mathcal{H}$ of $\mathcal{A}$. A Cartan subalgebra consists by definition of a maximal set of mutually commuting generators of $\mathbf{A}$. And indeed the other generators in $\mathcal{A} - \mathcal{H}$ can be regrouped in a complete set of raising and lowering operators.

A full set of step and symmetry operators satisfying equation (II.5.21) is called the *spectrum generating algebra* for the obvious reason that they allow you to walk through the sample space, in principle finding all the energy eigenstates and their quantum numbers referring to a framework compatible with the energy operator.

Generating the spectrum (sample space). Let us assume that by some means we succeeded in constructing a complete set of step operators which bring you from one energy level to another, one could in principle imagine looking for the ground state(s) (the state(s) that are 'annihilated' by all the lowering operators) and then, using the spectrum generating algebra of all step and symmetry operators, to generate the whole spectrum of eigenstates of the Hamiltonian.

We have seen that symmetries, and in particular the maximal set of mutually commuting symmetry operators, yield the set of quantum numbers that allows us to label and distinguish a relevant basis for all states. And as the labels of such base states corresponds to eigenvalues of symmetry operators they are conserved in time. Therefore, in a general sense, such a maximal set allows us to 'name' the properties of the system, since 'names' are useful precisely because they do not change all the time. On the other hand if the system undergoes interactions, the properties may change and also then it is important to have a proper identification of property names or quantum numbers. For example, the interaction may excite the system and therefore basically act like a raising operator.

Symmetry algebra and symmetry group

So far we have talked about the observables Q_i that commute with the Hamiltonian. They are conserved and we have seen that they generate a symmetry. That means that acting with them gives an infinitesimal displacement corresponding to a tiny symmetry transformation. This applies of course only to the case of continuous symmetries. You might wonder what a *finite transformation* then would look like and how they are described. It is here that we have to move from the mathematical concept of a (Lie)-algebra to that of a Lie group. This question is briefly addressed in the *Math Excursion* on Vectors and Matrices on page

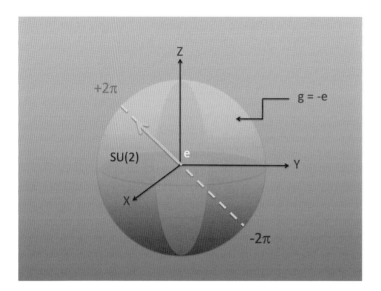

Figure II.6.4: *The group manifold of* $SU(2)$. $SU(2)$ can be represented as a solid three-dimensional ball with radius 2π. A point in that space corresponds with a rotation around the vector by an amount that corresponds to its length. All points on the surface are identified and represent minus the identity element: a rotation of about any axis by 2π yields an overall phase minus one.

179, and we have used in Chapter II.3 in the section on the Berry phase on page 113.

Exponentiation of the algebra. Let us return to the question of frame rotations for a qubit corresponding to a two-dimensional (complex) vector .

We considered the Z-frame and the X-frame and these frames are clearly related to each other by a finite rotation over an angle of $45°$ around the y-axis (perpendicular to the $z-$ and $x-$axes). Let us make an angle rotation over an angle θ around the Y axis[4] and use the matrix version

of the Euler identity:

$$e^{i\theta Y/2} = 1\cos\theta/2 + iY\sin\theta/2\,;$$

$$\Leftrightarrow R_y(\theta) = \begin{pmatrix} \cos\theta/2 & \sin\theta/2 \\ -\sin\theta/2 & \cos\theta/2 \end{pmatrix}. \quad \text{(II.6.5)}$$

Let us apply this to see what it does with the basis vectors:

$$\begin{pmatrix} \cos\theta/2 & \sin\theta/2 \\ -\sin\theta/2 & \cos\theta/2 \end{pmatrix}\begin{pmatrix} 1 \\ 0 \end{pmatrix} = \begin{pmatrix} \cos\theta/2 \\ -\sin\theta/2 \end{pmatrix}.$$

If we put $\theta = 90°$, we get exactly the finite rotation of state $|+1\rangle$ to $|-\rangle$ as indicated in Figure II.2.1 where the frame choices are discussed and how these choices are related to the unitary group transformations we denoted as U in our discussion in Chapter II.1. We also know how to apply this transformation to the operators, We have to act from both sides for example:

$$Z \to R_y(\theta)\,Z\,R_y(-\theta) = -X\,,$$

where we have used the fact that $R_y(\theta/2)^\dagger = R_y(-\theta/2)$. This explicitly resolves a puzzle that you may have felt uneasy about. The algebra is three-dimensional with $X/2$, $Y/2$ and $Z/2$ as basis vectors, and indeed by rotating Z around the Y axis with $\theta = 90°$ yields $-X$, exactly as you would expect, but applying the same transformation to the qubit rotates the two-dimensional 'vector' only over 45 degrees. How is that possible? Well to be precise the qubit is not a vector in the usual sense it is therefore that we introduced the term *spinor* exactly to make this distinction.

From the above considerations one may show that any finite $SU(2)$ group transformation can be parametrized as

$$g(\{\gamma^a\}) = e^{i\sum_a \gamma^a T_a} \quad \text{with } \{T_a\} = \{X/2, Y/2, Z/2\}.$$

Finite translations. For the translations one can do a similar exponentiation,

$$T(a) = e^{iaP}\,. \quad \text{(II.6.6)}$$

---

[4]Here the factor a half comes back and becomes relevant. The parameter is θ, but the generator satisfying the su(2) commutation relations is Y/2, and therefore it looks like a rotation by $\theta/2$, but it is not.

which gives that on an operator which depends on X, and P we obtain after a finite translation by any amount a:

$$f(X, P) \rightarrow T(a)f(X, P)T(-a)$$
$$= e^{iaP}f(X, P)e^{-iaP} = f(X + a, P). \quad (II.6.7)$$

In particular one has the property that $T(a)XT(-a) = X + a$., showing that the X operator has been shifted by a.

In the same vein you can show that if $[H, P] = 0$ and P is conserved. That also means that

$$T(a)HT(-a) = H,$$

which literally says that it leaves the Hamiltonian invariant, i.e. the translations are a symmetry of the Hamiltonian.

What I am trying to make plausible is that by 'exponentiating the algebra' we do get the corresponding group. Whereas the algebra describes infinitesimal transformations you need the group to do finite transformations. And whereas the algebra is a linear vector space, the group is some smooth curved manifold.

The group space or manifold of $SU(2)$. You can think of a group as a smooth manifold or space. For example, the group $U(1)$ is just a circle as we mentioned before. For the real space translations it is $\mathbb{R}^3$ because a finite translation in space is fixed by the three components of the displacement vector.

The group $SU(2)$ is isomorphic to the three-sphere S^3 as we discussed in Chapter II.1 on page 20. So exponentiating the $su(2)$ algebra (note the use of lowercase) we get the $SU(2)$ group (in capitals). The $su(2)$ algebra has generators X, Y, and Z, and is therefore three-dimensional. The dimensionality of the algebra is the same as that of the group (manifold). The group $SU(2)$ has therefore three independent parameters, or coordinates. You can think

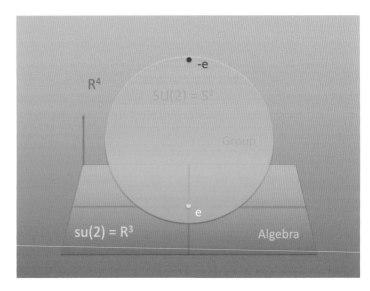

Figure II.6.5: *The group* $SU(2)$ *and its algebra* $su(2)$. $SU(2)$ can also be represented as a unit three-sphere S^3 embedded in $\mathbb{R}^4$. The $su(2)$ algebra can then be thought of as the $\mathbb{R}^3$ tangent space to the group manifold in the origin (the point corresponding to the trivial or unit element e).

of the algebra as the tangent (hyper) plane to the group manifold in the unit element e (corresponding to the trivial transformation). That plane has of course the same dimension but is a linear, flat space like $\mathbb{R}^n$. In Figure II.6.5 we give illustrated this relation between the $SU(2)$ group and the $su(2)$ algebra. If you stay near the unit element, a change in the tangent plane is almost as good as moving on the group manifold. It's like assuming that the Earth is flat, which is not such a bad approximation if you look on the scale of kilometers, but causes serious trouble if you start thinking in terms of thousands of kilometers! Thinking locally amounts to making a linear approximation, as for small $a \simeq \varepsilon$ we may write

$$T(\varepsilon) \simeq 1 + i\varepsilon P.$$

This terminology is that the algebra *generates* infinitesimal transformations. In short: thinking local acting global is bad, while thinking global and acting local is fine.

Gauge symmetries

We have argued that the equations that form the starting point for quantum fields are basically the same equations that one can write down for classical fields. Those classical fields change from being just functions on the configuration space to operator valued fields. And these then have to be quantized typically using canonical methods where the fields become like 'field coordinates' and their derivatives like 'field momenta'.

Electrodynamics revisited. Let us go back to the Schrödinger or better the Dirac equation in three plus one dimensions and ask how we could implement the interactions with the electromagnetic field. Somewhere in the equations there ought to appear terms that describe this interaction. Now we go through a beautiful argument where you will see how a number of rather peripheral remarks we have been making before all fall into place and yield a profound insight. That insight amounts to the fact that nature has a hidden symmetry and that imposing that symmetry completely fixes the precise form of the interactions (fundamental forces) between the elementary constituent particles.

I give the argument in relativistic notation, because that keeps things simple and elegant. The argument also holds true in non-relativistic situations. We want to use space-time vectors that have four components: for example instead of using the usual momentum vector $\mathbf{p}$ we switch to the four-momentum written p_μ where $\mu = 0, \ldots, 3$ and the time component of the four momentum is defined as $p_0 \equiv E/c$. Now if you look at the equations describing the interaction of charged particles with the electromagnetic field, then it turns out that you can get those interaction exactly right if you use a simple trick that goes by the name of 'minimal substitution'. It is a recipe that says: for a particle with a charge e replace everywhere the momentum p_μ by $p_\mu + eA_\mu$. The four vector $A_\mu = (V, \mathbf{A})$ are the electro-

magnetic potentials where V is the electrostatic or scalar potential and $\mathbf{A}$ as the vector potential.

These were introduced in the section on electrodynamics in Chapter I.1, together with the electromagnetic *field strength* $F_{\mu\nu}$:

$$F_{\mu\nu} = \partial_\mu A_\nu - \partial_\nu A_\mu. \qquad \text{(II.6.8)}$$

The three spatial components F_{ij} correspond with the components of $\mathbf{B}$, and the space-time components F_{0i} correspond with the components of $\mathbf{E}$.

Gauge invariance. In Chapter I.1 we argued that there is some redundancy in keeping all the six components of the fields $\mathbf{E}$ and $\mathbf{B}$ and one could do with only the four components of the gauge potential A_μ. That is indeed the case but as a matter of fact even that doesn't eliminate all redundancy. In the formulation with the gauge potentials there is still some redundancy left, because we can make a transformation on the gauge potentials that leave the field strength F and thus the physical $\mathbf{E}$ and $\mathbf{B}$ fields invariant. This transformation is called a gauge transformation and involves a space-time dependent function $\Lambda(x, t)$:

$$A_\mu(x, t) \rightarrow A'_\mu(x, t) \equiv A_\mu + \partial_\mu \Lambda(x, t). \qquad \text{(II.6.9)}$$

If you substitute the transformed field into (II.6.8), you immediately see that the extra terms cancel each other out, and that proves the invariance (and the efficiency of the relativistic notation).

This invariance is of another type than we have been discussing before, because the transformation depends on space-time. It is called a *local* transformation because by choosing the transformation you fix the amount by which you transform in every point independently, as long as it changes smoothly from one space-time point to the next. This means that we are effectively dealing with only three components for the gauge potential, because one may choose the gauge function in such a way as to 'gauge away' one of the components of the gauge potential. So why don't we get rid of it you may say, and strip the description of the electromagnetic field to the bare minimum. This is not so easy and you could say that keeping the redundancy is the price we pay for the transparency and compactness of the theory, and most importantly its linearity. This theory is beautiful like a peacock, with the exceptional property that it can fly as well! We are a bit like dealers in options when we talk about the field strengths which correspond to the invariant physical degrees of freedom, but these are in fact *derivatives* of the underlying potentials to which the particles couple.

Covariant derivative. The minimal substitution means that for charged particles we change the momentum operator to

$$P_\mu = -i\hbar\partial_\mu \to -i\hbar D_\mu \equiv -i\hbar(\partial_\mu + i\frac{e}{\hbar}A_\mu)\,; \quad \text{(II.6.10)}$$

where e is of course the charge of the particle. In other words, the recipe is to replace the ordinary derivative ∂_μ by the covariant derivative D_μ.

We also remarked before that the Schrödinger or Dirac field is complex and therefore has a real and an imaginary part. And we furthermore made the point that there is always one overall phase that is unobservable and has no physical meaning therefore. Transforming that phase into another phase would not matter; it reshuffles the real and the imaginary parts of the wave function but the combination of the two has exactly the same content. Nevertheless, there is a phase symmetry because there is a phase transformation that leaves the physics invariant

$$\psi(x_\nu) \to \psi'(x_\nu) = e^{i\alpha}\psi(x_\nu)\,. \quad \text{(II.6.11)}$$

Furthermore, the equations with the interaction term also are invariant under this phase transformation. This transformation is often called a *global*, meaning space-time independent gauge transformation.

Now we pose the interesting question whether these equations are also invariant under *local*, which means space-

time dependent phase transformations:

$$\psi(x_\nu) \to \psi'(x_\nu) = e^{i\alpha(x_\nu)}\psi(x_\nu)\,.$$

On first inspection the answer is no, because the equations have derivatives that 'see' that space-time dependent phase factor and are going to make trouble about it because:

$$\partial_\mu\psi \to \partial_\mu\psi' = e^{i\alpha(x_\nu)}(\partial_\mu + i\partial_\mu\alpha(x_\nu))\psi\,;$$

and the transformed equation would be different because of this extra term involving the derivative of the space-time dependent phase. But wait a minute, what if we include the gauge potentials as we are supposed to do if we adopt the minimal substitution doctrine. Then we get:

$$D_\mu\psi \to (D_\mu\psi)' = e^{i\alpha(x_\nu)}(\partial_\mu + i\partial_\mu\alpha(x_\nu) - i\frac{e}{\hbar}A'_\mu)\psi\,.$$

Now please observe a tiny miracle, if we just substitute the expression (II.6.9) for gauge transformed A'_μ and make the judicious choice $\Lambda = (\hbar/e)\alpha$ then net the effect of the two transformations is zero and we get that the gauge covariant derivative transforms exactly as we want,

$$D_\mu\psi \to (D_\mu\psi)' = e^{i\alpha(x_\nu)}D_\mu\psi\,.$$

It transforms 'covariantly' just like the field ψ itself and therefore the complete theory involving also matter fields becomes gauge invariant. This result implies that the equations transform now simply by an overall local phase, which we can divide out and we have not changed anything.

We conclude that the complete system of Maxwell equations coupled to the Schrödinger or Dirac equations exhibits this local gauge invariance.

Gauge connection and parallel transport. The gauge invariant part of the electromagnetic field are the **E** and **B** fields, or the components of $F_{\mu\nu}$. But as we have been discussing already in the previous section on particle statistics and anyons there is a more subtle *non-local* quantity that is gauge invariant, namely the Aharonov–Bohm phase factor or Wilson loop defined in equation (II.3.3).

If there is curvature (field strength) then the transport between point x_0 and x_1 becomes path dependent. The linear covariant equation:

$$D_\mu \psi(x) = 0;$$

has a general path dependent solution:

$$\psi(x_1) = e^{-i\frac{e}{\hbar}\int_{x_0}^{x_1} A_\mu dx^\mu} \psi(x_0).$$

It looks quite daunting, but think of it as just a phase factor, where the phase equals this integral of A_μ along the path, which is after all just a real number. This expression tells you precisely what *parallel transport* means: it tells you how the electromagnetic phase changes if you move in position space. And the covariant derivative in (II.6.10), is the infinitesimal version of that. The first term with the derivative generates a translation, while the second generates the phase transformation. This also connects with the entries in the table on page 213, the exponent is a phase factor corresponding to a group element of the group $U(1)$ which is just a circle. And A_μ is the *connection one-form* which takes a value in the Lie algebra which is just the phase itself. $U(1)$ is one-dimensional group, and it is generated by a 'one by one hermitian matrix': in other words a real number.

The other point is that this ties in perfectly with our earlier observations in the previous section concerning the Aharonov–Bohm phase factor, as a means of measuring the magnetic flux up to multiples of the basic flux quantum $2\pi\hbar/q$. The remarkable aspect is that the path may entirely lie in a region where the electric and magnetic fields themselves are zero, yet the closed loop measures a nontrivial and gauge invariant quantity. It measures a topological aspect of the theory.

We finally recall the other application of the parallel transport notion as a way to measure some Hamiltonian landscape by means of the so-called Berry phase, as we discussed in Chapter II.3. There, the notion of parallel transport was used to detect 'curvature' or 'field strength' differences between a flat and curved surface.

Charge conservation. We have emphasized over and again that one of the reasons why symmetry is important is that it corresponds to conservation laws. In fact there is a basic theorem by the German 19th century mathematician Emmy Noether that to any one parameter continuous symmetry there is an associated conserved 'charge.' Local symmetries include the corresponding global symmetry and one therefore expects that the gauge symmetries will also correspond to conserved quantities. For the electromagnetic gauge symmetry that is – not surprisingly – the local conservation of electric charge.

A rather direct proof of this was already presented in the subsection on gauge invariance on page 33 of Chapter I.1. Recall that the interaction of the field with an external current gives a contribution to the Lagrangian density of $A^\mu j_\mu$. So if we make the gauge transformation we get only one extra term which equals $+ie(\partial^\mu\Lambda/\hbar)j_\mu$ in the Lagrangian density, because the current itself is assumed to be gauge invariant. Invariance of the theory requires this extra term after integration over space-time to vanish. This in turn requires that the current has to satisfy $\partial^\mu j_\mu = 0$ which amounts to the local conservation of charge. This equation tells you that the change of the charge in that volume exactly equals the current going through the surface bounding that volume. This is the relativistic form of what we in general call a *continuity equation* which is a local conservation law indeed.

Turning arguments around. A question that you might have raised is whether we could have turned the arguments around and have said: let us *impose* this invariance under local transformations on the Dirac or Schrödinger equations, what do we have to do? The answer would have been: you have to introduce a gauge potential A_μ that transforms in such a way that it absorbs the troublesome extra term coming from the derivative. So introducing gauge fields is a necessary consequence of imposing local gauge invariance.

It was through arguments along these lines that in 1954 the physicists Chen Ning Yang and Robert L. Mills discovered the structure of *non-abelian gauge theories* that form the backbone of the acclaimed Standard Model.

Non-abelian gauge theories

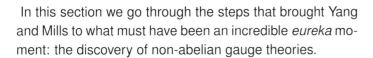

In this section we go through the steps that brought Yang and Mills to what must have been an incredible *eureka* moment: the discovery of non-abelian gauge theories.

Think of our familiar qubit as a column vector with two complex entries, but now we make it into a complex two-component spinor or doublet field, which we denote it by $\psi(x_\nu)$ and we have the derivative ∂_μ which can act on it. Next we want to make a field theory for ψ that is locally gauge invariant. The first thing is to ask what invariance there is under constant or global transformations. Well, it is not just a single phase but it can be any unitary frame rotation U as we discussed for example in the *Math Excursion* on page 179 of Part III. Such rotations correspond to elements of the group $SU(2)$, and we learned that any element of the can be written as the exponent of an element of the $su(2)$ algebra which is a linear combination of the Pauli matrices:

$$U(\boldsymbol{\gamma}) = e^{iC} \text{ with } C = \gamma_1 X + \gamma_2 Y + \gamma_3 Z \equiv \boldsymbol{\gamma} \cdot \mathbf{T}.$$

By construction C is hermitian $(C^\dagger = C)$ and U therefore unitary $(U^\dagger = U^{-1})$. Now we want to repeat the exercise we did for the phase factor with this matrix valued 'phase'.

Gauge covariant derivative. First we observe that the derivative has still no problem with the constant complex rotation by which we mean that the three components of γ are constant. But what if the parameters become spacetime dependent, if we write $\gamma = \gamma(x_\nu)$, and look what happens with at the two-component derivative if we transform $\psi(x_\nu) \to U(x_\nu)\psi(x_\nu)$

$$
\begin{aligned}
(D_\mu\psi) &= (1\partial_\mu + iqA_\mu)\psi \to \\
(D_\mu\psi)' &= (1\partial_\mu + iqA'_\mu)U\psi \\
&= U(1\partial_\mu + U^{-1}\partial_\mu U + iqU^{-1}A'_\mu U)\psi \\
&= U\,(D_\mu\psi)\,.
\end{aligned}
\tag{II.6.12}
$$

In the first line we should now think of the covariant derivative as a matrix where the derivative is multiplied with the unit matrix and A is some matrix with a structure we are about to determine. The strength of the coupling between the A and ψ fields is given by the charge q. In the intermediate line we have inserted the trivial factor $UU^{-1} = 1$ in front, in order to obtain the expression in the desired form, which appears in the bottom line. But that expression only holds if the gauge field A has the interesting structure which is more or less dictated by the derivative term:

$$U^{-1}\partial_\mu U = U^{-1}(\partial_\mu\boldsymbol{\gamma}) \cdot \mathbf{T}\, U\,.$$

Because the factors U, U^{-1} and $\mathbf{T}$ are matrices they do not commute and one cannot just change the order in which they appear in an expression.

Lie algebra valued gauge fields. Apparently this derivative brings down the Lie algebra element and takes the derivative of that, and the result of this gets rotated by the U factors around it. The upshot is that this non-abelian gauge field has to be an element of that same Lie algebra so:

$$A_\mu = \mathbf{A}_\mu \cdot \mathbf{T}$$

and it has to transforms like:

$$A_\mu \to A'_\mu = UA_\mu U^{-1} + \frac{i}{q}(\partial_\mu U)\,U^{-1}\,.$$

For the case at hand the conclusion is now clear, the gauge field itself has to be an element of the Lie algebra in this case $su(2)$, and has to transform like a connection. The is algebra is three-dimensional as it has three independent generators, and consequently there are three independent gauge fields needed, which represent three different gauge particles.

Principle fiber bundles. The appropriate mathematical setting of gauge theories is that of *fiber bundles*, as we discussed already in the section on the 'Physics of geometry' on page 78 of Chapter I.2. These bundles are defined as a triple $\{E, M, \pi\}$ corresponding to a *bundle space* E, a *base manifold* M (which would be our space-time manifold) and a *gauge (or structure) group* G. The dimension of E equals the sum of the dimensions of M and G. And the space E looks locally like a tensor product $M \otimes G$, but can be different globally, in which case we speak of a non-trivial bundle. Given is a *projection* π from E onto M, and the inverse of that projection at a point $x_\mu \in M$ gives you the *fiber* above that point which is a copy of (isomorphic to) G. Choosing a smooth *section*, meaning that you choose a particular group element out of each fiber, produces an explicit form of a gauge covariant derivative on M. Gauge transformations are related to the changing of sections of the bundle.

This setting allows you to naturally define topologically non-trivial gauge field configurations that can be characterized by topological invariants like the *Chern classes*. Deep results relevant for physics were obtained. For example, a variety of the so-called index theorems, like the *Atiyah–Singer index theorem*, that links the topological invariant of the gauge field configuration to the net number of left- versus right-handed solutions of the zero-mass Dirac equation coupled to that (background) field. Interestingly the Yang–Mills equations were not considered before they appeared in the physics literature, and only afterwards became a major mathematical topic in the 1970s.

Once more the Standard Model. We mentioned that the number of gauge particles is equal to the dimension of the Lie algebra, which is just the number of independent parameters or generators. But the argument does not depend on the particulars and basically holds for any gauge group, including the groups $U(1), SU(2)$, and $SU(3)$ that appear in the Standard Model. The weak and electromagnetic interactions have the gauge group $SU(2) \times U(1)$, where the charged $W^\pm$ bosons correspond to the raising and lowering operators $T_\pm$, while the photon and the neutral Z boson are linear combinations of the neutral W^0 boson and the Y boson associated with the $U(1)$ factor of the gauge group. The three W bosons correspond thus with the three-dimensional (iso) spin 1 representation in Figure II.6.2, while the fermionic quarks and lepton fields form doublets corresponding to the (iso) spin-$1/2$ representation.

Colors and Flavors. Quantum Chromodynamics (QCD), the theory for the strong interactions, has gauge group $SU(3)$, which has dimension eight. The eight gluons correspond with the weights of the root diagram (including two zero weights in the center) as shown in Figure II.6.6. In this figure we have also marked the color (anti-)triplet representations corresponding to the weights of the (anti-)quark fields.[5]

At this point you may experience a *deja vu* moment, because Figure I.4.33 in Chapter I.4 flashed back in your mind which indeed looks very similar to Figure II.6.6. Yes, true, but it actually refers to a very different context. There we were talking about the *flavor symmetry*, the classification scheme discovered by Gell-man and Zweig. It is indeed also an $SU(3)$ symmetry, and it also applies to the quarks but on the other hand it is a very different type

---

[5]The gluon circles carry a quark and anti-quark color, and we have given the anti-quarks the anti- or better complementary color in the figure. In Figure I.4.36 the gluons are also bicolored but there both the quark and antiquark have the same color but have arrows in the opposite direction.

of $SU(3)$ symmetry. Firstly, it is not a gauged symmetry, but instead an approximate global or rigid symmetry, so there are no gauge particles associated with it. And as the quarks of different flavors have different masses it is indeed only an approximate symmetry, because the particle states are not really degenerate. Our knowledge at this point suggests that this symmetry is accidental, and once you accept that it is only approximate you may as well declare that there is a $SU(4)$ or even $SU(6)$ flavor symmetry. This would be the case if you in addition take the charm, top and bottom quark flavors along. Anyway, the physics related to these two $SU(3)$ groups is entirely different: the flavour symmetry is manifest in the spectrum of observed particles, as the figure in Chapter 4 shows. The mesons for example belong to an octet and these are free particles. The color property of particles is hidden because of the confinement phenomenon which only allows color neutral or singlet states to be free particles. This made it so hard to uncover the color symmetry in the first place.

Color singlets. The singlet property has to do with constructing colorless combinations of quarks (and gluons). This requires that we look in the possible multi-quark spectrum for those combinations which have that property. Here I recall the fact that multi-particle states are described by so-called tensor products of single particle Hilbert spaces. The single (anti-)quark color states form a color (anti-)triplet representation denoted as 3 and $\bar{3}$ respectively. The tensor products can be split up again in irreducible components or representations. Like for example:

$$3 \times \bar{3} = 1 + 8$$
$$3 \times 3 = \bar{3} + 6$$
$$3 \times 3 \times 3 = 1 + 8 + 8 + 10. \tag{II.6.13}$$

The dimension of the tensor product space is the product of the dimensions of the two factors. The weights of the tensor product states are obtained by adding the weights of the individual representations. This you may verify in the SU(3) weight space of Figure II.6.6. What is clear from equation (II.6.13) is that the simplest ways to make a color singlet '1' representation is by combining a quark and an anti-quark, making a *meson*, or making a particular combination of three quarks making a *baryon*.

Is Einstein gravity a gauge theory? So we have found that the gauge symmetry principle underlies the particular way the force carrying particles appear in nature. Does this trick then also work for the gravitational force you may wonder. Yes indeed, it does! One interesting way to interpret the Einstein theory is actually to look at it as a gauged version of the combined *local* Lorentz and translation groups, usually referred to as the *Poincaré group*. So in this perspective the Einstein equations are an expression of a local Poincaré symmetry.

Kaluza–Klein theory. You could also argue the opposite way and say that the E and B fields, the field strengths of electromagnetism, correspond to electromagnetic 'curvatures' of some internal space that is defined in every point in space-time. Yet another way to understand it is to say that space-time has in fact extra spatial dimensions, which have particular geometries corresponding to circles, spheres or group manifolds for that matter. These compact extra spaces are then squeezed to zero size, by a procedure called 'dimensional reduction' or 'dimensional compactification.' This remarkable idea in fact goes back to the early days of general relativity where Theodor Kaluza and Oskar Klein proposed to unify electromagnetism and gravity in a five-dimensional theory using this symmetry principle.

The proper mathematical setting for the classical versions of gauge theories is that of *fiber bundles* with some Lie group G or representation thereof as fibers, as we introduced them in the section on 'The physics of geometry' on page 78 of Chapter I.2. These geometric structures attracted the attention of the physicists only long after the not so geometric Maxwell, Einstein and Yang–Mills equations were written down. In fact the formalisms were developed to a large extent independently in physics and mathematics.

Non-abelian field strengths. You might complain that I am choking my highly esteemed readers with math, but to my defence I would argue that we have exposed some of the core ideas of modern physics, in only a few pages , and even without too much cheating! In fact the 1954 paper of Yang and Mills is just a short article that appeared in the *Physical Review Letters* (PRL) journal, and its influence is inversely proportional to the length of the paper. There is an ironic aspect to that paper, since the authors in fact proposed that this non-abelian gauge theory should describe the 'pions' as these particles were at that time believed to mediate the strong nuclear interactions. This idea didn't work out at all, and so these beautiful equations went into the 'fridge,' and it took about 15 years before they were taken out again and found their true vocation in the Standard Model as we have described it.[6] It is one of those rare occasions where the elegance and beauty of an idea make it irresistible and fortunately also inescapable, so one just had to wait for it to find its proper place.

You might object by noting that the Kaluza–Klein idea of dimensional compactification apparently has *not* properly landed, in spite of being attractive and elegant as it 'produces' gauge fields with the correct interactions. The K–K approach returned as a necessary ingredient of string theory, but nevertheless has not yet found its true vocation, and I am afraid it has to spend some more time in the 'fridge.' Science is patient and even if an idea clearly 'does not work,' it is extremely hard to put stickers stating 'Consume before date indicated on the bottom' on ideas.

---

[6]A hallmark of great institutions is not only that they attract extremely gifted people, but also that they are the guardians of research fields, keeping alive a collective memory of failed attempts and almost forgotten, unsolved problems; of all that ended up in the 'fridge of ideas' so to speak.

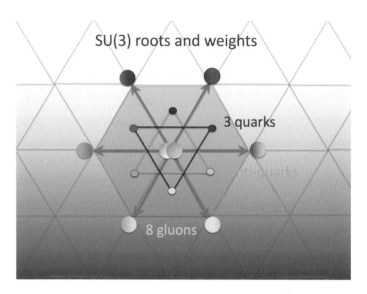

Figure II.6.6: $SU(3)$ *roots and weights.* In this figure we represented the root diagram of $SU(3)$. with the 6 non-zero roots given by the green arrows. The gluons form the 8 representation corresponding to the six non-zero roots and the two in the center, marked by the bi-colored circles. Then there are the triplet (3) and the anti-triplet ($\bar{3}$) representations corresponding to the three colored (anti-)quarks.

The Yang-Mills equations

So are we done? No, not quite, we have to check one other thing: what will happen to the analogue of the Maxwell equations for the gauge fields? And what happens to the electric and magnetic fields, so nicely encoded in the field strength $F_{\mu\nu}$, if we go non-abelian? Two remarks are to be made, (i) as F is linear in the gauge field it also will live in the Lie algebra and should therefore simply transform as $F \rightarrow F' = UFU^{-1}$ and (ii) this is only achieved if the definition of F for the non-abelian theories is generalized in a logical and elegant way to:

$$F_{\mu\nu} = \partial_\mu A_\nu - \partial_\nu A_\mu + iq[A_\mu, A_\nu]; \qquad (II.6.14)$$

logical and elegant because the commutator is antisymmetric in the indices and also keeps you in the Lie algebra. An equivalent, more covariantly looking definition is to say that $F_{\mu\nu} = -\frac{i}{q}[D_\mu, D_\nu]$. The extra commutator term in the field strength has huge physical consequences it turns out.

Clearly the definition of the non-abelian electric and magnetic fields are nonlinear in the potentials, and this means that the Yang–Mills equations, which are the generalizations of the Maxwell equations to the non-abelian case, are nonlinear as well. The Yang–Mills equations really are the dynamical expression of non-abelian gauge symmetry. These equations take the following form:

$$D^\mu F_{\mu\nu} = \partial^\mu F_{\mu\nu} + ig[A^\mu, F_{\mu\nu}] = 0.$$

They are strongly nonlinear indeed, in the first place because the definition of the field strength is non-linear in A, and secondly because of the presence of the commutator term of A with F in the equation itself.

Symmetry dictates the structure of interactions. The non-linearities mean that the theory is self-interacting right from the start. Whereas photons don't see each other, gluons do, as we already showed in Figures I.4.36 and I.4.37. We have reproduced the latter here to take a closer look at how it connects to the more detailed description of non-abelian gauge theories we have given.

The local Lagrangian density is a Lorentz invariant expression for non-abelian gauge fields (gluons) coupled to Dirac fermions (quarks) and looks deceivingly simple:

$$\mathcal{L}(x_\mu) = -\frac{1}{4}F_{\mu\nu}F^{\mu\nu} + i\bar{\psi}\slashed{D}\psi, \qquad (II.6.15)$$

with $\slashed{D} = \gamma^\mu D_\mu$ the Lorentz invariant Dirac operator as it works on a four-component Dirac field $\psi(x_\mu)$. In Figure II.6.7 we see two interaction vertices: on the left we see a self-interaction of the gauge field corresponding to the third order term in A from the F^2 term in the Lagrangian and on the right we see the gauge field interact with the Dirac field corresponding to the cubic interaction term from the covariant Dirac operator in the Lagrangian. There is a lot

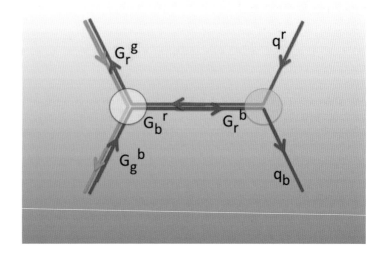

Figure II.6.7: *Color-flow diagram in QCD.* A nice way to visualize the interactions in QCD. Quarks carry a single color line, while gluons carry two (different) lines. In the vertices the color charge is conserved, so, the colors and arrows have to match. The upper index goes into the vertex, the lower index goes out.

of index gymnastics hidden in the notation however. This becomes evident if we for example write out the latter term in glorious detail. It looks quite horrendous:

$$i\frac{q}{\hbar c}\bar{\psi}(x_\nu)^i_a \gamma^\mu_{ij} A(x_\nu)^\gamma_\mu T^{\ ab}_\gamma \psi(x_\nu)^j_b. \qquad (II.6.16)$$

There are a few remarks to make with respect to this intricate expression:

(i) the interaction is local as all fields depend on the same space-time point x_ν;

(ii) all fields carry a space-time index that tells you how they transform under Lorentz transformations, and a gauge index that tells you how it transforms under gauge transformations;

(iii) the Dirac fields carry two indices, a space-time spinor index i with $i, j = 1, \ldots, 4$, and a 'color' index a with $a, b = 1, \ldots, n$ with n the dimension of the color representation (n=3 for QCD);

(iv) the four gamma matrices carry a space-time (vector) index μ and each of them is a matrix in spinor space and has therefore two spinor indices i, j;

(v) the gauge field has a space-time index μ and a gauge group index γ with $\gamma = 1, \ldots, \dim \mathcal{A}$ (dim $\mathcal{A} = 8$ for QCD);

(vi) the representation matrices or generators T carry a gauge group label γ and each of them is a matrix in the representation space, thus with two indices a, b;

(vii) all indices are pairwise contracted, and thus have to be summed over. This amounts to making invariant inner products in the spaces the indices refer to. In a sense the expression is therefore extremely simple because once you know what the symbols stand for, there is a strict logic which tells you where to put the various indices. It is dictated by the requirement of invariance of the interaction under independent changes of basis in either space-time, or spinor space, or in the Lie algebra or group representation spaces;

(viii) It is these delicate balancing act of indices that is for example reflected in the way the 'color 'lines in the diagram of Figure II.6.7 are strictly continuous through the vertices.

Some people might say that it is ugly to exhibit all these indices, while others say that that is exactly what makes the very beauty of the construction manifest. The ultra compact notation of equation (II.6.15) demonstrates how effective the symbolic notation is that the physicists have developed over the years. The expression (II.6.16) in contrast shows very explicitly how a particle in fact lives in many spaces simultaneously, all with their own indices and metrics. All of us agree that to do real calculations you have to go all the way down into this index jungle, it is a must, a *conditio sine qua non!* And once you realize in addition that this is only the lowest order interaction diagram you can imagine that it takes a fully dedicated PhD researcher to complete a single higher order calculation of some physically relevant proces that is measured in an accelerator.

Such calculations involve hundreds or even thousands of diagrams to be added to get the full probability amplitude for the process. The actual execution of such calculations involves nowadays high level AI in large scale computing efforts and it is thanks to the rigorous underlying symmetry structures that these calculations can be automated to such a large extent.

Self-interactions and the confinement problem. Free fields are sometimes not as free as one would think. And this in turn makes perturbative approximations dangerous, which basically means that you start with setting the coupling strength q to zero, and then take only low orders of q into account. The problem is that if a field is self-interacting the theory becomes nonlinear and may end up in a phase which is entirely different from what you naively would expect. The relevant or observable degrees of freedom can be very different from the degrees of freedom you started out with. For example the enigmatic problem of *quark confinement* can be traced back to the self-interacting nature of the gluons. Free quarks have never been observed, because they are doomed. They have to spend their whole life as a pair, or a *ménage a trois* but always confined within a hadron.

Understanding and proving these quantum confinement properties of Yang–Mills theories from first principles is still an open question and is one of the Millennium problems in mathematics. It is a problem that attracts the minds of brilliant mathematicians and theorists because it is a very well-defined problem. The starting point is a familiar object called a non-abelian gauge theory, or a principle fiber bundle with a compact structure group. The quantum problem to be solved is: prove the conjectured confinement property of the 'color-electric' fields. That this property holds has been demonstrated by numerous computer simulations of the theory, where the theory is formulated on a discrete space-time lattice but that amounts basically to a study of the strong coupling (large q) limit of the theory. This is basically a perturbative approach in $1/q$. And in that limit the theory does confine, but to settle the question one has to prove that there is not a phase transition between the strong and weak coupling regime.

From experience – think for example of Fermat's last conjecture – we know that such conjectures can linger around for centuries before they finally get turned into a theorem. A humble observation is that making the conjecture already can make you famous. So the least we can say is that we are exploring deep waters!

The conclusion is that the principle of local gauge invariance provided a valuable clue to the construction and understanding of the fundamental equations underlying the Standard Model. ■ ■

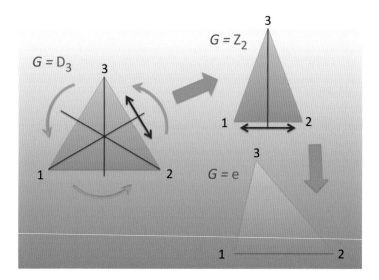

Figure II.6.8: *The breaking of symmetries.* Breaking symmetry by deformation of an object. The D_3 symmetry of the equilateral triangle (with six elements) gets broken to a Z_2 of isosceles triangle (with two elements), which subsequently gets broken to the trivial group for an arbitrary triangle.

The symmetry breaking paradigm

Having argued that symmetry principles play an important role in modern-day physics, the same can be said about the concept of symmetry breaking which has found many beautiful and surprising applications in basic high-energy physics as well as in many branches of condensed matter and molecular physics. Where symmetry unifies states and makes them degenerate, it is the breaking of symmetries which creates non-uniformity and diversity. We are going to explore some typical cases which illustrate the power of this quantessential idea.

Symmetry breaking in objects. It is paradoxical that I first let you suffer by talking so extensively about how beautiful symmetries are, and then immediately after confront you with how to break them. It is like a small child building a beautiful tower from woodblocks and then destroying it while screaming and dancing around it. Apparently there is some thrill in the act of destruction! Let us look for similar thrills, and first go back to the 'symmetries of objects', like an equilateral triangle, a circle or a sphere,

and then it is not hard to imagine how to break the symmetry.

For example you could squeeze the object one way or another as to reduce its symmetry. You could do it step wise like in Figure II.6.8, where you first go from an equilateral to an isosceles triangle, and then to a generic one. In that case you first pass from the discrete group D_3 with six elements (3 rotations and 3 reflections) to the group Z_2 of two elements (the identity element and a reflection), and in the second step you end up with no symmetry at all: you are left with only the identity element. Breaking has the property that the residual symmetry group after breaking is just a subgroup of the original symmetry group.

If you squeeze a ball top down, you typically get an ellipsoid, where the symmetry is reduced to rotations around the vertical axis only, and a reflection symmetry through the horizontal plane and vertical planes through the center.

If you then make it into a standing egg shape, you lose the reflection property in the horizontal plane but still keep the vertical symmetry axis, and so on. By the way this makes you wonder why eggs have the shape they have. Why not celebrate the perfection of life in perfect spheres? One reason that has been given is that egg-shaped objects do not roll away, if you put them on the table and push them away they tend to 'boomerang' in a little circle. 'They like to stay near their starting point!' I hear my mother say. And maybe the biology of how to lay an egg – to push it out by contraction – plays a role as well in the optimal egg design. What came first, the egg or the design? This is not even a 'chicken or egg' question, instead, this is an 'egg or egg' question. Anyway, more a topic in evolutionary biology than in quantum physics I fear, so it is better to leave it to the *cloaca* experts. The shapes created by symmetry breaking are more and more diverse and need more and more parameters to specify. In that sense their information content and therefore entropy increases. And many will say that with that their beauty increases as well.

Symmetry breaking by solutions of equations. The next step up is to talk about the symmetry of equations, and the first question that comes to mind is what do the solutions of equations with symmetries look like? Do they indeed manifestly exhibit the symmetries of the equations? The answer is clearly: No! Think of our nice Newtonian example again. The great step forward was exactly to discover and understand that the planetary orbits are *not* circles or even epicycles, but conic sections, ellipses, parabolas and hyperbolas. So, where did the spherical symmetry of the gravitational field around the sun go, which is so clearly present in the equations? Why and where does the immaculate perfection of the heavenly spheres get lost?

A little thinking yields the answer: the symmetry is still there. But the symmetry transformations act on the space of solutions. What they do is that given a particular solution, and acting with a symmetry operator on it, it will in

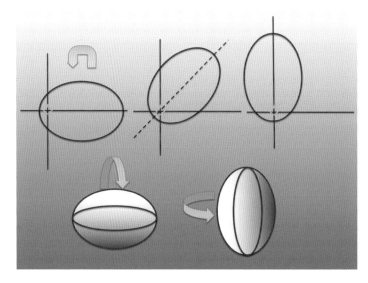

Figure II.6.9: *Action of rotational symmetry on an elliptic orbit solution.* The Newtonian Earth–Sun system has spherical symmetry but that symmetry is not manifest in a particular solution, like for example an elliptic orbit. The symmetry transforms different equal energy solutions into each other.

general generate a different solution. The symmetries map solutions onto each other, and as they keep the equations fixed, they transform solutions with equal energy into each other. With the rotations that is quite obvious, as we have illustrated with the elliptic orbits of the spherically symmetric Newtonian sun-earth system in Figure II.6.9. It turns out that the Runge–Lenz symmetry changes the eccentricity of the elliptic orbit and that is not so obvious. It is in this sense that you may say that most particular solutions break the symmetry of the equation, and the symmetry acts in the space of solutions. It creates a subspace of degenerate solutions in the space of all solutions. That space gets 'stratified' according to its energy values and solution shapes.

This brings us in fact close to the observations we have made with respect to the role symmetries play in quantum theory, labeling the degenerate states but also moving (stepping) between them. They walk you through the degenerate subspace of the total sample space of your favorite framework.

Symmetry breaking in the atom. Symmetry breaking is an important concept. What does symmetry breaking look like in a quantum setting? Imagine that we have a symmetry, then we could make that symmetry visible by 'breaking it'. In other words by adding a term to the Hamiltonian that explicitly breaks the symmetry. For example we put an atom in a magnetic field say along the z-direction, then there will be an extra term in the Hamiltonian proportional to L_z and the magnitude B of the magnetic field. Now the three-dimensional rotational symmetry is broken to rotations around the z-axis only. The consequence is that the energy levels which where at first degenerate and therefore hard to distinguish will now split up proportional to the value of their magnetic quantum number m. This is the famous splitting first observed by Pieter Zeeman we discussed in Chapter I.4. This is an example of *explicit symmetry breaking* where we change the Hamiltonian. But also in quantum theory we can have the phenomenon of *spontaneous symmetry breaking* which refers to a situation where we change external parameters of the system – say the temperature or a coupling – such that the Hamiltonian itself does not change and still has all the symmetries, but it is the ground state that changes to one in which the symmetry is broken.

Low energy modes. This brings us to a follow-up question: what happens if the ground state is not invariant and does not respect all the symmetries? In other words, what if the ground state breaks the symmetry? Well, by what we argued above, it will then necessarily be the case that that ground state is not unique and itself degenerate. If that ground state breaks a *continuous* symmetry, we will have a *continuous* set of equivalent ground states. And what that means is intuitively quite clear: the system can easily move from one ground state to one nearby and it would cost basically no energy.

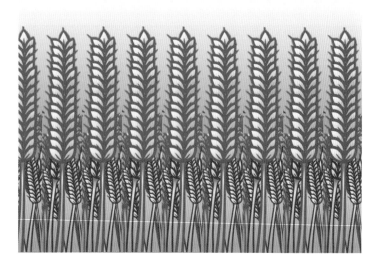

Figure II.6.10: *Long range orientational order.* The collective of wheat plants is in a state that exhibits a long range order. Bij growing out of spherical seeds, the original rotational symmetry is broken.

Saying it yet differently, the generators of the symmetries that are broken create 'zero (energy) modes' of the system. This is an important physical signature of broken symmetry: the appearance of low energy modes in the system that are easy to excite. And if we talk about (relativistic) field theory where the energy includes also the mass, our observation asserts that there will be massless particles around. Such particles are called Goldstone particles or modes, after the MIT physicist Jeffrey Goldstone who discovered the mechanism. Ideally these modes are exactly massless, but there can be additional effects that give those particles a mass. However that mass should be small compared with the scale of the interaction energy that caused the breaking.

Think of wheat seeds, if we assume them to be spherical, spreading them on a field gives a 'ground' or better 'down to earth' state that is rotationally invariant, which means to say that we can rotate each of the seeds by the same amount and nothing will change. Now we wait

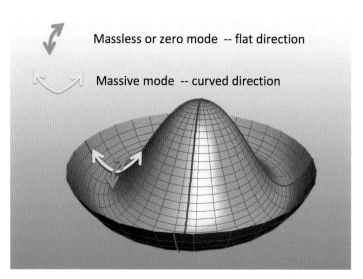

Massless or zero mode -- flat direction

Massive mode -- curved direction

Figure II.6.11: *Wheat waves as low energy excitations.* The wheat field at rest shows tha long-range order typical for a broken symmetry. It has low energy excitations. These are the 'wheat waves' that propagate easily and can already be excited by a gentle breeze.

Figure II.6.12: *Breaking of global symmetry.* The breaking of a $U(1)$ global symmetry leading to a 'Mexican hat' potential. The minimum is not unique but there is a continuum of ground states forming a circle. The breaking leads to one massless and one massive mode as indicated in the figure.

a month or more, and the seeds turn into plants nicely growing up, all beautifully lined up vertically, so the ground state has changed to a 'field' in a completely ordered state that certainly is a state of broken symmetry. There is a spontaneous, average length which is non-zero, and furthermore a long-range vertical orientational order in the system which breaks the original spherical symmetry (see Figure II.6.10).

Now where is the zero mode? Those modes correspond to what you get if a light breeze goes over the field and you see gentle plane waves traverse the wheat plants (see Figure II.6.11). It is a low energy collective mode that originates in the broken symmetry of the ground state. Amusing and playful for sure, but we better take it serious because there are many examples of this so-called Goldstone mechanism, from spin waves or *magnons* in magnets, to the appearance of three nuclear particles known as *pions*, $\pi^{\pm}$ and π_0 we have mentioned in Chapter I.4.

Chiral symmetry breaking. A famous application of the symmetry breaking concept is provided by the three pion particles ($\pi_{\pm}$ and π_0). The interpretation is that they are the Goldstone particles associated with what is called *chiral symmetry breaking*. It refers to an ingenious scenario proposed by Japanese/American physicist Yoichiro Nambu, who indeed received the Physics Nobel prize in 2008, for – I quote – 'the discovery of the mechanism of spontaneous broken symmetry in subatomic physics.' The scenario starts with massless *up* (u) and *down* (d) quarks. These are described by massless Dirac equations, but the massless Dirac equation can be split into two non-interacting pieces, the right (R) and left (L) polarized components. Said differently, it is precisely the mass term in the equations that couples the left to the right polarized components. If you look at the tables of the standard model in Figure I.4.35, you see that there is the horizontal so-called *isospin* symmetry between u and d quarks. This means that the massless equations have an $SU(2)_L$ symmetry transforming u_L and d_L into each other (so they form an isospin one-half representation), and an $SU(2)_R$ symmetry transforming the right-handed components u_R and d_R into each other. So at this stage the model has a six-dimensional $G = SU(2)_L \otimes SU(2)_R$ symmetry. This is called the *chiral symmetry group*, which is a global symmetry. Nambu suggested that a quark anti-quark condensate forms spontaneously, so that the particular diagonal combination of fields u and d becomes the order parameter and acquires a vacuum expectation value:

$$\langle \phi \rangle = \langle (\bar{u}_L \, u_R + \bar{d}_L \, d_R) \rangle = f_\pi \neq 0$$

Now this condensate breaks the symmetry G, but not completely. What is left you can see from the condensate, namely, if we *simultaneously* transform left *and* right then the condensate is invariant. This in turn tells us that from the six generators a particular 'vector like', 'left plus right' $SU(2)$ subgroup survives, while the rest, the three 'left minus right' generators, will be broken. These give rise to three Goldstone particles with exactly the quantum numbers that correspond to the three pion particles. The fact that these particles in the end do have a relatively small mass is accounted for by the fact that the masses of the quarks were not quite zero to start off with.

The breaking systematics. In the chapters on condensed matter physics we will return to this topic of symmetry breaking in the context of many body physics. The general picture boils down to a situation where the theory has a continuous symmetry group G of dimension $\dim G$, and some field gets a non-zero ground state expectation value. That particular vacuum state is only invariant under a residual symmetry group $K \subset G$ which is a subgroup of G. Then there will be $\dim G - \dim K$ broken symmetries and therefore the same number of Goldstone modes. The field that acquires the non-zero expectation value in the ground state and breaks the symmetry is called an *order parameter* field. The nomenclature is that the broken state is the state in which everything is neatly lined up some way and therefore exhibits 'order', where order is defined as the

presence of long-range correlations in the medium.

Ferromagnetism. As an example think of a metal where all the nuclear magnetic spins in the absence of an external field are pointing in random directions in the medium, and therefore there is no over-all magnetization, and no macroscopic direction of the magnetic field is discernible. If one then lowers the temperature below what is called the *Curie temperature*, the thermal energy gets so small that the weak interaction between the tiny magnets starts to become dominant and the spins minimize their energy by lining up and thereby 'spontaneously' make a magnet. So, by cooling down a metal spontaneous magnetization occurs and conversely, by heating up a magnet to high temperature it will lose its magnetization and the symmetry will be restored. Spontaneous magnetization serves as the prototype of spontaneous symmetry breaking in a many-body system. And indeed the low energy modes are just the spin waves which are easy to excite in a magnetized medium.

Topological defects. In Volume III of the book we will address another crucial aspect of symmetry breaking, which is the appearance of what are called *topological defects*. Defects are collective excitations which are usually 'heavy' and not so simple to excite, but once they exist they are equally hard to get rid of. A dramatic instance you are all familiar with from watching the news is the phenomenon of tornadoes or vortices in liquids. In that case there is a ground state that is symmetric if there is no wind, but when a wind starts blowing there is at once everywhere at any given point in space we have a local vector pointing in the direction of the wind. On the surface of the earth we can think of the non-zero two-dimensional vector field representing the wind as an order parameter. As a consequence of some 'massive' obstacles it may happen that somewhere a pair of vortices with opposite vorticities is created, and once these get well separated they are highly stable objects. As a matter of fact you cannot destroy single vortices by locally disturbing them, you have to wait till their energy gets dissipated, for example by causing a lot of damage. There are many examples of remarkably stable collective excitations in all kinds of fields of science and technology that can be thought of as topological defects that originate in a state of broken symmetry.

Hidden gauge symmetries: the Higgs particle. So far we have only looked at rigid or global symmetries: we considered transformations that were the same at any point in space and we found the remarkable directly observable phenomena of low energy Goldstone modes and high-energy defects as hallmarks of their breaking. The next question that naturally arises in field theory is what happens if we somehow 'break' a local gauge symmetry? You may think of the $U(1)$ gauge symmetry of electrodynamics, or the $SU(2)$ gauge symmetry of the weak interactions. Again this may happen *spontaneously,* meaning to say that the system of equations still has the full symmetry, but that the solution, in particular the ground state, does not. The first question to answer is whether this can be done at all. Is it possible to maintain the local gauge symmetry and yet have a ground state in which some field acquires a non-zero expectation value? The answer turns out to be 'approximately yes.' A first example was exhibited by Landau and Ginsberg in their effective description of superconductivity. Later it was understood and explained in full detail in the modern theories of Bardeen, Cooper and Schrieffer, and later Anderson, about which we have more to say in Chapter III.3.

The Brout–Englert–Higgs (BEH) mechanism

A beautiful example of the spontaneous breaking of a non-abelian gauge symmetry is the Brout–Englert–Higgs mechanism, accounting for the heavy mass of the weak force mediating $W^{\pm}$ and Z^0 particles in the weak and electromagnetic interactions, and more indirectly for the existence of the Higgs particle. Let me illustrate how that comes

about in a simpler model due to Sheldon Glashow, without going into much detail.

Breaking in an $SU(2)$ model. Let us consider an $SU(2)$ (or $SO(3)$) gauge theory coupled to a 'matter' field that transforms like a triplet or iso-vector under the gauge group. This means that we should think of the gauge field as $A_\mu^a T_a$, where the T_a are now the three 3×3 matrices generating the $SO(3)$ symmetry. It has three gauge particles (like the W-bosons we discussed before) because the group is three-dimensional. The 'matter' field $\phi(x)$, is a triplet of space-time scalar fields, that transform like a 3-dimensional 'iso-vector' under the $SO(3)$ gauge group. In the quantum context the field $\phi(x)$ would therefore describe three types of scalar particles. Let us now assume that this field $\phi(x)$, or rather its square which is gauge invariant, develops a constant vacuum expectation value $\langle |\phi|^2 \rangle \neq 0$. So a condensate forms. The situation is similar to the magnets we just discussed, but now we think of it happening in some internal space where the force field is active, and where the ϕ field describes an *iso-vector* degree of freedom at every point in space.

As long as the vacuum expectation value vanishes the symmetry is not broken, but if the iso-vector is non-zero, and chooses some fixed direction it is like a wheat field and the non-zero vector field is only invariant under rotations around the axis in the direction in which the nonzero iso-vector points, corresponding to an $SO(2)$ subgroup of dimension one. So we expect there to be two massless Goldstone particles, like in the case we discussed before. But now in addition we have the gauge fields that are coupled to this iso-vector through a covariant derivative. The question is then what the effect of the vacuum expectation for the scalar field has on the gauge fields. The resulting mechanism is powerful and quite universal.

To see what happens we write for the iso-vector (and think of it as a three component column-vector) in the 'broken' phase:

$$\phi(\mathbf{x}) = \phi_0\,\hat{\mathbf{e}}_3 + \delta\phi(\mathbf{x}) ,$$

where ϕ_0 is the constant non-zero vacuum expectation value pointing in the third direction of iso-space and the delta describes the field fluctuations around that ground state value. Now the interactions are generated by the co-variant derivative:

$$D_\mu\phi = \left(\mathbf{1}\partial_\mu + iqA_\mu^a\,T_a\right)\phi ,$$

where the T_a are the three generators of rotations in iso-space. At this point the crucial observation is that there are two components of the gauge field that 'see' or sense the vacuum value, while the third component does not be-cause it linked to the generator of the residual symmetry which leaves the condensate unchanged. The Lagrangian density $\mathcal{L}$ of this theory contains a term proportional to $(D_\mu\phi)^2$. Of interest here is only what the effect is of the constant ϕ_0 in the Hamiltonian. When you work out the interaction between the gauge field and the vacuum term you discover that it leads to a quadratic term proportional to $|\phi_0|^2$ of the form:

$$\Delta L = |\phi_0|^2\big((A^1)^2 + (A^2)^2\big) ;$$

and this is exactly what a mass term for the two compo-nents of the gauge field would look like. Apparently we have generated a mass for two of the three force carrying particles, a mass proportional to the non-zero expectation value ϕ_0. So, we end up with one massless force com-ponent (A^3), which is long-range like the photon, and two massive force particles A^1 and A^2. The latter two can be recombined in the components $A^\pm$ which are charged with respect to the massless A^3 field. Because of their mass these fields mediate a short-range interaction described by a Yukawa potential as we explained in Chapter I.4. They would be the lookalikes of the $W^\pm$ particles. What we just described amounts to a simplified analogue of the Brout–Englert–Higgs mechanism in the Standard Model, which indeed explains the masses of the W and Z bosons me-diating the weak interactions, and the photon remaining massless.

Searching for the Higgs. The remaining question is where does the celebrated Higgs particle reside in this scenario? I have not yet mentioned it. To understand its origin we have to do some counting of the degrees of freedom of the particles before and after the condensate forms.

Let us start with a massless force mediator like the pho-ton. In Chapter I.1 we showed that the photon field A_μ has two transversal polarization states orthogonal to its propa-gation direction. It is important to know that this transver-sality has everything to do with the fact that the photon is massless and, as we have argued before, it is the gauge invariance that effectively removes one degree of freedom from the three-component 'vector' potential. It is indeed the gauge invariance that – so to speak – protects the masslessness of a gauge particle like the photon. To get massive it would need the extra (longitudinal) component which is just not there, *basta*!

To continue our counting exercise, each component of the iso-vector field ϕ_i represents one field degree of freedom. independent of whether it is massive or massless. Sup-pose we take it to be a massive field, then after break-ing, we create two massless Goldstone degrees of free-dom while the third iso-component remains massive. Now comes the magic of the Higgs mechanism: the massless modes of the ϕ field get 'eaten' by the corresponding gauge particles, who become *stante-pede* massive after this ex-quisite meal. Because a massive vector field needs three polarization states, it has two transversal components like the photon, but also a longitudinal component, which the massless photon does not have. So, the upshot of the exercise is crystal clear: if we 'break' a gauge symmetry then the the forces in the unbroken group stay unchanged but the force mediating particles that correspond to the broken generators, become massive and therefore short-range. And they become massive by absorbing the would-be Goldstone modes, which consequently disappear from the spectrum. There are no massless Goldstone particles but instead we have two massive vector bosons!

And now, to finally answer the question that got us into all this counting in the first place, where is that Higgs particle? The answer can only be that that particle corresponds exactly to the single leftover massive degree of freedom, the third component of that iso-vector Φ we started of with. So it is not the massless Goldstone degree of freedom that signals the breaking in this gauge symmetry setting, but the smoking gun is a neutral (it does not couple to surviving photon-like particle) massive scalar particle. What we learn is that the Higgs particle is not the condensate which gives the force carriers mass, but rather the quantized wave that rides on top of that condensate! It is a bit like having a transition from vapor to liquid water, which after the transition allows for waves propagate on the water surface. The degrees of freedom that acquire mass are the ones that have to wade through the water which makes them feel heavy indeed. The Higgs particle is the necessary a witness without alibi of this beautiful but intricate mechanism. The discovery of this unique feature that vindicates the BEH mechanism, a backbone of the Standard Model, by the ATLAS and CMS collaborations at CERN in 2012 was therefore a landmark discovery.

The mixing of weak and electromagnetic interactions. In the example above we have looked at the breaking of an $SO(3)$ symmetry by a non-zero vacuum expectation value of an iso-vector or triplet field ϕ, giving rise to masses for two of the three gauge fields. This is not quite the way the symmetry breaking works in the Standard Model. In the sector of the weak and electromagnetic interactions we have a gauge group $SU(2) \times U(1)$ involving the three gauge fields $W^{\pm}$ and W^0 for the $SU(2)$, and a gauge field Y for the $U(1)$ factor. This group is broken to a a residual $U(1)_\gamma$, corresponding to the massless photon. This can be achieved by a non-vanishing expectation value for a scalar field that transforms like a doublet under the $SU(2)$ and is also charged with respect to the $U(1)_Y$ field. The net effect is that one is left with three massive gauge particles: the $W^{\pm}$ and the neutral Z_0 boson, which is a linear combination of the W_3 and Y fields. The other, orthogonal linear combination of those two neutral fields corresponds to the photon. This intricate mixing of symmetries shows reminds us of the fact that nature not always celebrates ultimate simplicity.

A symmetry not broken, but hidden. The above account of the BEH mechanism can be criticized on valid grounds. It may even be called misleading. I used this narrative for pedagogical reasons, because it borrows some of the vocabulary of the global symmetry breaking scenario. But a deeper fact is that the vacuum expectation value as I discussed it is gauge dependent. Because of the local gauge invariance, I can locally transform that vacuum vector in any direction I want, so the analogy with the phenomena of magnetization where that direction is directly observable and fixed is wrong. The good way to talk about the BEH mechanism is to say the the invariant square of the covariant derivative acquires a vacuum expectation value, which directly translates into the mass terms for the vector particles. In other words there is a way of talking about this so-called breaking in a gauge invariant way. But then we have arrived at a *contradictio in terminis*, because if the mechanism can be cast in gauge invariant terms, then the gauge symmetry cannot be broken! Indeed! This is the reason that we rather speak of a *hidden symmetry*, the gauge invariance is still present, but is no longer manifest in the physics (the mass degeneracy), it is hidden. It is better to say that the gauge symmetry is not really broken at all, but realized in a different way in this physical model. This point of view is strongly supported by the technical fact that there is not necessarily a real phase transition between the hidden and manifest symmetric (confining) phase of the system.

Other forms of symmetry. We have in passing already referred to other symmetry types then the ones we have been considering here.

An important extension of space-time symmetries to so-called *supersymmetries* was a remarkable achievement.

The related super-algebras are not of the Lie algebra type, because they also involve fermionic generators that obey anti-commutators. If these extended symmetries are made local by gauging them, you need to introduce a spin-3/2 *gravitino* as the super partner of the graviton. As the names suggest these symmetries play a vital role in super string theory and super gravity theories and we commented on them at the end of Chapter I.4. The experimental program at the Large Hadron Collider at CERN has been searching for the lightest super particle that should exist in any supersymmetric theory with broken supersymmetry. And as we have not run into any superpartner of any particle in the Standard Model we have to assume that supersymmetry should be broken already at a high energy well above 1 TeV.

Later, a remarkable class of algebra's were discovered,: these are called infinite dimensional Lie algebras that are also known as *Kac–Moody algebras*. They have found interesting applications in two-dimensional physics both in string and condensed matter theory. It is a very high level of symmetry. After what we have said before one expects in this case there to be an infinite number of conservation laws, which almost tantamount to saying that models in which they feature, in spite of being very nonlinear are basically exactly solvable.

Finally there is a class of symmetries related to what we called topological phases in matter, which are called *Hopf algebras* or *quantum groups*. The remarkable aspect of their application in two-dimensional physics is that their representations describe both the ordinary excitations, and the topological defects and their dyonic mixtures called anyons. These correspond to the exotic particles we briefly described towards the end of the previous chapter .

A detailed discussion of the symmetries we just mentioned is beyond the scope of this book, but we mention them to emphasize the richness of the symmetry concept in mathematical physics.

Symmetry concepts and terminology

We have explored many aspects of the notion of symmetry in this chapter. First we searched for the observables Q_i that commute with the Hamiltonian. These correspond with *conserved quantities* and form some Lie-algebra including the Hamiltonian H, which is then called the *symmetry algebra* $\mathcal{Q}$. The states of the system at some fixed value of the energy will form a degenerate set that corresponds to certain representations of the symmetry algebra. The degenerate states can be labeled by the eigenvalues of some mutually commuting subset of the symmetry generators, forming a so-called *Cartan subalgebra* $\mathcal{H}$ of the symmetry algebra. The choice of Cartan subalgebra corresponds to choosing a framework $\mathcal{F}$. The other symmetry operators that are not in the Cartan subalgebra can be combined into *raising and lowering operators* that walk you through the sample space of the chosen framework. In the following table we have summarized the correspondence between the physical and mathematical concepts underlying the notion of symmetry.

Math: *Group theory* $\supset$	Continuous symmetries $\subset$	Physics: *Quantum theory*
$\vdots$ $\quad$ $\vdots$		Hilbert space of states Algebra of observables
Lie algebra $\mathcal{A}$ $\dim \mathcal{A} = d$	Observables Hermitian Commutator algebra Infinitesimal transformations Invariant polynomials (Casimirs)	$\{A_i\} = \{A, B, \ldots\}, \quad i = 1\ldots, d$ $A^\dagger = A$ $[A, B] = iC$ $\Delta_A |\psi\rangle = iA |\psi\rangle$ $\{C_k\} \ (k = 1, \ldots, \text{rank } \mathcal{A}) \ [C_k, \mathcal{A}] = 0$
Cartan subalgebra $\mathcal{H}$ $\dim \mathcal{H} = \text{rank } \mathcal{A} = r$	$\mathcal{H} \subset \mathcal{A} \Leftrightarrow$ Framework $\mathcal{F}$ Mutually commuting (= Abelian) Labels basis states of representation N Weight vectors $\{\lambda_m\}$	$\{H_i\} \quad i = 1, \ldots, r \leftrightarrow \mathbf{H}$ $[H_i, H_j] = 0$ $|\psi\rangle_N = \sum_m c_m |\{\lambda_m\}\rangle_N$ $\mathbf{H} |\{\lambda_m\}\rangle_N = \lambda_m |\{\lambda_m\}\rangle_N, \ m = 1, \ldots, N$
Cartan-Weil basis: $\mathcal{A} = \{H_i, E_{\pm\alpha_k}\}$ Root system $\{\pm\boldsymbol{\alpha}_k\}$ of $\mathcal{A}$ in $\mathbb{R}^d$	Raising and lowering operators	$E_{\pm\alpha_k} \quad k = 1, \ldots, (d-r)/2$ $[\mathbf{H}, E_{\pm\alpha_k}] = \pm\boldsymbol{\alpha}_k E_{\pm\alpha_k}$ $[E_{\pm\alpha_k}, E_{\pm\alpha_k}] = \pm\boldsymbol{\alpha}_k \cdot \mathbf{H}$
Symmetry algebra $\mathcal{Q}$ $\dim \mathcal{H} \leq \dim \mathcal{Q} \leq \dim \mathcal{A}$	Subalgebra $\mathcal{Q} \subset \mathcal{A}$ All Q_i commute with Hamiltonian H_0 $Q_i \sim$ conserved quantities $Q_i \sim$ generate symmetry transformations Time independent labeling of states	$\{Q_i\}$ $[Q_i, H_0] = 0$ $\dfrac{dQ_i}{dt} = 0$ if $H_0 \in \mathcal{H} \Rightarrow \mathcal{H} \subset \mathcal{Q} \Rightarrow \{\lambda_i\} \subset \{q_i\}$
Lie group $\mathcal{G}$ $\dim \mathcal{G} = \dim \mathcal{A}$	Unitary reps Transformation group on Hilbert space $\mathcal{H}_0$ Finite transformations: $\mathcal{G} \simeq e^{i\mathcal{A}}$ Group space coordinates	$U^\dagger = U^{-1}$ $|\psi\rangle \rightarrow |\psi\rangle' = U|\psi\rangle$ $A \rightarrow A' = UAU^\dagger$ $g = e^{i \sum \gamma^i A_i}$ $\{\gamma_i\}$

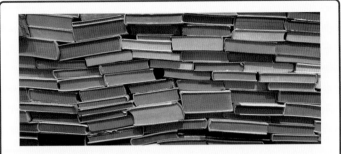

On symmetries:

— *The Theory of Groups and Quantum Mechanics*
Hermann Weyl
(Reprint of 1931 Edition)
Martino Fine Books (2014)

— *Symmetries in Fundamental Physics*
Kurt Sundermeyer
Springer (2013)

— *Symmetries and Conservation Laws in Particle Physics:*
An Introduction to Group Theory for Particle Physicists
Stephen Haywood
Imperial College Press (2010)

— *Concepts of Elementary Particle Physics*
Michael E. Peskin
Oxford University Press (2019)

— *Aspects of Symmetry: Selected Erice Lectures*
Sidney Coleman
Cambridge University Press (1985)

On non-abelian gauge theories:

— *Quantum Field Theory and the Standard Model*
Matthew D. Schwartz
Cambridge University Press(2013)

— *Gauge Theories in Particle Physics*
A Practical Introduction, Volume 2: Non-Abelian Gauge Theories: QCD and The Electroweak Theory
Ian J.R. Aitchison (Author) and Anthony J.G. Hey
CRC Press (2013)

Indices

Subject index Volume II

W bosons, 199
Z boson, 199

wavefunction, 19, 20, 25, 31, 39, 146, 149
wavefunction in momentum space, 158

Abigail, 42
AC current, 27
adiabatically, 114
Aharonov–Bohm phase, 109, 182, 197
algorithm, 17
Alice and Bob, 126, 127
amplitude, 89
anti-commutator, 168
anti-matter, 168
anti-triplet ($\bar{3}$) , 201
anyons, 176
approximate symmetry, 191
Atiyah–Singer index theorem, 199
ATLAS, 211
axiomatic approach, 49

Banach spaces, 49

Barbie on a globe, 51
baryon, 200
base manifold, 199
basis vectors, 50
BCS theory, 170
beam splitter (BS), 96
Bell inequality, 128
Bell states, 134
Berry connection, 114, 119
Berry phase, 113, 197
Bertlmann's socks, 35
Bit mechanics, 17
bit-force, 16
bit-momentum, 16
black hole information paradox, 43
Bloch sphere, 21
Bohr-model of the atom, 150
Boolean algebra, 17, 74
Born rule, 23
Bose–Einstein distribution, 181
Botzilla, 42
bounded operators, 48
bra vectors, 22

Bracket, 45
bracket, 22
Bragg diffraction, 93
breaking of light, 93
Brout–Englert–Higgs mechanism, 209
butterfly effect, 14

Cartan subalgebra, 192, 212
Casimir operators, 190
certain uncertainties, 79
Chand Baori, 161
charging energy, 27
Chern classes, 199
chiral symmetry breaking, 207
choice of a framework, 78
classical determinism, 84
classical wave theory, 89
CMS, 211
CNOT-gate, 17, 18
coherent states, 163
collapse of the wavefunction, 66, 72
color (anti-)triplet, 200
commutation relations, 153

commuting generators, 192
compatible observables, 57
complementarity, 146, 148
completeness relation, 58
Complex rotations, 21
complexification, 50
composite particle, 183
configuration space, 15, 145
confinement, 200
Conjugate states, 45
conjugate vectors, 22
conjunction, 74
connection one-form, 197
conservation law, 197
conserved quantities, 187,
    212
consistent framework, 71,
    76
continuity equation, 197
Cooper pair density, 25
Copenhagen interpretation, 23,
    62
correspondence principle,
    14
covariant derivative, 196
creation and annihilation
    operators, 163, 167
cryptography, 143
Curie temperature, 208

dagger, 48
DC current, 27
De Broglie wavelength, 90
decoherence, 41, 44
Degeneracies, 53
degenerate states, 189
delayed choice experiment,
    107
density matrix, 11, 38–41,
    44

density operator, 31, 39
deterministic chaos, 13
differential operator, 48, 152,
    188
dimensional compactification,
    200
discrete dynamics, 16
dispersion, 91
displacement operator, 188
Dissipation, 92
double slit experiment, 102
dynamical symmetry, 190
dynamical system, 16

eigenstate, 49, 51, 60, 65, 66, 71,
    72, 82, 83, 87
eigenvalues, 47–53, 60, 65, 77,
    87
eigenvector, 49, 87
eigenvectors, 50–52, 54, 57, 58,
    65, 77, 87
Einstein–Bohr debate, 62,
    126
elementary projectors, 77
energy conservation, 188
entangled pair, 123, 125,
    134
entangled two-qubit state,
    34
entanglement, 31, 36
entanglement entropy, 41
envelope, 159
EPR paradox, 62
Euler identity, 151
exclusion, 171
exclusion principle, 171
Expansion of state, 45
expectation value, 39, 51
explicit symmetry breaking,
    206

factorization, 141
Fermi energy, 181
Fermi–Dirac distribution,
    181
fermion, 171
fiber bundles, 185, 199
field coordinates, 195
field modes, 168
field momenta, 195
field strength, 195
finite transformation, 192
flavor symmetry, 199
flux quantization, 112
Fock space, 168
Fourier transform, 141
Frame choices, 54
Frame rotations., 54
framework, 71, 76, 78, 81, 87,
    212
frequency, 90

gamma matrices, 203
gauge invariant, 196
gauge particles, 199
gauge potential, 195
gauge symmetry, 185
gauge transformation, 195
geometric optics, 89
GHZ experiment, 130
GHZ-state, 132
global symmetries, 185
Goldstone mechanism, 207
Goldstone particles, 206
golf ball, 85
gravitino, 212
ground state, 148
group manifold, 193
group velocity, 92, 159
Grover's search algorithm,
    143

h-bar, 14
Hadamard gate, 139
half-integral spin, 171
half-mirror, 96
Hamiltonian landscape, 118
Hamiltonian operator, 52, 77
Heisenberg equation, 156,
        187
Heisenberg uncertainty relation,
        79, 80, 154
hermitian, 48
hermitian adjoint, 48
hidden symmetry, 211
hidden variables, 62, 126
Higgs particle, 211
Hilbert space, 12, 20, 45, 47,
        150
holonomy, 118
homotopy classes, 174
Hopf algebras, 212
Hopf or monopole bundle,
        51
Huygens' principle, 89, 93

idealized experiments, 66
improper mixtures, 41
incompatible observables, 57, 78,
        81
indistinguishability, 145, 171
inequivalent representations,
        187
inner product, 22, 45
input-output table, 17
interactions, 169
interference, 89
involutive automorphism, 48
ions in an optical lattice, 29
irreducible representations,
        189
iso-vector, 209

iterative map, 17

Josephson effect, 112
Josephson junction, 25

Kac–Moody algebras, 212
Kaluza–Klein theory, 200
ket vector, 20
Klein–Gordon field, 167
Kopenhagener Deutung, 62
Kronecker 'delta', 23

laddering, 60
Lagrangian, 202
Leaving a trace, 63
Lie algebra, 116, 185, 187, 188,
        190, 197, 198, 201,
        212
Lie group, 116, 185, 192,
        200
lightest super particle, 212
linear *operators*, 48
linear dispersion, 92
linear superposition, 24
linear superposition principle, 50,
        136
Linearity, 48
local gauge invariance, 185,
        204
local Poincaré symmetry,
        200
local realism, 126
local symmetries, 185
long-range order, 207
longitudinal, 90
loop integral, 111, 115, 119
lowering operator, 60

Mach–Zender interferometer,
        107

macroscopic quantum state,
        181
magnetization, 208
many worlds, 62
matrix mechanics, 156
matter waves, 147
Maxwell–Boltzmann distribution,
        180
meaning, 71
meaningful statement, 76
measurement, 48, 49, 51, 53, 58,
        62–66, 69, 74, 84
measurement outcome, 47, 62, 87,
        98
Meissner effect, 112
meson, 200
Minimal uncertainty state,
        163
mixed state, 31, 37, 45
momentum, 15
momentum conservation,
        188
momentum operator, 152
multi-particle Hilbert space,
        168
multi-qubit states, 30
multi-qubit system, 137
mutually commutative, 77

new quantum logic, 78
NEWTON-gate, 18
no cloning theorem, 64
non-abelian gauge theories,
        198
non-commutativity, 56
non-commuting observables,
        81
normalization condition, 20,
        149
NOT-gate, 17

object and subject, 62
observables, 47–49, 51, 56
observer, 63
ontology, 77
operators, 12
optical thickness, 56
order parameter, 208
orthogonal, 22
orthogonal complement, 58
orthogonal subspace, 59
orthonormal basis, 53
orthonormal frame, 23
overall phase, 25

parallel transport, 197
parallelism, 137
parametric down converter,
          97
particle interchange, 171
particle-wave duality, 146
Pauli matrices, 49, 65, 77
perturbative approach, 169
phase gate, 139
phase space, 15, 74, 146
phase velocity, 92, 159
photon, 147
Planck's constant, 14
Planck-Einstein relation, 82
Poincaré group, 200
Pointillism, 79
polarization, 90
polarization operator, 65
polarization state, 29, 56, 123,
          126
polarized electrons, 29
polarizer, 59
polarizing beam splitter, 96,
          97
position operator, 152, 153
Preferred frames, 87

preperatory device, 99
Prime factoring, 139
Probabilistic interpretation,
          45
probability amplitude, 22, 63, 67,
          72, 78, 150
probability amplitudes, 65
probability density, 147, 150
projection, 199
projection operator, 58, 77
projection postulate, 66
projective decomposition, 58
Projective measurement, 87
projector P, 58
proper mixture, 38, 39
property, 15
propositions, 77
punctuated equilibrium, 86
pure state, 37

QCD, 199
Quantum Chromodynamics,
          199
quantum computation, 124, 137,
          138
quantum computing, 141,
          144
Quantum copying, 64
quantum dots, 29
Quantum entropy, vi, 6, 41,
          45
quantum eraser, 104
quantum gates, 138
quantum groups, 212
quantum interference, 104
quantum measurement, 61
quantum observables, 47
quantum principles, 45
quantum registers, 30
quantum software, 142

quantum statistics, 173
quantum supremacy, 142
Quantum teleportation, 133
quantum tunnelling, 120
quark confinement, 203
qubit, 20, 48
qubit gate, 49
qubit observable, 49
qubit realizations, 29
Qubit state, 45
qubit state, 60
qubit state space, 51
qubit uncertainties, 83

Racah invariants, 190
raising and lowering operators,
          154, 192
raising operator, 60
Ray-Ban, 59
rays, 90
Real states, 21
reflection, 92, 93
refraction, 93
relative phase, 25
representation theory, 187
ribbon diagram, 178
rigid, 185
root diagram, 201
Runge–Lenz vector, 191

sample space, 49
sampling spaces, 74
scanning tunnelling microscope,
          121
Schrödinger equation, 146,
          154
Schrödinger's cat, 32, 61
section, 199
self-adjoint, 48
self-interference, 102

separable states, 45

separable two-qubit state,
        34

Shor algorithm, 139

single framework, 78

Snellius' law, 93

sources, 13

space of solutions, 205

spatial translations, 153

spectrum, 49

spectrum generating algebra,
        192

spin waves, 208

spin-statistics, 171, 179

spin-statistics connection, 145,
        177

spinor, 193

spinor representations, 190

spontaneous symmetry breaking,
        206

square integrable, 149

stability of matter, 148

Standard Model, 199

standing wave pattern, 101

state counting, 179

State decomposition, 21

State operators, 160

state vector, 12, 20, 23, 24, 30, 31,
        39

Stationary states, 155

step operators, 60, 159

Stern–Gerlach device, 66,

97

STM, 120

Stokes' law, 110

strong measurement, 69

superconducting ground state,
        25

superconductor, 112

Superposition, 87

supersymmetries, 211

symmetries of objects, 204

symmetry algebra, 157, 212

symmetry breaking, 185,
        204

syntactic rule, 78

tensor product, 30

The Delft experiment, 129

time evolution, 159

topological defects, 208

topological matter, 177

topological order, 177

topological phases, 212

topological quantum computing,
        138

topology of particle exchange,
        173

tracking information, 104

transversal, 90

triplet (3), 201

truth value, 74

tunneling current, 25

two-particle configuration space,

173

uncertainty relation, 78,
        80–84

unit hypercube, 22

unitary group, 55

unitary transformation, 55

universal set, 139

unpredictability, 84

updating algorithm, 17

vector representations, 190

Von Neuman entropy, 39, 41

wave packet, 158, 163

wave plates, 56

wavefronts, 90

wavelength, 90

wavenumber, 90

wavepacket, 92

weak and electromagnetic
        interactions, 211

weak measurements, 69

weak values, 69

which-way experiment, 107

winding number, 111, 112

Yang–Mills equations, 202

zero (energy) modes, 206

zero point energy, 84

zero-mass Dirac equation,
        199

Name index Volume II

Aquinas, Thomas, 24
Aspect, Alain, 107, 129

Bardeen, John, 170
Bell, John, 35, 126
Bennett, Charles, 124, 134
Berry, Michael, 113
Bohm, David, 62
Boltzmann, Ludwig, 41
Born, Max, 23, 62, 76
Bragg, Lawrence, 93
Bragg, William Henry, 93
Brassard, Gilles, 124

Cartan, Élie, 157
Clauser, John F., 129
Cooper, Neil, 170

Dali, Salvador, 61
Deutsch, David, 124
Dieks, Dennis, 64
Dirac, Paul, 12, 22, 76

Ehrenfest, Paul, 32
Einstein, Albert, 13, 61, 123
Escher, M.C., 89
Escher, Maurits, 171
Everett, Hugh, 62

Feynman, Richard, 13, 62

Gibbs, J. Willard, 41
Glashow, Sheldon, 209
Goldstone, Jeffrey, 206
Gould, Jay, 86

Hanson, Ronald, 129, 130
Heisenberg, Werner, 66, 76, 145

Josephson, Brian, 28

Kaluza, Theodor, 200
Kitaev, Alexei, 184
Klein, Oskar, 200
Klitzing, Klaus von, 183
Kuhn, Thomas, 86

Laughlin, Robert, 183
Leinaas, Jon Magne, 177

Matisse, Henri, 151
Maxwell, James Clerk, 13
Mills, Robert L., 198
Milnor, Yuri, 124
Myrheim, Jan, 177

Nambu, Yoichiro, 207
Newton, Isaac, 13
Noether, Emmy, 197

Pauli, Wolfgang, 171

Podolsky, Boris, 123

Quincke, Georg Hermann, 99

Rosen, Nathan, 123

Schrödinger, Erwin, 31, 61, 76
Schrieffer, Robert, 170
Seurat, Georges, 79
Shannon, Claude, 41
Shor, Peter, 124, 139

Tajiri, Shinkichi, 173
Tensey, Mark, 123

von Neumann, John, 11, 39, 66, 76

Weinberg, Steven, 186
Weyl, Hermann, 185
Wheeler, John Archibald, 47, 78
Wilczek, Frank, 176, 183
Wootters, William, 64

Yang, Chen Ning, 198

Zeilinger, Anton, 129, 134
Zurek, Wojciech, 64